FUNDAMENTALS OF

Neurology

Third Edition, Illustrated

ERNEST GARDNER, M.D.

Professor of Anatomy

Wayne State University College of Medicine, Detroit

W. B. Saunders Company

PHILADELPHIA & LONDON

To LaVearl Gardner

Preface to the Third Edition

IN THE present revision, special attention has been paid to sensory endings, particularly those in muscle, to vision, and to basal ganglia. It also seemed worth while to provide a brief account of neurochemistry, an important field of increasing importance. In bringing material up to date, new illustrations have been added, and some replaced.

Certain arrangements are unchanged. The references cited are intended to provide the interested student with a starting point for further reading. The short biographical sketches are of those men whose names are mentioned in the text, or who were outstanding in neurology.

I am indebted to Evelyn J. Erickson of the Department of Medical Illustration, and to Mrs. Geraldine Fockler of the same department, for their preparation of the illustrations. I am also indebted to Mr. Charles Pickard and Mr. Robert Wright of the Department of Medical Photography for aid in preparation of illustrations.

I wish to thank Dr. Ferdinando Morin, Department of Anatomy, Wayne State University, Dr. Otto Neuhaus, Department of Physiological Chemistry, Wayne State University, and Dr. Frederick Crescitelli, Department of Zoology, University of California at Los Angeles. All contributed valuable criticisms and suggestions during the preparation of the revision, particularly in connection with the chapter on neurochemistry.

Special thanks are due my wife, LaVearl Gardner, Mrs. Barbara Stopke, and Miss Gwen Gerada, for typing the manuscript.

Finally, I am indebted to the W. B. Saunders Company for the help and many courtesies they extended me.

ERNEST GARDNER

Detroit, Michigan

Contents

vii

CHAPTER 20

CHAPTER 1

Descriptive and Analytical
Methods

THE MATERIAL in this volume is based upon dissection and microscopic study of the nervous system, analysis by experimental methods, and the study of neurological disorders. Because this knowledge has accumulated over many centuries, a confusing terminology has arisen. Names were often given to portions of the body before the functions of these parts were known. For instance, an area of the brain which in general configuration somewhat resembles a sea horse was named the *hippocampus*. Often the name of the investigator who first described a structure became associated with that structure, as, for example, the *vein of Galen* (p. 5).

Various national and international anatomical groups have attempted to clarify and simplify anatomical terminology. The most recent revision is that by the International Anatomical Nomenclature Committee, and the list of Nomina Anatomica submitted by that committee to the Sixth International Congress of Anatomists in Paris, 1955, was approved by that Congress. Anatomical terms in this book for the most part are those of the Nomina Anatomica, translated into English where appropriate.

Orientation

Information as to the position of any object, such as a house in a city, is expressed in terms of direction, such as east and west, or right and left. When the human body is in the *anatomical position*, that is to say, when it is upright, with the upper extremities

1

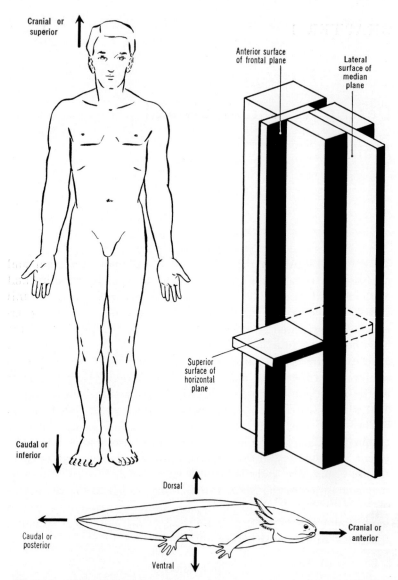

Figure 1. The anatomical position and synonymous terms of direction; a block diagram showing the primary planes and surfaces; and an amphibian, illustrating comparative anatomical nomenclature.

at the sides and the palms facing forward, three primary planes may be defined (Fig. 1). These are the *sagittal, frontal,* and *horizontal* planes. A sagittal plane in the middle of the body (*median* plane) divides the body into right and left halves. A frontal plane is a vertical plane at right angles to the sagittal that divides the body into front and back parts. A horizontal plane is any plane at right angles to the preceding ones that divides the body into upper and lower parts.

Structures toward the front of the body are *anterior;* toward the back, *posterior.* Cranial (or *superior*) refers to upper, and *caudal* (or *inferior*) to lower structures. The fact that man stands upright has led to a difference from the terminology used in comparative anatomy. In lower forms, structures which in man are toward the front of the body are *ventral,* those toward the back, *dorsal.* Cranial and anterior become synonymous, as do caudal and posterior (Fig. 1). In connection with the nervous system, the comparative anatomical nomenclature is often followed, particularly as regards "dorsal" and "ventral." For instance, the roots of the spinal cord usually are termed "dorsal" and "ventral" rather than "posterior" and "anterior" (pp. 24 and 35). "Ventral" is sometimes used to indicate structures at the base of the human brain; the comparable surface in animals that walk on all fours is ventral.

Other important terms are *medial,* nearer the median or mid-sagittal plane, and *lateral,* farther from that plane. *Proximal,* in referring to a limb, indicates a position nearer the trunk or central axis of the body; *distal,* a more peripheral position. For other terms of position and directions one should consult the textbooks of anatomy cited at the end of this chapter.

Techniques for Gross and Microscopic Study

Many important characteristics of the nervous system, such as size, shape, position and surface markings, may be noted by ordinary inspection. Details may be revealed by dissection of the nervous system, that is, by separating it from other tissues or organs, or by cutting it in various ways so as to obtain access to structures not apparent on the surface. The minute anatomy can be studied by examining portions of the nervous system under the microscope. Tissues examined by this means must be thin and transparent so that light can pass through them into the microscope and eventually to the eye. Although it is desirable to study tissues in the living state, thin sections are difficult to obtain and structures in the tissues may not be readily distinguishable. Therefore, special techniques are used to kill tissues and obtain thin slices to which dyes are applied so as to color structures differentially.

In order to preserve a structure in a state resembling the living as closely as possible, small pieces of fresh tissue are *fixed* in a chemical solution which simultaneously kills them and preserves them from alteration during subsequent treatment. Solutions of formalin or alcohol are the fixatives most commonly used for nerve tissue. After fixation, water in the tissues is slowly removed by transferring them through increasing concentrations of alcohol. Water-free tissues are then infiltrated with some substance which can be hardened later. Melted paraffin or a solution of nitrocellulose (celloidin) is used for such purposes. The hardened blocks can be cut into thin slices (as thin as 1 or 2 *microns* or less) without marked damage or distortion. This is done with a sharp knife and a special machine, the *microtome*. The thin slices or sections are then stained. Because all parts of tissues are not of the same chemical composition, some stains will color one structure, some another. Numerous dyes are available, and their choice depends upon the structures being studied. The stained sections are then made transparent by immersing them in a substance such as xylol. To prevent the drying and destruction which occur on exposure to air, they are placed on glass slides, covered with a solution of a transparent resin, and sealed with a thin piece of glass. As the resin dries, it remains clear and forms a hard, protective coat for the sections which will last for many years.

In hospitals, where a rapid method is often necessary, fresh pieces of tissue are quickly frozen into hard blocks by contact with solid carbon dioxide, "dry ice." Sections may be cut immediately, stained and mounted.

Experimental Methods of Study

There are many methods of studying the living nervous system. Most of them are carried out in animals other than man. The function of a particular portion or structure in the nervous system may be adduced by stimulating it with an electric current and observing the results directly. A part of the nervous system may be removed surgically and any effect or loss of function noted. Habit formation, behavior, reactions to stimuli, and the like, may be observed before and after surgical procedures in animals and in man. Drugs may be given which affect or stimulate certain elements of the nervous system and thereby alter their functions. The inception of function may be observed by correlating physiological and morphological development during embryonic, fetal and infant life. Finally, there are methods involving special techniques. Some of these will be discussed in subsequent chapters. For instance, living tissue, especially that of the nervous system, undergoes electrical changes during an alteration in activity. These changes can be studied and recorded, usually by means of special electronic equipment, and the methods allow one to examine a variety of phenomena. Some of these are nerve conduction, the localization of active nerve centers and the tracing of pathways in the central nervous system. The effect of various drugs, such as anesthetics, on electrical activity can also be included.

Clinical Methods of Study

A disease or injury of the nervous system usually causes a loss of function or may give rise to an abnormal condition. If a patient with a neurological disorder dies, the signs and symptoms which that patient presented during life may be correlated with pathological changes found after death. Over many years the study of great numbers of such cases has yielded considerable information. Data may also be obtained when operations are necessary. These clinical methods are the only comprehensive ones available for neurological studies in man, if one excludes special tests used by psychologists and psychiatrists.

Names in Neurology

Galen, of Pergamum (about A.D. 130–200)

Galen was a Greek physician who, after many years of study, settled in Rome. Here, as the founder of experimental physiology, he did an incredible amount of work. He knew of the effects of cutting the spinal cord, with its resulting sensory losses and motor disturbances. Galen studied the heart and knew that the arteries contained blood. He saw and described the cerebral aqueduct. His knowledge of anatomy was comprehensive and accurate. He set so high a standard that for thirteen centuries his works were the only authoritative sources. Since he rarely, if ever, dissected

human cadavers, the errors he made in attributing animal structures to man were perpetuated. In spite of the fact that during
medieval times it became heresy even to question these errors,
there is no doubt that Galen was one of the great scientific figures
of all time.

References

The following textbooks are general anatomical ones, of which the following three
are standard volumes. The first two are widely used in medical schools of Great
Britain and Ireland, and the third in the United States.

Brash, J. C., ed.: Cunningham's Textbook of Anatomy. 9th ed. London, Geoffrey
Cumberledge, Oxford University Press, 1951.

Johnston, T. B., and Whillis, J., ed.: Gray's Anatomy. 31st ed. London, Longmans
Green and Co., 1954.

Schaeffer, J. P., ed.: Morris' Human Anatomy. 11th ed. Philadelphia, Blakiston
Company, 1953.

The following textbook is one of the best on comparative anatomy in the English
language. The chapters on sense organs and the nervous system are of particular
interest here.

Romer, A. S.: The Vertebrate Body. 2nd ed. Philadelphia, W. B. Saunders Company, 1955.

The following two volumes are suitable both for the beginning and the advanced
student. The textbook (the first listed) is simply and clearly written, the body being
discussed according to regions, in contrast to the three listed above, which discuss
the body according to systems (muscles, vessels, etc.).

Grant, J. C. B.: A Method of Anatomy. 5th ed. Baltimore, Williams and Wilkins
Company, 1952.

Grant, J. C. B.: Atlas of Anatomy. 4th ed. Baltimore, Williams and Wilkins Company, 1956.

The following two textbooks for the beginning student present elementary facts
about the structure and function of the human body.

Marshall, C., and Lazier, E. L.: Introduction to Human Anatomy. 4th ed. Philadelphia, W. B. Saunders Company, 1955.

Millard, N. D., King, B. G., and Showers, M. J.: Human Anatomy and Physiology.
4th ed. Philadelphia, W. B. Saunders Company, 1956.

CHAPTER 2

The Central Nervous System

DURING THE course of development in the embryo, the nervous system becomes a tubular structure, and this tubular arrangement is found in the adult in a considerably modified form (Chap. 5). That part of the tube in the head region develops into the *brain* and its various subdivisions. The rest of the tube becomes the spinal cord. The brain and spinal cord constitute the *central nervous system.*

Nerve cells in the brain and spinal cord have processes of various lengths. Many of these processes connect parts of the brain and spinal cord, while others collect in bundles, leave the brain and spinal cord as cranial and spinal nerves, and are distributed to muscles and glands. Other nerve cells are found adjacent to the brain and spinal cord, and their processes convey sensory impulses from non-nervous structures to the brain and spinal cord. The *cranial* and *spinal nerves,* their peripheral combinations, and the peripheral portions of the *autonomic nervous system,* constitute the *peripheral nervous system.*

In order to pave the way for more detailed anatomical and physiological discussions, this and the next two chapters will be devoted to a general presentation of the gross or macroscopic anatomy of the nervous system.

Location and Coverings of the Central Nervous System

The brain and spinal cord are protected by the *skull,* the *vertebrae,* and their ligamentous connections. The brain occupies the cranial cavity in the interior of the skull. This cavity is commonly

7

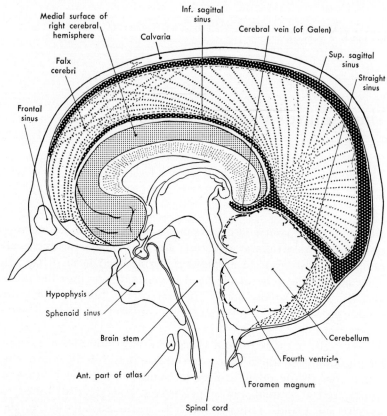

Figure 2.   Diagram of a median section of skull and brain showing relationship of various parts of brain to skull and dura mater. The falx cerebri and its contained sinuses are also shown in Figure 3. Veins in the cerebral hemispheres empty into the sinuses. Blood flows posteriorly, and, from the junction of straight sinus and superior sagittal sinus, is carried by other sinuses (not shown) to the internal jugular veins.

of 1200 to 1500 cc. capacity. There are numerous openings or foramina in the base of the skull for blood vessels and nerves. Through an especially large one, the *foramen magnum,* the brain is continuous with the spinal cord (Figs. 2 and 19).

The vertebrae are irregularly shaped bones joined so as to form a long column. Each vertebra has a heavy body from which an arch extends backward, enclosing a large opening. The vertebrae are arranged so that these openings form a continuous channel, the *spinal canal.* The spinal cord occupies the spinal canal and

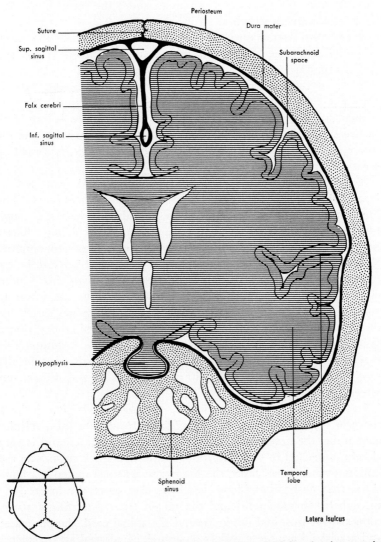

Figure 3. Diagram of a frontal section of skull and brain, showing certain features of the meninges. The small figure shows the plane of section. Note that the dura mater forms a fold (falx cerebri) between the cerebral hemispheres, and contains two venous sinuses. This plane is at right angles to that of Figure 2. Note also that the dura mater is continuous through the suture with periosteum on the outer surface of the skull.

extends from the foramen magnum to about the level of the first or second lumbar vertebra.

There are lateral openings between the vertebrae, the *intervertebral foramina,* through which nerves and blood vessels run (Fig. 20, p. 33).

There are seven *cervical* vertebrae in the neck; twelve *thoracic vertebrae* for chest or thorax; five *lumbar vertebrae* for the abdomen; a *sacrum* for the pelvis (the sacrum develops before birth as five sacral vertebrae that later fuse into a single bone). At the lower end of the column is a small bone, the *coccyx,* representing several vertebral segments.

The brain and spinal cord are surrounded and protected by layers of non-nervous tissue collectively called *meninges.* The outer layer is the *dura mater* (Figs. 2 and 3). This is a tough fibrous membrane that in the cranial cavity is found immediately internal to bone. When bone is removed preparatory to entering the cranial cavity, dura mater is the first meningeal layer to be encountered. In certain regions the dura mater contains venous channels or *sinuses* that carry venous blood from the brain to veins in the neck and thence to the heart. In the spinal canal, the dura mater is separated from bone by an interval, the *epidural space,* which contains fat and many small veins. A comparable space is not found in the cranial cavity except when artificially produced, for example, by bleeding between skull and dura mater after trauma (p. 48).

Just internal to the dura mater, and separated from it by a space of capillary thickness, the *subdural space,* is a thin, cellular membrane, the *arachnoid.* Around the brain the arachnoid is very closely connected by a meshwork of connective tissue strands to the innermost meningeal layer, the *pia mater.* The pia mater is a loose tissue that ensheathes blood vessels as they enter the brain. The space between arachnoid and pia mater, the *subarachnoid space,* contains cerebrospinal fluid. Around the spinal cord, the pia mater and arachnoid are more widely separated. Meningeal arrangements are shown in Fig. 29 and cerebrospinal fluid is discussed in Chap. 4.

The Brain

The part of the neural tube that develops in the head region forms the brain. Three enlargements of this tube are found early in development. These are forebrain, midbrain and hindbrain, and from these the subdivisions of the adult brain are formed. The cavity of the neural tube persists in the adult as cavities called *ventricles.*

The forebrain forms the *cerebrum* and the *interbrain (diencephalon).* The *cerebrum* is composed of two *hemispheres* that form the bulk of the brain.

The midbrain persists as the *midbrain* of the adult.

The hindbrain forms the *pons, medulla oblongata,* and *cerebellum.*

The term *brain stem* refers to midbrain, pons, and medulla oblongata, and often includes diencephalon as well. These regions collectively form a stem or stalk between the expanded cerebral hemispheres and the spinal cord.

Cerebral Hemispheres. The huge size of the hemispheres relative to the rest of the brain is due, in man, to the development of regions concerned with motor, sensory and higher mental functions.

A prominent longitudinal fissure partially divides the cerebrum into two cerebral hemispheres. This fissure is occupied by a downward projection or fold of dura mater. When the arachnoid and pia mater are removed, it is seen that the hemispheres are folded or convoluted. The convolutions are called *gyri,* the depressions or intervals between gyri, *sulci.* Most gyri and sulci are named, and the more constant of these are shown in Figs. 4 and 5.

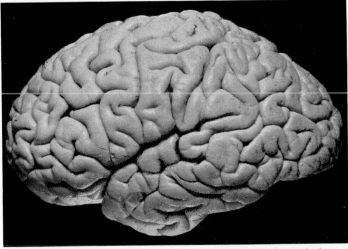

Figure 4. Photograph of lateral surface of human cerebral hemisphere. The arachnoid and pia mater have been removed.

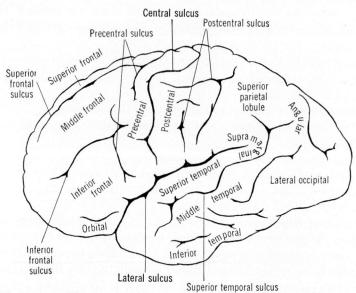

Figure 5. Outline sketch of the lateral surface of the cerebral hemisphere shown
in Figure 4. The gyri are directly labelled (except the superior frontal), while the
sulci are indicated by leaders.

Thus, between the *central sulcus* and *precentral sulcus* is the
precentral gyrus, a region concerned in motor activities. There is
considerable individual variation in size, shape and position of
gyri and sulci, and none can be identified with certainty unless
arachnoid and pia mater are removed.

Some sulci separate parts of the hemispheres called *lobes*. Each
lobe supposedly has specific functions. To a certain extent this is
true; the occipital lobe, for example, is concerned with vision.
But it is generally found that functional distinctions between lobes
are quite arbitrary. The lobes are shown in Fig. 5. The *frontal lobe*
is in front of the central sulcus, the *parietal lobe* behind it and
above the lateral sulcus. The *temporal lobe* is below the lateral
sulcus. The *occipital lobe* is posterior to temporal and parietal
lobes, but there is usually no definite sulcus separating them on
the lateral surface of the hemisphere. Figure 12 shows how the
various lobes extend to the medial surface of the hemisphere.

The two hemispheres are united by several bands (commissures)
of nerve tissue that cross the midline. The most prominent of these
is the *corpus callosum* (Fig. 13).

Diencephalon. The diencephalon or interbrain lies between cerebrum and midbrain. Its largest part is the *thalamus* (Fig. 14), a region concerned with sensory functions. Just below the thalamus is the *hypothalamus,* concerned with visceral functions.

Base of Cerebrum and Diencephalon. The nerves connected to the brain, and the blood vessels supplying the brain, enter or leave from below, so to speak. Hence the brain must be removed and its base studied. Figures 6 and 7 show the base of the brain. The only lobes readily visible in this view are parts of the frontal and temporal lobes. Between the two temporal lobes is a part of the brain

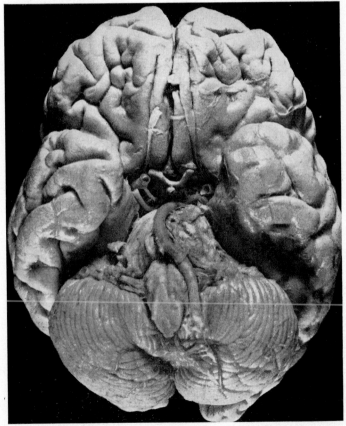

Figure 6. Photograph of the base of a human brain, with the arachnoid and pia mater largely removed. One vertebral artery is enlarged; the other, smaller one is cut at the beginning of the basilar artery. The right olfactory bulb is removed.

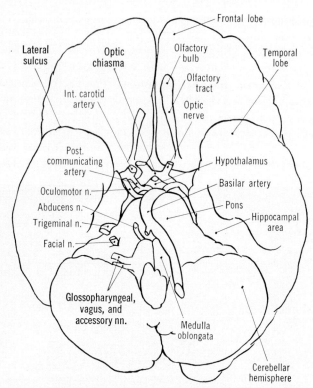

Figure 7. Outline sketch of the base of the brain shown in Figure 6.

marked by two prominences, the *mammillary* bodies (Figs. 8 and 9). These are parts of the diencephalon. There is a large bundle of nerve tissue, the *cerebral peduncle,* on each side just behind the mammillary bodies. The two cerebral peduncles are part of the midbrain.

The *olfactory nerves* are groups of tiny nerve filaments that ascend through openings in the front part of the floor of the cranial cavity. These nerves are the first of twelve pairs of cranial nerves. They end in *olfactory bulbs,* from which *olfactory tracts* are directed backward to the base of the frontal lobes (Fig. 7).

The *optic nerves,* the second pair of cranial nerves, are good sized structures that, shortly after leaving the orbital cavities through the *optic canals,* join to form the *optic chiasma,* from which *optic tracts* proceed backward around the cerebral peduncles.

Close to each optic nerve, near the chiasma, is a large blood vessel, the *internal carotid artery*, which supplies the orbit and brain. Just behind the optic chiasma is a stalk of tissue connecting the base of the brain with the *hypophysis (pituitary gland)*, which is contained in a fossa in the base of the skull (Figs. 2 and 3). Near the optic nerves, and entering the orbit where they supply muscles that move the eye, are the *oculomotor, trochlear,* and *abducens* nerves, the third, fourth, and sixth pairs of cranial nerves respectively.

Also at the base of the brain is the *arterial circle* (circle of Willis, see Chap. 4), formed by communications between branches of the internal carotid and basilar arteries, and from which branches are distributed to the brain.

Midbrain. The front of the midbrain or mesencephalon is

Figure 8.   Photograph of the base of the brain. Most of the cranial nerves have been removed, as well as one olfactory bulb. The temporal lobe on one side has been cut away to expose the right optic tract as it winds around the cerebral peduncle.

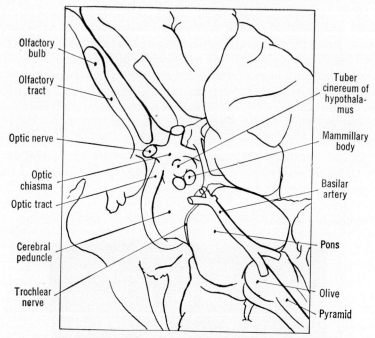

Olfactory bulb

Olfactory tract

Optic nerve

Optic chiasma

Optic tract

Cerebral peduncle

Trochlear nerve

Tuber cinereum of hypothalamus

Mammillary body

Basilar artery

Pons

Olive

Pyramid

Figure 9.   Outline sketch of the base of the brain shown in Figure 8.

formed by the two cerebral peduncles, which contain nerve tracts connecting the cerebrum with brain stem and spinal cord. On the posterior surface of the midbrain are four rounded eminences. The upper two are the *superior colliculi,* the lower two the *inferior colliculi.* The superior colliculi are concerned with visual functions, the inferior with auditory. The posterior limit of the diencephalon, at the junction of the diencephalon and midbrain, is marked by a small, oval body, the *pineal body,* which is attached in the midline just above the superior colliculi. The function of the pineal body is obscure. It often becomes calcified with advancing age, and hence more radiopaque. It thereby becomes visible in radiograms and thus serves as a useful landmark or reference point in interpreting radiograms of the brain and skull.

The oculomotor nerves attach to the front of the midbrain, between the cerebral peduncles. The trochlear nerves arise in the midbrain, but leave from its posterior surface.

Pons.   The midbrain continues below into a massive, rounded structure, the *pons.* The pons serves in part as a bridge or connection between the two cerebellar hemispheres, and contains various nerve tracts and collections of nerve cells. The fifth pair of cranial nerves, the *trigeminal nerves,* is attached to the sides of the pons. The abducens nerves are attached to the front of the pons, just above its junction with the medulla oblongata. The seventh and eighth pairs of cranial nerves, the *facial* and *stato-acoustic* (often called *acoustic* or *auditory*), are attached at the sides, at the junction of pons and medulla oblongata.

Medulla Oblongata. The pons continues below into the medulla oblongata, which in turn continues into the spinal cord, the junction being at the level of the foramen magnum.

The front of the medulla oblongata is marked by the longitudinally directed *anterior median fissure,* on each side of which is an elevation, the *pyramid.* Lateral to the upper part of each pyramid, separated from it by the *anterior lateral sulcus,* is an ovoidal elevation, the *olive.* Details of the posterior surface of the medulla oblongata are discussed with the ventricular system.

The ninth, tenth and eleventh pairs of cranial nerves, the *glossopharyngeal, vagus* and *accessory* nerves respectively, are attached to the side of the medulla oblongata, between the olive and *inferior cerebellar peduncle.* The *hypoglossal nerves,* the twelfth pair, emerge on each side between pyramid and olive, from the anterior lateral sulcus.

The medulla oblongata contains, in addition to various nerve tracts, important collections of nerve cells dealing with vital functions, such as respiration, circulation and special senses.

Two vertebral arteries enter the cranial cavity through the foramen magnum, ascend in front of the medulla oblongata, and unite to form the basilar artery. This in turn ascends in front of pons and midbrain, ultimately entering into the arterial circle (p. 46).

Cerebellum. The cerebellum is a deeply fissured structure behind the brain stem, formed of two hemispheres connected by a median portion, the *vermis.* The cerebellum is connected to the brain stem by paired peduncles, whose position and direction are shown in Fig. 10. The *superior cerebellar peduncles* connect the cerebellum and midbrain, the *middle cerebellar peduncles* connect cerebellum and pons, and the *inferior cerebellar peduncles* connect cerebellum and medulla oblongata.

The cerebellum is an important organ concerned with various aspects of control of muscular activity.

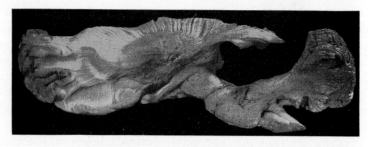

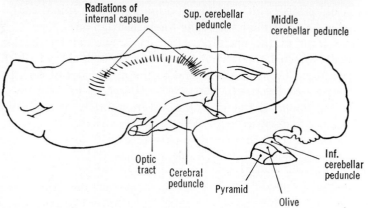

Radiations of
internal capsule

Sup. cerebellar
peduncle

Middle
cerebellar peduncle

Optic
tract

Cerebral
peduncle

Pyramid

Olive

Inf.
cerebellar
peduncle

Figure 10. *Upper,* photograph of human brain stem. The lateral part of the cerebral hemisphere is removed to show the internal capsule, and the cerebellum is dissected to show its peduncles. Only a small part of the superior peduncle is visible, because it extends longitudinally on the dorsal aspect of the brain stem (see Fig. 19, p. 30). *Lower,* outline sketch of the photograph.

The Ventricular System. Figures 11 and 12 show a brain separated into right and left halves by a median cut. This cut exposes some of the *ventricles,* the adult derivatives of the cavity in the embryonic neural tube. The ventricles contain cerebrospinal fluid (Chap. 4). There is a lateral ventricle in the interior of each cerebral hemisphere. Each lateral ventricle joins the front end of the *third ventricle* by an *interventricular foramen.* The third ventricle is a narrow space within the diencephalon. Posteriorly it is continuous with the *cerebral aqueduct (aqueduct of Sylvius).* The aqueduct is a narrow channel within the midbrain, continuous below with the *fourth ventricle,* between the cerebellum behind, and pons and medulla oblongata in front. The fourth ventricle continues below into a narrow channel, the *central canal,* found in

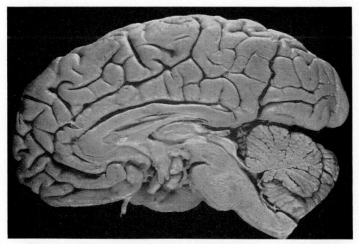

Figure 11. Photograph of a brain sectioned in the median plane.

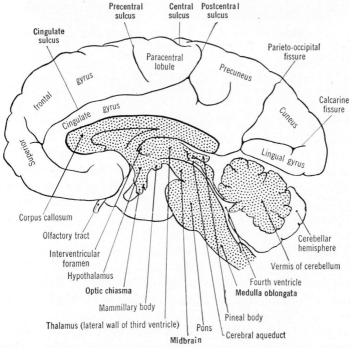

Figure 12. Sketch of the medial surface of the brain shown in Figure 11. The gyri are directly labelled, while other structures are indicated by leaders.

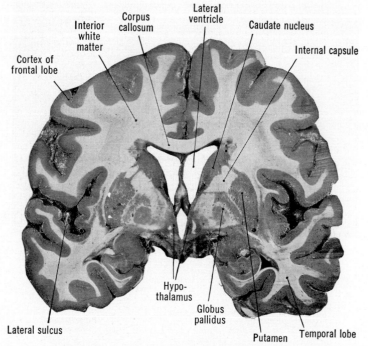

Figure 13. Photograph of a coronal slice of brain, stained by a method which colors gray matter and leaves white matter relatively unstained.

the lower part of the medulla oblongata and throughout the length of the spinal cord.

Below the cerebellum, the fourth ventricle is roofed by a thin membrane in which there is an opening by means of which the ventricle communicates with the subarachnoid space. An opening is also found laterally, on each side. Cerebrospinal fluid circulates through the ventricles, into the subarachnoid space (Chap. 4). In the lateral, third, and fourth ventricles there are complex tufts of small blood vessels, the *chorioid plexuses*. These are concerned with the formation of cerebrospinal fluid and are discussed in Chap. 4.

The floor of the fourth ventricle is formed by the pons and medulla oblongata (Fig. 19). There is, in the midline, a *median sulcus*, lateral to which are various elevations. Among these, in the lower part of the medulla oblongata, are two on each side, the *funiculus gracilis* and *funiculus cuneatus*, marking nerve tracts ascending from the spinal cord.

Gray and White Matter of the Brain. If a cerebral hemisphere is cut into slices (Figs. 13 and 14), certain structural features are evident. The surface or *cortex,* in fresh brains, is grayish in appearance, and is accordingly termed *gray matter,* in contrast to *white matter.* Gray matter is composed largely of bodies of nerve cells, while white matter is formed largely by processes or fibers of nerve cells. More detailed explanations of these differences are given on pp. 77 and 78. Figures 13 and 14 also show that the interior of the hemispheres is composed partly of white matter, and partly of well demarcated areas of gray matter known collectively as *basal nuclei* or *basal ganglia.* In each hemisphere, these masses of gray matter form a medial group, including *caudate nucleus, thalamus,* and *hypothalamus,* and a lateral group, including *lentiform nucleus* (composed of *putamen* and *globus pallidus*) and *amygdaloid body.*

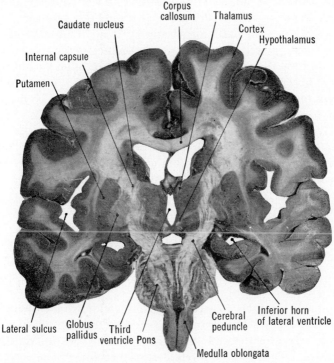

Figure 14. Photograph of a coronal slice of brain, posterior to that of Fig. 13, and stained by the same method. This is in the same plane and relatively same region as the microscopic sections of Figs. 137 and 138 (pp. 296, 297).

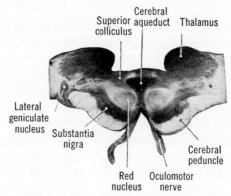

Figure 15.   Horizontal slice of midbrain. Staining method as for Fig. 13.

These lateral and medial groups are separated by a band of white matter known as the *internal capsule*. Each internal capsule emerges from the base of the brain as a cerebral peduncle. While technically the term basal nuclei applies to all the masses of gray matter listed, as well as several smaller masses not listed, in common usage the thalamus and hypothalamus are often excluded.

Nerve fibers in the internal capsule that connect caudate nucleus and lentiform nucleus are arranged in parallel groups so that this region has a striated appearance. Hence these structures are collectively termed the *corpus striatum.*

The thalamus and hypothalamus belong to the diencephalon, and are often included with the brain stem. Most of the other basal nuclei belong to the cerebral hemisphere, and are concerned with important aspects of motor activity and behavior (Chap. 17).

Figure 15 illustrates a slice through the midbrain. There are two masses of gray matter in an intermediate position. In the fresh condition, they are pinkish and are accordingly named the *red nuclei.* Just in front of each nucleus, in the cerebral peduncle, is an area, the *substantia nigra,* in which the nerve cells contain a dark pigment (melanin).

Figures 16 and 17 are slices of pons and medulla oblongata. These show that white matter is found anteriorly; mixtures of white and gray matter, the *reticular formation,* are intermediate; and gray matter is next to cerebral aqueduct, fourth ventricle and central canal.

The slices shown in Figs. 16 and 17 include parts of the cere-

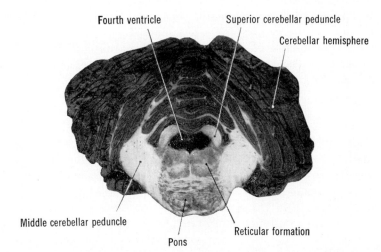

Fourth ventricle   Superior cerebellar peduncle

Cerebellar hemisphere

Middle cerebellar peduncle

Reticular formation

Pons

Figure 16. Horizontal slice of pons and cerebellum. Staining methods as for Fig. 13.

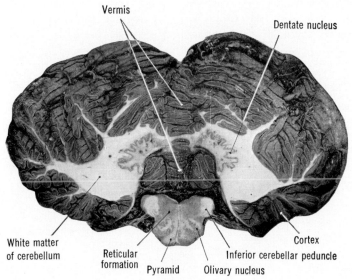

Vermis

Dentate nucleus

White matter
of cerebellum   Reticular
                       formation   Pyramid   Olivary nucleus

Cortex

Inferior cerebellar peduncle

Figure 17. Horizontal slice of medulla oblongata and cerebellum. Staining method as for Fig. 13.

bellum. As is true of the cerebral cortex, the cortex of the cerebellum is composed of gray matter. The cerebellar peduncles and the interior of the cerebellum are composed of white matter. But within the interior of the cerebellum, in and near the roof of the fourth ventricle, are paired masses of gray matter, among which are the *dentate nuclei* (Fig. 17) and several known collectively as *roof nuclei.*

The Spinal Cord

The spinal cord does not occupy the whole length of the spinal canal, but ends at about the level of lower part of the first lumbar vertebra or upper part of the second. Below this level the spinal canal is occupied by meninges, including subarachnoid space, and nerve roots. There is also a thin, fibrous strand, the *filum terminale,* that continues downward from the spinal cord to the coccyx. Above, its fibrous components fuse with pia mater, below, with dura mater.

In the midline of the spinal cord posteriorly, there is a slight longitudinal groove, the *posterior median sulcus.* There is a continuous series of nerves, the *dorsal roots,* which enter the *posterior lateral sulcus* of the spinal cord at regular intervals (Fig. 18). There is commonly a *posterior intermediate sulcus* in the upper

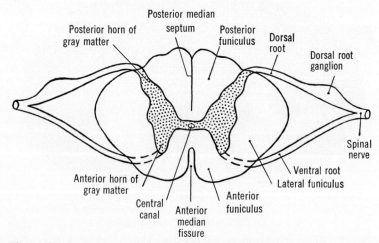

Figure 18.   Transverse section of spinal cord, showing spinal roots and arrangement of white and gray matter. Note that a septum continues inward from the posterior median sulcus to divide the white matter into two posterior funiculi. Compare with Fig. 124 (p. 247).

half of the spinal cord, between lateral and median sulci. There are also a variable number of small arteries and veins on the posterior surface of the cord. In the cervical region the arteries form definite longitudinal vessels on each side, the *posterior spinal arteries.*

Anteriorly, in the midline, the spinal cord has an *anterior median fissure,* occupied by the *anterior spinal artery,* and one or two small veins. *Ventral roots* leave at regular intervals from the anterolateral region of the spinal cord.

The spinal cord has cervical and lumbosacral enlargements, corresponding to the attachments of dorsal and ventral roots supplying the limbs. The collection of roots in the spinal canal below the spinal cord resembles the tail of a horse, hence the name *cauda equina* given to this collection.

A slice through any level of the spinal cord reveals a characteristic structure (Fig. 18). In contrast to the cerebral hemispheres, gray matter is found in the interior, surrounded by white matter. The gray matter is arranged somewhat like the letter **H**, with anterior and posterior horns, and a connecting bar of gray matter. A lateral horn is also found in the thoracic part of the spinal cord. The central canal is found in the connecting bar. Not uncommonly, in the adult, the canal is obliterated at various levels.

Nerve fibers leaving the anterior horns enter ventral roots. Nerve fibers of dorsal roots, entering the spinal cord at the posterior lateral sulcus, reach the posterior horns.

The white matter of the spinal cord is arranged into *funiculi.* A septum extending inward from the posterior median sulcus divides the white matter here into two *posterior funiculi.* In the upper half of the spinal cord, and especially in the cervical region, a thin septum extending inward from each posterior intermediate sulcus, divides each posterior funiculus into a laterally placed *fasciculus cuneatus* and a medially placed *fasciculus gracilis.* These are continuous with the corresponding funiculi of the medulla oblongata.

Each *lateral funiculus* is the white matter between dorsal and ventral root fibers. Each *anterior funiculus* is the white matter between the ventral root fibers of that side and the anterior median fissure.

The white matter of the spinal cord contains nerve tracts connecting dorsal and ventral root fibers with various parts of the spinal cord, and with the brain. The gray matter contains cells concerned with sensory impulses, with the activity of muscles, and with the functions of various viscera and blood vessels.

Summary

The central nervous system includes the brain and spinal cord. It is surrounded by the meninges, composed of the dura mater, arachnoid and pia mater. The subarachnoid space lies between the last two membranes and contains cerebrospinal fluid.

The brain includes the convoluted cerebral hemispheres, the brain stem and the cerebellum. The hemispheres (frontal, temporal, parietal and occipital lobes) have a surface, or cortex, composed of gray matter. They contain the lateral and third ventricles, and the internal masses of gray matter known as the basal ganglia. The internal capsules lie between portions of the basal ganglia and emerge at the base of the hemispheres as the cerebral peduncles.

The brain stem is composed of diencephalon, midbrain, pons and medulla. The cerebellum is connected to the brain stem by three pairs of peduncles. Between the cerebellum and the pons and medulla lies the fourth ventricle. This is connected to the third ventricle by the cerebral aqueduct, which runs through the midbrain. The interior of the brain stem is composed of gray and white matter in varying proportions. The cerebellum has an interior of white matter and a surface of gray matter.

The spinal cord is continuous with the medulla oblongata at the foramen magnum. It terminates at the upper border of the second lumbar vertebra. Its interior gray matter is arranged like the letter H, surrounded by white matter arranged into funiculi. Ventral roots of the spinal nerves arise from the anterior horn of gray matter, while the dorsal roots terminate in the posterior horn of the gray matter. The cord is larger in the cervical and lumbosacral regions.

Names in Neurology

Monro, Alexander (1697–1767)

In 1700, J. Monro settled in Edinburgh. At the age of twenty-two, he became professor of anatomy, the first of a long line of distinguished anatomists. His son, Alexander Monro, followed in his father's footsteps as professor of anatomy, and it is his name that is attached to the interventricular foramina. The grandson, also named Alexander, held the same chair as professor of anatomy. The three Monros occupied this chair for a period of 126 years (1720–1846), and the first two Monros themselves taught at least 12,800 students.

Sylvius (also known as Jacques DeBois) (1478–1555)

Sylvius was a Parisian teacher and such a devoted follower of Galen's teachings that he would not admit the possibility of errors in Galen's descriptions, believing rather that the human body had changed since Galen's time. He named the jugular, subclavian, renal and other blood vessels, but the cerebral aqueduct which bears his name was *not* first described by him. Galen, more than 1000 years before, had seen and described it.

References

Detailed descriptions of the anatomy of the central nervous system are available in the textbooks of human anatomy cited on p. 6.

Herrick, C. J.: Introduction to Neurology. 5th ed. Philadelphia, W. B. Saunders Company, 1931. A classic presentation of fundamental principles of the nervous system.

Krieg, W.: Functional Neuroanatomy. 2nd ed. Philadelphia, Blakiston Company, 1953. This textbook is valuable, not only for the text material, but also for the excellent phantom drawings which present neuro-anatomical structures in three-dimensional form.

Ranson, S. W., and Clark, S. L.: Anatomy of the Nervous System. 9th ed. Philadelphia, W. B. Saunders Company, 1953. This is one of the more popular of the current neuroanatomy textbooks. It is well arranged, contains a great deal of information, and has excellent illustrations.

Strong, O., and Elwyn, A.: Human Neuroanatomy. 3rd ed. Baltimore, Williams & Wilkins Company, 1953. This textbook contains some particularly good illustrations and presents clearly the fundamental aspects of neuroanatomy.

CHAPTER 3

The Peripheral Nervous System

THE PERIPHERAL nervous system includes the cranial nerves, dorsal and ventral roots, and spinal nerves with their peripheral branches, as well as certain portions of a special division, the autonomic nervous system. The term *peripheral nerve* ordinarily refers to those nerves arising from plexuses formed by spinal nerves. This terminological distinction between spinal and peripheral nerves is important from the standpoint of differences in the distribution of these two types of nerves. These differences are discussed in the section on Spinal Nerves and Peripheral Nerves (p. 34).

A nerve is a collection of nerve fibers visible to the naked eye. Each fiber is so small that it cannot be seen with the naked eye, and hundreds or thousands are necessary to form a nerve. Thus, according to the number of constituent fibers, a nerve may be as large as a man's finger, or so small as to be barely visible. The nature of these fibers is discussed in Chap. 6. An idea of their function can nevertheless be introduced at this time. Each fiber in a nerve is a process of a nerve cell, a nerve cell with all its processes being often called a neuron. Nerve fibers conduct nerve impulses between non-nervous tissues and the central nervous system, and between various parts of the central nervous system. Those impulses that travel toward or into the central nervous system are *sensory* or *afferent;* those that leave are *motor* or *efferent.* Nearly all nerves contain both afferent and efferent fibers and are, therefore, mixed nerves.

Many nerves are distinguished by the presence of a local en-

28

largement called a *ganglion,* consisting mainly of bodies of neurons. Ganglia associated with afferent fibers are located nearer the central nervous system than those in efferent paths. Ganglia associated with efferent fibers are always part of the autonomic system.

Cranial Nerves

Cranial nerves are complex structures that follow complicated paths to the peripheral structures they serve. Detailed descriptions of their distributions can be found in anatomical textbooks. At this time only the general areas that they supply will be indicated. The usual method of description groups the cranial nerves into twelve pairs.

I. Olfactory Nerve. The filaments composing this nerve arise in the olfactory mucous membrane of the upper part of the nasal cavity. The fibers end in the olfactory bulb. The olfactory tract runs backward from the bulb and ends at the base of the brain near the optic chiasma (Fig. 9, p. 16). All these structures are associated with the sense of smell (Chap. 12).

In lower forms there is a nerve which is anatomically associated with the olfactory system. This is the *nervus terminalis.* Functionally, it appears to mediate the taste of substances entering the nasal cavity. The nervus terminalis in man is so rudimentary that it will not be considered here.

II. Optic Nerve. This nerve arises from the *retina* of the eye (p. 191). It runs posteriorly and, in joining the other optic nerve, forms the optic chiasma (Fig. 9, p. 16). Two bundles, the *optic tracts,* extend posteriorly from the chiasma, proceed around the cerebral peduncles, and end near the superior colliculi. These structures are concerned with vision (see Chap. 12). The optic nerves and tracts are not true peripheral nerves, but rather fiber tracts of the central nervous system, connecting brain and retina. The retina is a part of the central nervous system.

III. Oculomotor Nerve. After its origin from the midbrain (Fig. 15, p. 22), the oculomotor nerve runs anteriorly into the orbit, where it ends in muscles that attach to the eyeball and move it in various directions. A portion of the nerve is distributed to certain involuntary muscles within the eye.

IV. Trochlear Nerve. The trochlear nerve is a bundle of fibers that arises from the back of the midbrain around which it winds

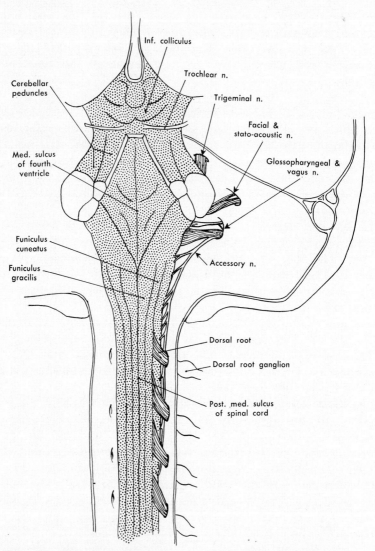

Figure 19. Diagram of the posterior aspect of the brain stem, spinal cord, and certain cranial and spinal nerves. The cerebellum has been removed to expose the floor of the fourth ventricle. The glossopharyngeal, vagus and accessory nerves leave the skull through the same foramen (jugular foramen). The upper one or two filaments constitute the glossopharyngeal nerve. The portion of the accessory nerve arising from the medulla oblongata joins the vagus nerve and is distributed to the larynx; that portion derived from the spinal cord continues separately (but is not shown) to the sternocleidomastoid and trapezius muscles. The hypoglossal nerves are not visible in this view.

(Fig. 19), to run anteriorly into the orbit. Here it ends in a single muscle attached to the eyeball.

V. Trigeminal Nerve. The trigeminal nerve has a motor and sensory root, both attached to the side of the pons. Near the pons, the sensory root has an enlargement, the *semilunar ganglion,* from which three large branches arise to be distributed to the muscles of mastication, to the skin of the face and part of the scalp, to the mucous membrane of the mouth and nasal cavity, to the eye (especially the cornea), to the teeth, and to the dura mater. The motor root joins that branch which is distributed to the muscles of mastication.

VI. Abducens Nerve. The abducens nerve arises from the front of the pons, just above its junction with the medulla oblongata (Fig. 7, p. 14). It enters the orbit, where it supplies a single muscle attached to the eyeball.

VII. Facial Nerve. This nerve is attached laterally, just at the junction of the pons and medulla oblongata (Fig. 7, p. 14). Its main distribution is to the muscles of expression (the facial muscles), located around the mouth, nose and eyes, and on the forehead and scalp. Some fibers are also distributed to the mucous membrane of the anterior two-thirds of the tongue (for taste), and some to certain of the salivary glands and to the lacrimal gland. The *geniculate ganglion* is found on the nerve in its course through the skull.

VIII. Stato-acoustic. Formerly called auditory or acoustic, the new term better reflects its function, but for simplicity it can be called the eighth nerve. It is attached, laterally, at the junction of the pons and medulla oblongata (Figs. 19 and 109, p. 207). It has *cochlear* and *vestibular* divisions, each of which arises in the inner ear. Each has a small ganglion along its course in the inner ear, called *spiral* and *vestibular ganglia,* respectively. These nerves are associated with the sense of hearing and of balance or equilibrium.

IX. Glossopharyngeal Nerve. This nerve is closely associated with, and hard to distinguish from, the next nerve. There is a series of nerve rootlets attached to the lateral surface of the medulla oblongata (Fig. 19). The upper one or two of these rootlets form the glossopharyngeal nerve, which supplies the mucous membrane and a muscle of the throat (pharynx), a salivary gland, and the mucous membrane of the posterior third of the tongue for taste. There are two ganglia along its course, the *superior* and the *inferior*.

X. Vagus Nerve. The majority of the rootlets mentioned previously form the vagus nerve, which supplies the mucous membrane of the pharynx and larynx and also the muscles of these organs. In addition, it has a complex distribution to viscera in the thorax and abdomen. It has two main ganglia, the *superior* and the *inferior,* which are found on the nerve within and just below its foramen of exit. The position of the vagus is shown in Fig. 19.

XI. Accessory Nerve. The lower of the nerve rootlets from the medulla oblongata joins others which have ascended through the foramen magnum from the cervical spinal cord. The accessory nerve formed by this mingling of fibers (Fig. 19) then divides. One division is composed of fibers arising from the medulla oblongata. This part joins the vagus nerve and is distributed with it to the muscles of pharynx and larynx. The other division is composed of fibers arising from the spinal cord and ultimately supplies two muscles, the *trapezius* and the *sternocleidomastoid.*

XII. Hypoglossal Nerve. This nerve is formed from a number of rootlets attached to the ventrolateral surface of the medulla oblongata, between the pyramid and olive. It supplies the muscles of the tongue.

Spinal Roots and Spinal Nerves

Ordinarily a pair of dorsal roots and a pair of ventral roots can be traced to the foramina between adjacent vertebrae. Near or in each foramen is an ovoid swelling of each dorsal root, the *dorsal root ganglion.* Just beyond this point each dorsal root is joined by the corresponding ventral root. The spinal nerve formed by this junction then makes its exit through the foramen. The first pair of spinal nerves leaves between the first cervical vertebra and the base of the skull; consequently the remaining cervical spinal nerves leave above the corresponding vertebrae, with the exception of the eighth cervical nerve. Since there are but seven cervical vertebrae, the eighth nerve leaves above the first thoracic vertebra. Below this level the spinal nerves leave below the corresponding vertebrae. There are, then, seven cervical vertebrae and eight pairs of cervical spinal nerves; twelve thoracic vertebrae and twelve pairs of thoracic nerves; five lumbar vertebrae and five pairs of lumbar nerves; one sacrum but five pairs of sacral nerves, because embryologically there are five sacral verte-brae; and for the coccyx, usually one pair of coccygeal nerves. The remainder, if any, are rudimentary. The part of the spinal cord from which a pair of spinal nerves arises is sometimes called a segment (first thoracic nerves from first thoracic segment), mainly because of correspondence with the segmented vertebral column.

The nerve fibers in the dorsal roots carry afferent impulses to the spinal cord, while those of the ventral roots carry efferent im-pulses away from the spinal cord. The spinal nerves, because they

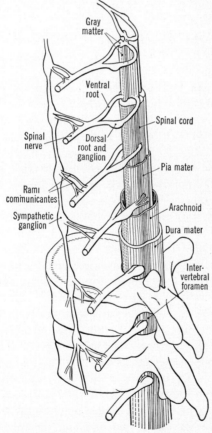

Gray matter

Ventral root

Spinal cord

Spinal nerve

Dorsal root and ganglion

Pia mater

Rami communicantes

Sympathetic ganglion

Arachnoid

Dura mater

Inter-vertebral foramen

Figure 20. The spinal cord and meninges within the vertebral canal. The rami communicantes join the ventral rami of spinal nerves. The dorsal rami are not shown.

are formed by dorsal and ventral roots, are mixed nerves, and carry both types of impulses.

Spinal Nerves and Peripheral Nerves

The spinal cord may be regarded as segmented, with one pair of spinal nerves for each segment. In the distribution of spinal nerves to the body this segmentation is more or less retained, in spite of the fact that in the brachial and lumbosacral regions the spinal nerves enter into complicated *plexuses.*

After leaving the intervertebral foramen, each spinal nerve divides into a dorsal and ventral ramus (Fig. 21). These are not distributed haphazardly, but in a fairly definite pattern over the body.

Distribution of the Dorsal Rami. These branches supply the muscles of the back, and the skin of the back in the areas indicated in Fig. 22.

Distribution of the Ventral Rami. The ventral rami of the first four cervical nerves supply the muscles of the front of the neck: those, for instance, which bend the head forward and turn it to one side or the other. Branches also supply the skin areas indicated in Fig. 22.

The ventral rami of the last four cervical nerves, as well as that of the first thoracic nerve, form the *brachial plexus* by a series of communicating branches (Fig. 23). Peripheral nerves emerge from this plexus and supply the skin and muscles of the shoulder and upper limb.*

It might be supposed that spinal nerves would lose their identity in this or in any plexus. As a matter of fact, the spinal nerves are still distributed in a segmental manner, and this is particularly true for the innervation of skin. That is to say, the upper spinal nerves entering the brachial plexus eventually supply the lateral part of the upper limb, while the lower spinal nerves supply the medial part. The distribution is shown in Fig. 24. This segmental supply has not been determined by dissection, however, because the fibers from the spinal nerves are too intermingled in the plexus. It has been possible to trace their ultimate distribution only by noting specific effects after disease, surgical operation, and animal experiments in which specific spinal nerves are destroyed.

---

* Those who are interested in the names of these nerves, their course and distribution, should refer to the anatomical textbooks cited in the first two chapters.

It is on the findings by such methods that the distribution shown in Fig. 24 is based. This figure also indicates that the areas supplied by peripheral nerves (see Fig. 22) are usually quite different, except in the thorax and abdomen, from the areas supplied by spinal nerves. The differences are illustrated in Fig. 25, which shows that any one spinal nerve may contribute to several peripheral nerves, and that any one peripheral nerve may carry fibers from several spinal nerves. Such distinctions are of the utmost importance in determining the location of neurological disorders

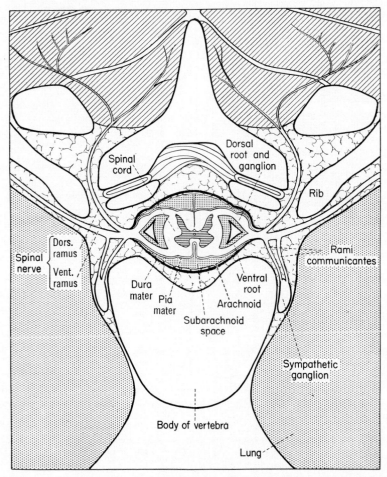

Figure 21. Drawing of a horizontal section of the spinal cord, meninges and spinal nerves.

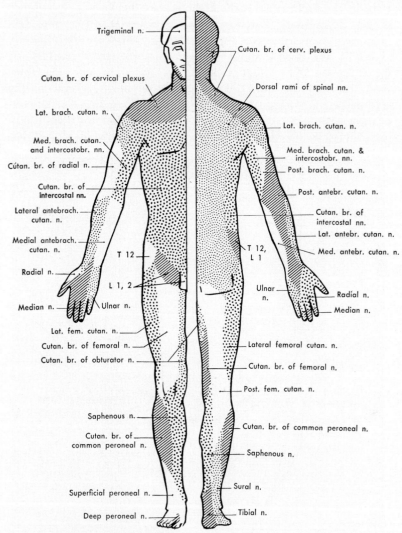

Figure 22. Diagram of the distribution of peripheral nerves to skin. The left half of the figure represents the anterior surface of the body, the right half the posterior. Note the differences between this type of distribution and that illustrated for spinal nerves in Figure 24. Only in the trunk are the patterns similar. The skin of the trunk is supplied segmentally by intercostal and subcostal nerves, by cutaneous branches of the lumbar plexus and by dorsal rami of spinal nerves.

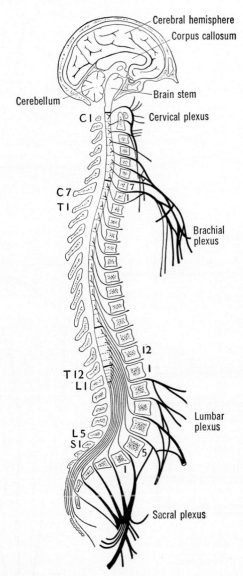

Figure 23. Drawing of the brain and cord in situ. The brain is shown in the median plane (see Fig. 11, p. 19). Although not illustrated, the first cervical vertebra articulates with the base of the skull. The letters along the vertebral column indicate cervical, thoracic, lumbar, and sacral. Note that the cord ends at the upper border of the second lumbar vertebra.

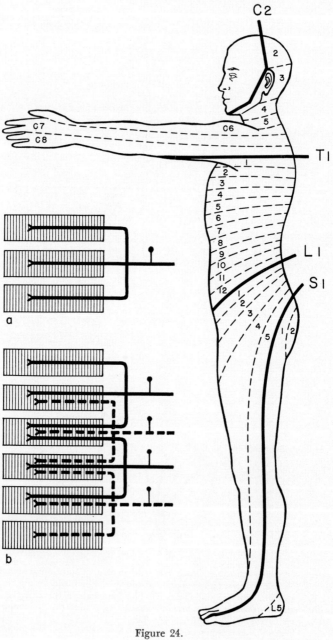

Figure 24.

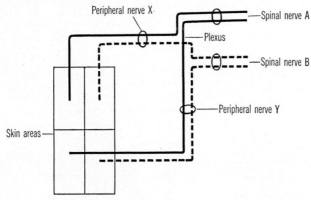

Figure. 25. Schematic representation of peripheral nerve distribution from a plexus formed by spinal nerves. Spinal nerve *A* enters a plexus and reaches an area of skin by way of peripheral nerves *X* and *Y*. Spinal nerve *B* also enters the plexus and reaches a different area of skin by way of peripheral nerves *X* and *Y*. Peripheral nerves *X* and *Y*, therefore, each contain parts of the two spinal nerves.

affecting these structures. There is, however, considerable overlap between sensory nerve distribution. The area which any one spinal or peripheral nerve supplies overlaps into the area supplied by its neighbor. When a nerve is cut or otherwise destroyed, the area in which function is lost is smaller than the area to which the nerve is distributed.

The ventral rami of the thoracic nerves course below the ribs and are distributed to the skin and muscles of the thorax and abdomen. These *thoraco-abdominal nerves* do not form plexuses, but, instead, remain separate so that their segmental distribution is quite apparent.

The ventral rami of the lumbar and sacral nerves unite to form the *lumbar, sacral* and *pudendal plexuses* (Fig. 23), from which

Figure 24. Schematic representation of the distribution of spinal nerves to skin. Each numbered zone refers to an area of skin supplied by the spinal nerve of the corresponding number. The letters refer to cervical, thoracic, lumbar and sacral. Thus, the zones between C 2 and T 1 are supplied by cervical nerves. The first cervical nerve rarely gives any significant supply to skin. Skin above C 2 is supplied by the trigeminal nerve. The diagram does not show variation or overlap. The latter is illustrated in *a* and *b*, showing, for example, that in the trunk region each spinal nerve sends branches to at least three segments (*a*), and each segment has branches from at least three spinal nerves (*b*). Therefore, if a single spinal nerve is cut, the segment it supplies will still receive fibers from adjacent nerves. Sensation will be diminished but not lost. (Data based on Keegan and Garrett, Anat. Rec., vol. 102, 1948.)

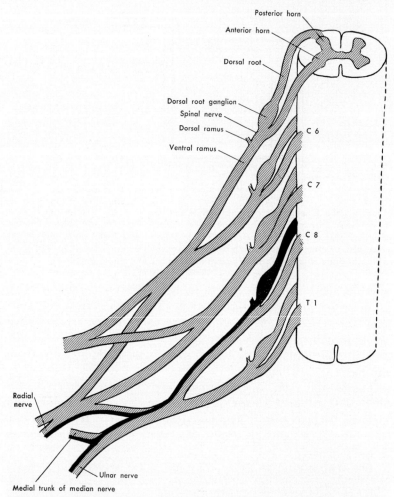

Figure 26. Diagram of the manner in which dorsal and ventral roots form spinal nerves, which in turn form a plexus (brachial). C 6, sixth cervical segment of the spinal cord, etc. Also shown is the fact that sensory fibers from a single dorsal root (C 8, solid black) may be distributed by several peripheral nerves. Many branches of the plexus are not shown.

peripheral nerves arise to supply the skin and muscles of the pelvis, hip region and lower limbs. Here, again, Fig. 24 illustrates the segmental nature of the spinal nerves in contrast to the peripheral nerves (Fig. 22).

The Segmental Supply of Muscles. Segmental distribution is less apparent in muscles than in skin because muscles, in their process of formation in the embryo and fetus, may migrate some distance from their place of origin. For instance, the diaphragm, which separates the thoracic and abdominal cavities, was originally formed in part in the cervical region. It later descends, but, in so doing, carries along its nerve supply from the cervical spinal cord. For many other muscles the complexity of their nerve supply is due to the fact that they develop in areas supplied by several spinal nerves. Because of this, most muscles are supplied by two or more spinal nerves. There is, nevertheless, a craniocaudal sequence in that the distal parts of limbs are supplied by more caudally situated spinal nerves. For example, muscles of the shoulder are largely supplied by the cervical nerves of the brachial plexus, whereas the muscles of the hand are mainly supplied by the first thoracic spinal nerve. Since most muscles are supplied by two or more spinal nerves, section of one such nerve will result in weakness, not total paralysis, of that muscle.

Differences between Cranial and Spinal Nerves. Cranial nerves are attached to the brain at irregular rather than regular intervals. Although not apparent by gross examination, the optic nerves are not true peripheral nerves, but are extensions of brain substance. Cranial nerves are not formed of dorsal and ventral roots; as a consequence, there is a marked variation in afferent and efferent components between them. Some cranial nerves have more than one ganglion, while others have none. There are other marked differences which, however, cannot be discussed until certain functional aspects are considered in subsequent chapters.

Autonomic Nervous System

Some branches of cranial nerves and certain branches of many spinal nerves contain motor fibers that supply viscera in the thorax, abdomen and pelvis, and most of the glands and blood vessels in the body. These special fibers supplying visceral structures comprise the peripheral portions of the *autonomic nervous system*.

Sympathetic Division of the Autonomic Nervous System. There is a long nerve trunk on each side of the vertebral bodies that extends from the base of the skull to the coccyx. Each is known as the *sympathetic trunk*. Ganglia are present at fairly regular intervals along these trunks. Three or more pairs of ganglia occur in the neck, usually ten to twelve in the thorax, and a variable number of pairs in the abdomen and pelvis. Branches of the trunks are distributed to the organs of these areas and form extensive plexuses. Ganglia also occur in the plexuses, and in the abdomen have been given the names *celiac, mesenteric, splanchnic,* and *renal.* They are of the same structure and function as those in the sympathetic trunks.

Branches from the sympathetic trunks are also given to all the spinal nerves just after they emerge from the intervertebral foramina. These are called *rami communicantes.* These rami are illustrated in Figs. 20 and 21, and are discussed further in Chap. 13.

The sympathetic trunks, their connections with the rest of the nervous system, and their branches to viscera constitute the sympathetic division of the autonomic nervous system.

Parasympathetic Division of the Autonomic Nervous System. Part of this division includes those cranial nerves supplying visceral structures. These are the oculomotor, facial, glossopharyngeal, vagus and accessory nerves. There is also a sacral portion composed of branches of the second and third (sometimes third and fourth) sacral nerves that supply viscera in the pelvis. Numerous ganglia occur in the parasympathetic division, but are not located in a definite trunk. Instead, they are scattered, being found in or near the organs supplied.

During the course of their distribution, sympathetic and parasympathetic fibers become intermingled. This is especially true in the thorax and abdomen, where branches of the sympathetic trunks and of the vagus nerves cannot be easily separated by dissection.

Physiological differences between sympathetic and parasympathetic systems are striking, and are discussed in Chap. 13.

Summary

Attached to the base of the brain and to the brain stem are twelve pairs of cranial nerves which have complex distributions to cranial, cervical, thoracic and abdominal structures.

Thirty-one pairs of dorsal and ventral roots are attached to the spinal cord at regular intervals. Each dorsal root joins the ventral root of the corresponding side and from the same cord segment to form a spinal nerve. Each spinal nerve leaves the spinal canal and divides into dorsal and ventral rami. The dorsal rami supply the skin and muscles of the back. Ventral rami supply the limbs and the sides and front of the body. In the cervical, brachial, lumbar and sacral regions they enter into plexuses.

Certain branches of spinal nerves, plus sympathetic trunks and associated ganglia, supply motor fibers to viscera, and constitute the sympathetic division of the autonomic nervous system. Branches of certain of the cranial nerves, plus branches of the second and third sacral nerves to the pelvis, form the parasympathetic division.

References

The anatomy textbooks cited in the first chapter contain detailed descriptions of the anatomy of the peripheral nervous system. These and the neuroanatomy textbooks cited in the second chapter also contain sections dealing with the segmental distribution of spinal nerves, as well as the anatomy of the autonomic system.

Haymaker, W., and Woodhall, B.: Peripheral Nerve Injuries. 2nd ed. Philadelphia, W. B. Saunders Company, 1953. This is clear, readable and well-illustrated.

CHAPTER 4

Blood Supply and
Cerebrospinal Fluid

AS BLOOD circulates in the lungs, oxygen becomes bound with hemoglobin, and is thus transported to the tissues. Here oxygen is released. Carbon dioxide is taken up and transported by the blood to the lungs. Blood carries the products of ingested food from the intestines to various tissues. These are but a few of the constantly occurring functions of the blood.

All exchanges take place through the thin walls of tiny vessels, the *capillaries*. The rest of the blood vascular system is designed to bring blood to or away from the capillaries. The arteries, which proceed from the heart, distribute blood to various large regions of the body. The smallest of the arteries (*arterioles*) are highly contractile and are thus able to regulate the amount of blood entering a given region or organ. The capillaries themselves may also open or close and thus affect the amount of blood circulating in an area. From the capillaries, blood enters small vessels, the *venules*. These in turn form larger vessels, the veins, by which the blood is ultimately returned to the heart. The number of capillaries in the body is so great that, if all were open at once, there would not be enough blood to fill them. In any given structure, such as a muscle, most capillaries are closed except during marked activity.

The blood vessels supplying the nervous system form an extensive capillary bed, especially in gray matter such as the cerebral cortex. A few minutes' deprivation of blood suffices to kill some portions of the nervous system.

Blood Supply of the Nervous System

Blood Supply of the Brain. The blood supply of the cranial cavity is derived from two pairs of arteries in the neck. These are the *common carotid* and the *vertebral arteries.*

The common carotid arteries ascend in the neck; below the base of the skull, each divides into *external* and *internal carotid arteries,* the branches of which supply cranial structures. Each internal carotid artery enters the cranial cavity through a canal in the base of the skull, emerges alongside the optic chiasma and

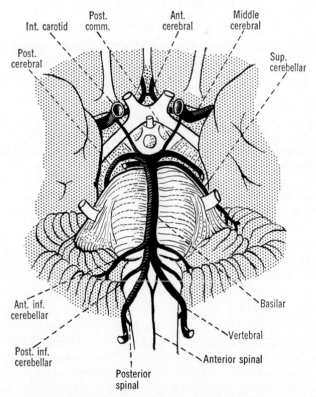

Figure 27. Drawing of the arterial circle at the base of the brain. All small branches and ramifications of various larger branches have been omitted. The anterior communicating vessel connecting the two anterior cerebral arteries is not labelled.

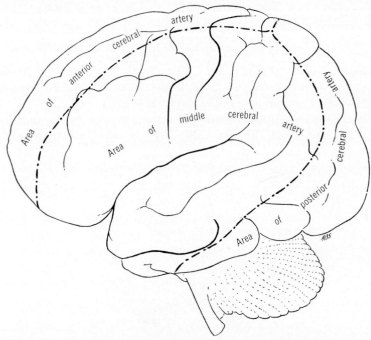

Figure 28. Drawing of the approximate areas on the lateral surface of the hemisphere supplied by the cerebral arteries. The brain stem and cerebellum are supplied by the vertebral and basilar arteries.

divides into an *anterior* and a *middle cerebral artery*. The two anterior cerebral arteries are united by a small communicating branch.

The vertebral arteries ascend in foramina in transverse processes of the cervical vertebrae and enter the cranial cavity through the foramen magnum. Here, on the ventral surface of the medulla oblongata, they join to form a single arterial stem, the *basilar artery*. This artery ascends in front of the brain stem and ends by dividing into two *posterior cerebral arteries*. Each of these is joined to the corresponding middle cerebral by a communicating branch. The various branches at the base of the brain thus form an *arterial circle*, the *circle of Willis* (p. 56). The arrangement of this circle and the branches issuing from it are illustrated in Fig. 27. The cerebral arteries are distributed to those areas of the brain indicated in Fig. 28, and to the interior and medial surface as well. The intercommunication in the arterial circle is extensive enough so that an interruption of blood flow in one of its component arteries does not impair the circulation of blood to the brain, provided there is no arterial disease and the occlusion occurs gradually.

As shown in Fig. 29, all vessels lie in the subarachnoid space before entering brain substance. This space continues for a distance along the vessels after they enter nerve tissue. After repeated branchings the arteries form capillaries. The veins arising from the capillaries return to the subarachnoid space and eventually empty into the dural sinuses. These in turn empty into the internal jugular veins by which the blood returns to the heart.

The brain stem receives its blood supply from the basilar artery as that vessel ascends on its ventral surface. The cerebellum receives branches from the vertebral arteries as well as from the basilar.

Blood Supply of the Meninges (Dura Mater). The main blood supply of the dura mater is by the middle meningeal branches of the external carotid arteries. Each ascends through a foramen in

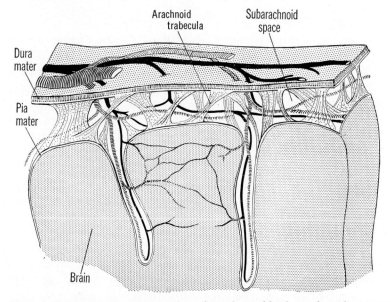

Figure 29. Schematic representation of meninges, blood vessels and nervous tissue. Arteries (black) and veins are shown as they pierce the dura mater and run in the subarachnoid space. The subarachnoid space is a meshwork filled with cerebrospinal fluid. The pia mater is structurally similar to arachnoid. It forms a condensation on the surface of the brain, together with neuroglial fibers on the inner side. Where vessels enter nervous tissue they carry with them the loose meningeal tissue, so that, in effect, potential spaces reach as far as nerve cells.

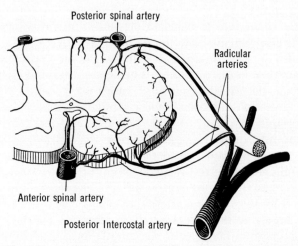

Figure 30. The arterial supply of one half of the spinal cord. Note the anas-
tomoses of the various branches. Most of the extensive branching within the substance of the cord has been omitted.

the base of the skull and then lies between the dura mater and the
skull. Their special importance is due to the fact that they may be
torn or otherwise damaged in skull injuries. In such cases there is
severe bleeding which, because it occurs between the dura mater
and the skull, is known as extradural or epidural hemorrhage, and
which may cause severe symptoms because of pressure on the brain.

Blood Supply of the Spinal Cord, Spinal Roots and Spinal Nerves.
As the vertebral arteries ascend, branches arise which run inward
through the intervertebral foramina. These in turn form branches
which accompany the spinal roots to the spinal cord. As the vertebral arteries unite to form the basilar artery, an anterior and posterior *spinal artery* arises from each. The two anterior spinal arteries
join. The resulting single vessel descends in the anterior median
fissure of the spinal cord. The posterior spinal arteries descend
separately, lateral to the posterior median sulcus, but communicate
frequently across the midline. Both these spinal vessels communicate with the branches entering with the spinal roots. The intra-
spinal blood supply is indicated in Fig. 30.

There are branches of the posterior intercostal and lumbar arteries (from the aorta) which enter the vertebral canal in the thoracic and abdominal regions at irregular intervals. These accompany
spinal roots to the portion of the cord which they supply. The blood

supply of the spinal cord, then, is derived from these and from the vertebral arteries. Blood is eventually returned by a system of vertebral veins which follow much the same anatomical course as the arteries.

The roots and spinal nerves receive their blood supply from those branches mentioned which accompany the roots to the cord. In addition, branches of the sacral arteries supply the roots in the sacral canal.

Blood Supply of the Peripheral Nerves. This involves more detail than can be given here. It can be stated simply that each nerve receives branches from the arteries in each of the different regions through which the nerve may happen to run. For instance, the

Anterior cerebral artery

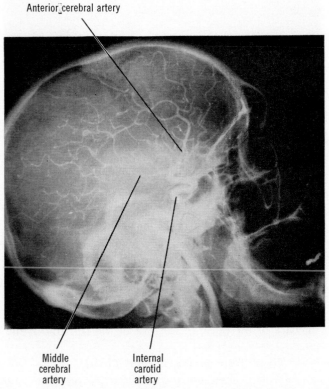

Middle
cerebral
artery

Internal
carotid
artery

Figure 31. Angiogram taken by injecting a radiopaque material into the common carotid artery, and x-ray photograph taken as the material circulated through the arterial system. The internal carotid, middle cerebral and anterior cerebral arteries are visualized. (Courtesy of Drs. E. S. Gurdjian and J. E. Webster.)

Basilar artery   Posterior cerebral artery

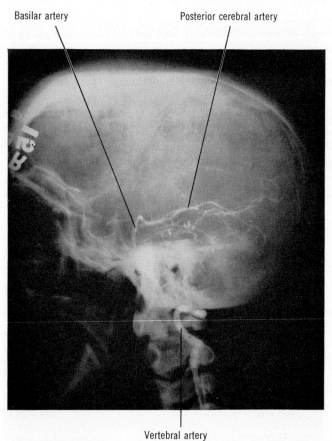

Vertebral artery

Figure 32.   Angiogram taken by injecting a radiopaque material into a vertebral artery. One of the vertebral arteries is visible, as is the basilar artery and several of its branches, including superior cerebellar and posterior cerebral. (Courtesy of Drs. E. S. Gurdjian and J. E. Webster.)

sciatic nerve with its branches extends from the sacrum to the toes. In so doing it receives blood from an artery in the pelvis, in the thigh, in back of the knee, in the calf of the leg, and in the ankle and foot.

Study of Blood Flow in the Cranial Cavity.   There are many ways to study blood flow, but few of them give any direct information. Most are nevertheless quite valuable. One can, for example, compare gas tensions in venous blood with those in arterial blood and thus get an estimate of metabolic activity. Nerves can be stimulated and the effect on blood flow observed. Observation in such cases usually involves opening the skull or else placing a transparent plastic window in the skull so that vessels can be watched and photographed. One type of study involves the visualization of blood vessels by injecting a radiopaque dye into an artery in the neck (either common carotid or vertebral) and then getting x-ray photographs as the dye circulates through the cranial vessels. This method is especially useful from a clinical standpoint, particularly in detecting abnormalities in vascular patterns, interruptions or blocks of blood flow and shifts in position of blood vessels from tumors or other lesions. The method is called *angiography*. Figures 31 and 32 illustrate some angiograms.

Experimental studies of arteries on the surface of the brain indicate that they are relatively unaffected by vasomotor impulses from the autonomic nervous system. Rather, they respond to changes in gas tensions, tending to increase in diameter as CO_2 tension increases, and decrease in diameter as O_2 tension increases.

Clinical Importance of Blood Supply

In vascular disorders the nervous system is frequently affected by derangements of its blood supply. The results are more or less familiar to all under the lay terms "stroke" or "apolexy." These terms, however, cover a multitude of events.

Arteries larger than 0.5 mm. in diameter may be affected by *atherosclerosis,* a degenerative process affecting the inner lining of the vessels. The thickening which results may partially close the lumen of a vessel, and this occlusion may become complete by a clotting of blood. This is known as a *thrombosis*. In such instances the area of the nervous system deprived of its blood supply degenerates and softens. If the portion of the nervous system so affected is an important one, the results may be severe and even fatal.

Arteries smaller than 0.5 mm. in diameter, that is to say, arterioles, are never affected by atherosclerosis, but instead by a diffuse thickening of the entire vessel wall, an *arteriolosclerosis*. If, as a result, the vessels become partially occluded, resistance to blood flow increases and blood pressure rises (hypertension). Vessels damaged by various disorders may rupture, and the consequence is an *intracerebral hemorrhage*.

These are but some of the so-called *cerebrovascular accidents,*

and occur most frequently in the region of the internal capsule of
the brain.

Formation and Circulation of Cerebrospinal Fluid

The anatomy of the ventricles with their chorioid plexuses was
discussed in Chap. 2. The ventricles are lined by a thin membrane, the *ependymal epithelium*. Where it separates the blood
vessels of the chorioid plexuses from the ventricular cavities, it is
known as *chorioidal epithelium*. The chorioidal blood vessels in
the lateral and third ventricles arise from the circle of Willis and,
in the fourth ventricle, from branches of the vertebral arteries.
Blood circulates through the plexuses, and from it is formed an
almost protein-free fluid which passes through the chorioidal epithelium into the ventricles. This cerebrospinal fluid circulates
from the lateral ventricles to the third ventricle, then through the
aqueduct into the fourth ventricle, being joined by more fluid in
the latter two ventricles. It then enters the subarachnoid space
through openings in the walls of the fourth ventricle. There is an
active circulation in the subarachnoid space around the brain and
spinal cord (Fig. 33). Eventually the fluid is absorbed into the
blood stream after filtration through small tufts or *villi* of arach-
noidal tissue which project into the dural venous sinuses (Fig. 33).
Thus the brain and spinal cord are literally surrounded by fluid,
and nowhere do they actually touch the dura mater.

It is possible that some cerebrospinal fluid is formed by nerve
cells, and reaches the subarachnoid space by way of loose tissue
around blood vessels. Also, some cerebrospinal fluid seeps along
cranial and spinal nerves to tissue lymphatics and thereby eventually reaches the venous system. It is difficult to tell how much is
absorbed by this route, but it is possible that the amount is considerable.

One of the important factors that keeps cerebrospinal fluid circulating is that the pressure in the capillaries at the site of formation is higher than that at the site of absorption. The dependence
of cerebrospinal fluid circulation upon this pressure gradient may
be illustrated by a simple experiment during the measurement of
fluid pressure at *lumbar puncture*. If both internal jugular veins
are compressed manually in the neck, there is shortly a prompt
rise in the pressure of cerebrospinal fluid, because the venous
occlusion prevents blood from leaving the cranial cavity. Venous

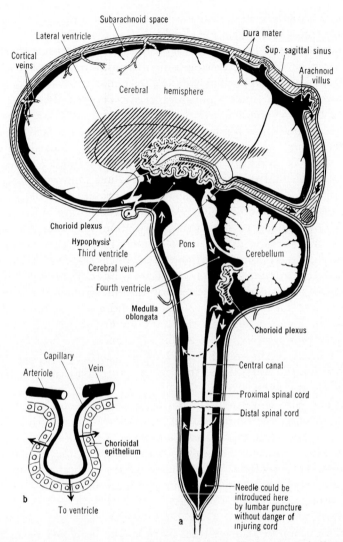

Figure 33. *a*, Circulation of cerebrospinal fluid (in black); arrows indicate the direction of circulation. The drawing represents a median section of the nervous system and therefore shows third ventricle, cerebral aqueduct, fourth ventricle, and central canal, with the approximate size and location of one of the lateral ventricles indicated by oblique lines. Note the aperture in the fourth ventricle by which fluid reaches the subarachnoid space. Note also one of the arachnoid villi through which fluid enters venous blood in a dural sinus. *b*, Fundamental plan of chorioid plexuses. Cerebrospinal fluid is formed from blood plasma and passes through chorioidal epithelium into the ventricular space. (Modified from A. T. Rasmussen: The Principal Nervous Pathways, 3rd ed. Macmillan Company, 1945.)

pressure promptly rises, and the gradient decreases. Since arterial blood continues to enter the cranial cavity, the only result can be a general increase in cerebrospinal fluid pressure. Other important factors in circulation are changes in the position of the body and changes in venous pressure with respiration.

By thrusting a lumbar puncture needle between the third and fourth lumbar vertebrae into the subarachnoid space, the pressure of the cerebrospinal fluid can be measured by an attached manometer. Figure 33 shows that, since the spinal cord ends above this level, there is no danger of injuring it by such a lumbar puncture. In the horizontal position, cerebrospinal fluid pressure ordinarily amounts to 10 to 20 mm. of mercury (approximately 100 to 200 mm. of water) at this region. Abnormal conditions, such as the growth of a tumor, by obstructing circulation, may cause the total intracranial pressure to rise to 400 or more mm. of water. Cerebrospinal fluid may also be withdrawn through the needle and examined for bacteria, cells or chemical compounds not normally present. The fluid may be tested for various serological reactions, such as tests for syphilis. Fluid that is withdrawn may be replaced by air, or by an opaque oil. Since the air or oil may be detected by x-ray photography, the position of a mass that may interfere with normal cerebrospinal fluid dynamics, such as a tumor, may be determined. Anesthetics, such as procaine, may also be introduced for spinal anesthesia.

Air may also be introduced into ventricles by means of a needle thrust through the brain into the ventricles after a small hole is drilled in the skull cap. A *ventriculogram* is a radiogram of ventricles filled with air. The subarachnoid space of the cranial cavity may be visualized by air introduced at lumbar puncture (*pneumoencephalography*). Such air enters the ventricular system in part, usually the fourth ventricle.

Not all the functions of the cerebrospinal fluid are known. It serves to minimize damage from blows to the head and neck; and it may be concerned in the transfer to the blood circulation of metabolic substances resulting from physiological activity of the brain and cord.

Of considerable importance is the fact that substances in the blood may not enter the brain (*blood-brain barrier*) or cerebrospinal fluid (*blood-cerebrospinal fluid barrier*). For example, many dyes, after intravenous injection, may stain tissues of nearly the whole body, but not the brain. Chemicals that are important in the metabolism of the nervous system may be difficult to study because, upon intravenous injection, they may not pass the blood-brain barrier (see glutamic acid, p. 351). The sites of these barriers are not known with any certainty. It may be postulated that if a substance is present in high concentration in the blood, it may diffuse through chorioidal cells into ventricles (perhaps also between cells) and thus enter cerebrospinal fluid. The main barrier is probably the chorioidal cells. The substance can enter brain tissue by diffusing through blood vessels. The barrier may be the endothelial cells of the capillaries. It is also held that pia-glial sheaths around capillaries constitute a barrier.

Clinical Importance of Cerebrospinal Fluid

The hydrodynamics of cerebrospinal fluid are important from a clinical standpoint. It was mentioned that such abnormal conditions as tumors may cause an increase in total intracranial pressure. When this occurs, it is because of interference with circulation or absorption of the fluid. For instance, if fluid is prevented from leaving the fourth ventricle, it nevertheless continues to be formed and cerebrospinal fluid pressure rises. In the adult the skull is rigid and cannot give way; therefore the brain is compressed.

Hydrocephalus is a disorder with excess cerebrospinal fluid, usually due to interference with circulation or absorption of the fluid. The skull bones do not unite for many years after birth, hence in hydrocephalus in children, the excess fluid forces the bones apart until the head reaches an enormous size, with the forehead overhanging and the skull thinned out. The brain is usually compressed, but not to the extent which may result from a severe hydrocephalus in the adult. In many cases, the damage is severe enough to interfere with normal development, and may even result in idiocy. In such cases, death usually occurs at a relatively early age by reason of interference with important areas in the brain stem or of lessened resistance to infectious processes.

Summary

The blood supply of the brain and meninges is derived from the common carotid and vertebral arteries; that of the spinal cord and its roots is derived from the vertebral, intercostal, lumbar and sacral vessels. The peripheral nerves receive their blood supply from the main arteries in the regions through which they pass.

Some of the branches of the arterial circle at the base of the brain supply the chorioid plexuses of the lateral and third ventricles; branches of the vertebral arteries supply those in the fourth ventricle. Cerebrospinal fluid formed in the plexuses enters the ventricles and circulates through them. Fluid then enters the subarachnoid space and is eventually absorbed into the blood stream through the arachnoid villi in the dural sinuses. The pressure of this fluid may be measured in the spinal subarachnoid space by introducing a hypodermic needle with a manometer attached.

Names in Neurology

Willis, Thomas (1621–1675)

An English physician, Thomas Willis probably holds first place among the seventeenth century neuro-anatomists. In 1664 he published his famous *Cerebri Anatome,* which classified the cranial nerves and was the most complete description of the anatomy of the nervous system of its day. In this work he described the circle of arteries which is now named after him.

References

Descriptions of the blood supply of the nervous system and the structures concerned with cerebrospinal fluid are available in the textbooks cited in the first three chapters. For discussions of the physiology and pathology of the cerebrospinal fluid, see the textbook by Grinker and Bucy cited in Chap. 18 (p. 328).

Davson, H.: Physiology of the Ocular and Cerebrospinal Fluids. London, J. & A. Churchill, Ltd., 1956. A well written book, dealing mainly with physiological and biochemical aspects of these fluids.

CHAPTER 5

Formation and Development
of the Nervous System

IN THE study of the structure of the adult nervous system, questions arise that may be answered more easily by reference to the conditions found in the embryo and fetus. For instance, how does it happen that the adult nervous system is cavitated? How do nerves and ganglia form? The answers to these questions may be had by examination of the embryonic nervous system and the correlation of its subsequent development with the adult arrangement.

General Characteristics of the Cell

A microscopic study of the different tissues of the body shows that they are composed of fundamental units called *cells,* plus "intercellular" substances which lie between them. Cells vary in structure and appearance according to the tissues they compose. Muscle cells, for instance, differ considerably from nerve cells. Nevertheless, cells have certain common characteristics. Each consists of a living, semifluid and complex colloidal substance known as *protoplasm,* which is usually organized into a *nucleus, cytoplasm,* and other structures. The surface of the cell is differentiated as a "cell membrane." The nucleus, a small, rounded or oval body, is separated from the cytoplasm by a "nuclear membrane," and contains variable amounts of *chromatin* material, which stains darkly with basic dyes such as hematoxylin. The chromatin is usually found in *chromosomes,* and part may also be condensed to form

Cytoplasm   Nucleolus

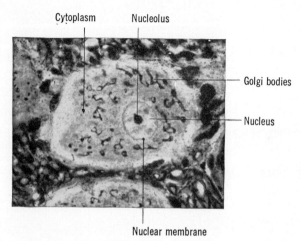

Golgi bodies

Nucleus

Nuclear membrane

Figure 34. Photomicrograph of a dorsal root ganglion cell showing the Golgi apparatus. (From a preparation by Dr. John Mohr.)

small, rounded intranuclear structures called *nucleoli*. The cytoplasm surrounding the nucleus and forming the greater part of most cells usually stains with an acid dye such as eosin, and contains specialized structures such as *mitochondria, Golgi bodies* (p. 69) and various types of granules (Fig. 34). A more elaborate discussion of these cytoplasmic inclusions, the functions of which have not yet been entirely determined, will be found in textbooks of histology, cytology and cytochemistry. Living cells are engaged in complicated chemical processes known collectively as *metabolism*. Most cells are able to reproduce themselves, that is, to divide and form new cells, and many are capable of movement. For a description of these processes one should again refer to special textbooks. In some cellular activities, particularly reproduction, the nucleus seems to be of primary importance.

Cells may vary in size and shape and are usually specialized to perform some particular function, such as secretion, contraction or conduction.

Fertilization and Early Development

The entire body develops from two highly specialized cells: one the *ovum* or egg of the female, and the other the *spermatozoon* or sperm of the male. The ovum is a relatively large cell, especially so in birds. The familiar hen's egg is a good example of a single cell of this type. In the human being it may just reach the limit of visibility, that is, about 100 microns or 0.1 mm. in diameter. The cytoplasm of most ova contains nutrient materials sufficient to provide energy for the early stages of development. The ova also bear, in the chromosomes of their nuclei, factors representing the hereditary characteristics of the female.

The spermatozoon is a small cell, not more than 50 or 60 microns long, consisting of a condensed nucleus and a motile "tail" which, by rapid, whiplike movements, enables the spermatozoon to swim about in the fluid semen. In the chromosomes of its nucleus are the factors representing the hereditary characteristics of the male.

The development of an individual begins with the penetration of an ovum by a sperm cell, thus initiating a process known as fertilization. A series of cell divisions follows the union of ovum and sperm, resulting in the formation of two cells, then four, eight, sixteen, and so on, a process which eventuates in the billions of cells which make up the infant at birth. The stimulation of cell division in the process of fertilization is equalled in importance by the combining of the factors representing maternal and paternal characteristics.

Germ Layer Formation and Differentiation

As the mass of embryonic cells increases in size, certain areas grow at different rates, so that metabolic or physiological gradients are said to exist. For instance, there are surface-interior gradients evidenced by the formation of sheets or layers of cells. There is also a change in growth rate from the head to tail regions, the cephalic region growing and differentiating more rapidly. Local patterns develop within this general axial gradient which are important in later developmental changes.

The sequence of development, then, is an increasing number of cells which are at first arranged in two layers. Within a short time, a third layer makes its appearance. Figure 35 illustrates this by schematic cross sections through young embryos.

Those cells on the back or dorsal portion of the embryo form a layer called *ectoderm*. The ventral layer of cells is referred to as *entoderm*, and the more diffuse collection of cells between the ectoderm and entoderm is termed *mesoderm*. Such structures as the outer skin and the nervous system develop from the ectoderm;

the skeleton, muscles, connective tissue, heart and blood vessels
are derived from mesoderm. From the entoderm come the digestive
and respiratory tracts and their glandular derivatives. This early
arrangement of yet unspecialized cells into a pattern of three germ
layers is characteristic of the vertebrate animal kingdom.

Development of the Nervous System

Formation of the Neural Tube. The dorsal sheet of cells, the
ectoderm, shows a higher metabolic rate in the midline. As a result, differentiation proceeds much more rapidly here, and there
is soon evident a thickened plate extending from head to tail. This
pattern is fundamentally the same for all vertebrates.

The cells at the edge of the plate grow faster than those in the
middle, so that a *neural groove* is formed. This deepens to form a
tubular structure as the cells increase in number. This process is
schematically represented in Fig. 35. As the tube separates from

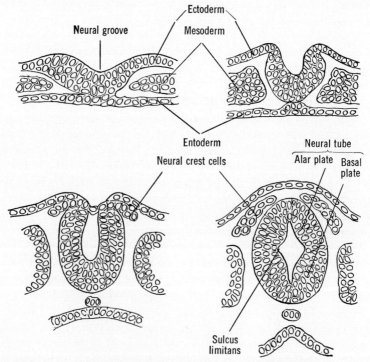

Figure 35.   Transverse sections through embryos of increasing age, illustrating the
formation of the neural tube and associated structures.

the overlying ectoderm, the ectodermal cells at the junction become separated from both and come to lie along the dorsal side of the detached *neural tube*. These cells are known as *neural crest cells* because of their early position over the neural tube. From the neural tube and the neural crest cells the entire adult nervous system is formed, except its blood vessels and certain supporting cells. In spite of subsequent complex morphological changes, the central nervous system remains a tube throughout the lifetime of an individual.

Figure 35 also illustrates the delimitation of the neural tube into alar and basal plates. Cells derived from the basal plate become associated with motor systems, whereas those from the alar plate align themselves with afferent (so-called sensory) mechanisms.

Subdivisions of the Neural Tube. The portion of the neural tube in the head region forms the brain, while that within the vertebral canal becomes the spinal cord.

With the more rapid growth and differentiation in the cranial end of the neural tube, three primary enlargements or vesicles are

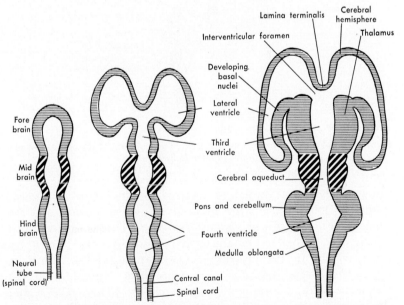

Figure 36. Schematic representation of three- and five-vesicle stage in the development of the brain, with early development of the cerebral hemispheres. The lamina terminalis of the adult brain represents the anterior end of the brain in the embryo.

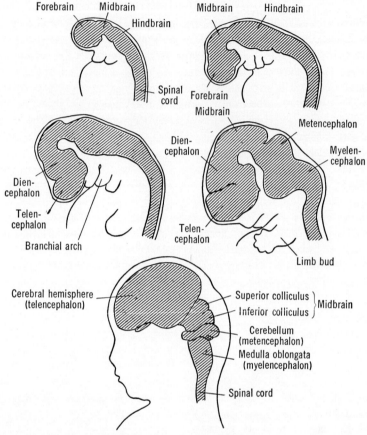

Figure 37.   Schematic representation of the changes in form of the embryonic and
fetal brain. (Modified after Patten.)

formed. The most cranial of these is the *forebrain* or *prosencephalon*. The middle is the *midbrain* or *mesencephalon,* and the caudal, the *hindbrain* or *rhombencephalon*. These are illustrated in Fig. 36. Secondary enlargements or subdivisions shortly become evident in the prosencephalon, forming the *endbrain* or *telencephalon* and *interbrain* or *diencephalon,* and also in the rhombencephalon, forming the *afterbrain* or *metencephalon* and the *marrowbrain* or *myelencephalon.* Figure 37 shows the changes in form throughout embryonic and fetal life. All these vesicles contribute to the brain, the adult derivatives being indicated in

Table 1. Derivatives of the Primary Vesicles

Primary Vesicle	Subdivision	Derivatives	Lumen
Prosen-cephalon	Telen-cephalon	Cerebral cortex, corpus striatum and rhinen-cephalon	Lateral ventricle and part of third ventricle
	Dien-cephalon	Thalamus and hypo-thalamus	Most of third ventricle
Mesen-cephalon	Mesen-cephalon	Collicular region and cerebral peduncles	Cerebral aqueduct
Rhomben-cephalon	Meten-cephalon	Pons and cerebellum	Fourth ventricle
	Myelen-cephalon	Medulla oblongata	Fourth ventricle and part of central canal
Remainder of neural tube		Spinal cord	Most of central canal

Table 1. The neurocele or cavity of the embryonic neural tube forms, in the adult, the ventricles of the brain and the central canal of the medulla oblongata and spinal cord.

Cellular Changes in the Neural Tube. The portion of the neural tube which forms the spinal cord changes less, so that the differentiation of its primitive cells into nerve cells is more easily studied. The neural tube at first consists of a layer of elongated cells, but continuous cell division results in an expansion of the lateral walls (Fig. 38). Some of the cells resulting from this repeated division migrate laterally within the tube to form a *nuclear* or *mantle layer* (Fig. 39), which, in the adult, becomes the gray matter of the spinal cord. Gray matter anywhere in the nervous system is composed mainly of cells. The cells immediately adjacent to the central canal form a single layer of *ependymal cells* which line the ventricular system of the brain and, where the chorioidal plexuses are present, differentiate into chorioidal epithelium.

The cells in the mantle layer of the neural tube follow either of two fundamental changes. They may become *spongioblasts,* which develop into the supporting cells of the nervous system, or they may become *neuroblasts* and develop into nerve cells. Each neuroblast develops an outgrowth or process, the *axon,* which extends peripherally, contributing to and forming with numbers of other

Alar plate of neural tube   Sulcus limitans

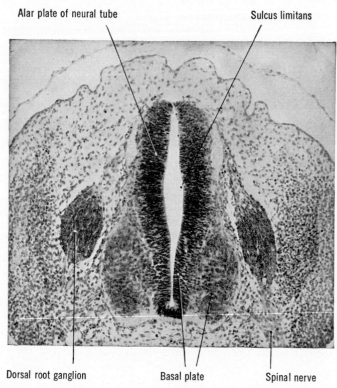

Dorsal root ganglion   Basal plate   Spinal nerve

Figure 38.   Photomicrograph of a cross section of the neural tube of a 10-mm. pig embryo.

axons an outer or *marginal layer* in the tube. This becomes the white matter of the spinal cord. Neuroblasts develop other processes (Fig. 40), called *dendrites,* which extend peripherally for a short distance, but do not reach the marginal layer. The cells are now *multipolar.* Thus, in the early stages, the neural tube exhibits three layers: an inner or ependymal, middle or mantle, and outer or marginal.

Those neuroblasts which lie in the ventral portion of the mantle layer or basal plate send their axons through the marginal layer or white matter and out of the cord (Fig. 38). Here, at regular intervals, larger numbers of axons are collected into ventral roots of spinal nerves. Each ventral root supplies a body area which may be thought of as a transversely oriented "embryo segment." The muscles which the ventral root fibers will supply develop from

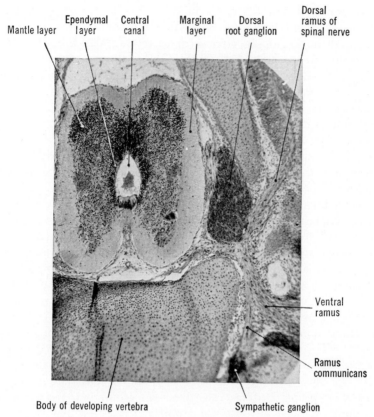

Mantle layer — Ependymal layer — Central canal — Marginal layer — Dorsal root ganglion — Dorsal ramus of spinal nerve

Ventral ramus

Ramus communicans

Body of developing vertebra   Sympathetic ganglion

Figure 39.   Photomicrograph of a cross section of the spinal cord of a 25-mm. pig fetus. Note the spinal nerve leaving through an intervertebral foramen.

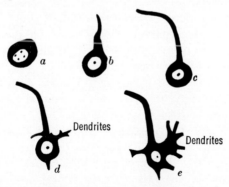

Dendrites

Dendrites

Figure 40.   Drawing of neuroblast growth. *a*, Germinal cell. In *b* and *c* an axon appears and nuclear chromatin forms a nucleolus. In *d* and *e* dendrites appear and increase in number.

tissue which at first lies but a millimeter or less from the neural tube. The first axons traversing this distance establish a path which fibers developing later seem to follow. The factors which determine the growth and termination of fibers may be termed *preneural influences* in that they are operative before the nervous system assumes its functions as a conducting mechanism. For instance, there is a general relationship between the region where a limb bud is developing and the spinal cord at that level such that nerves from this portion of the cord grow into the region. But there is no specific relationship between the axons of the spinal nerves and the muscle fibers developing within the limb bud. It may be predetermined that a certain axon enters a given embryo segment, but within that segment the axon may vary in the exact site of its termination. This is because the direction of its growing tip is influenced by the physical nature of the non-nervous environment, such as obstructions, changes in consistency, stresses and strains, and the like. These are prominent in regions of attachment of limb buds, where they probably influence the formation of plexuses. Once a path is established by the first fibers, however, growth of later axons is much less haphazard. Although growth is nonspecific, variation is not so marked as it might be, because of the short distances traversed and the pattern formed by the earliest fibers. It cannot be denied, however, that there is some specificity which determines that motor and sensory fibers form their proper endings once they have grown into their region of supply. This is an unsolved problem. It may be that this specificity is inherent in the nervous system itself.

Cranial nerves, so far as their efferent portions are concerned, likewise arise as outgrowths of neuroblasts, but the segmental arrangement is not apparent. Furthermore, in the brain the early lateral migration of the neuroblasts is such that many come to lie at the surface. Their axons grow inward, so that the white matter thus formed is internal to the gray matter. This accounts for the fact that the surface or cortex of the cerebral hemispheres and of the cerebellum consists of gray matter.

Migration and Differentiation of Neural Crest Cells. Growth and differentiation of the neural crest cells accompany neural tube changes. The crest divides longitudinally and then becomes segmented. Many of the cells in each neural crest segment develop two processes which grow in opposite directions (*bipolar cells*)

(Fig. 41). Later, there is an eccentric growth of the cell body so that the two processes become fused at their point of origin from the cell body. A *unipolar cell* is thus formed whose single process divides into two branches. From each segment of the neural crest all the peripheral processes (dendrites) accompany corresponding ventral root fibers to form a spinal nerve (Fig. 39). The central processes (axons) from each segment grow into the spinal cord, toward the dorsal portion of the mantle layer (alar plate), thereby forming a dorsal root. The collection of cell bodies in each neural crest segment gives rise to an enlargement, the dorsal root ganglion. With respect to the spinal cord, the dorsal root fibers are afferent in nature.

Afferent fibers in most cranial nerves arise by a similar process, but again the regular sequence is not apparent. The ganglion cells associated with the olfactory and acoustic nerves retain their more primitive cheracteristics as bipolar cells.

Many of the cells in the neural crest and in the mantle layer migrate peripherally and take up positions along the vertebral column and in the abdominal cavity. Here they differentiate into multipolar cells and collect into groups of cells, the sympathetic ganglia and collateral ganglia (celiac, mesenteric, and so forth). Some axons of these sympathetic ganglion cells go to viscera, others by way of rami communicantes to spinal nerves.

One important feature is the formation of the medullae of the adrenal glands by some of the cells migrating from neural crest and mantle layer. Thus, from early stages, the adrenal medullae are intimately associated with the sympathetic part of the autonomic nervous system.

Parasympathetic ganglion cells are probably similarly formed after migration from the central nervous system and neural crest.

There is uncertainty regarding the roles of the neural tube and

Figure 41. Illustration of the manner in which eccentric growth (more rapid growth on one side of the cell) transforms a primitive bipolar cell into a unipolar one.

the neural crest in the formation of autonomic ganglion cells. The latter are said by many to be entirely developed from the neural crest, but there is considerable evidence indicating that the ventral portion of the mantle layer is also concerned.

Not all cells in the neural crest and in the mantle layer become neurons. As mentioned previously, many cells in the mantle layer are spongioblasts. These differentiate into *neuroglia,* a type of specialized supporting cell in the central nervous system. Comparable supporting cells are found in peripheral nerves, where they are known as *neurilemmal cells.* They probably develop from cells which have migrated from the neural crest and ventral mantle layer. They are of ectodermal origin.

With the definitive formation of the vascular system in the embryo, blood vessels soon invade the central nervous system and, in so doing, carry with them a small amount of connective tissue, some of the cells of which apparently form a type of neuroglial cell known as microglia (see Chap. 6). These are said to be the only mesodermal elements of the central nervous system.

Growth and Differentiation after Birth and in the Adult.   At or shortly after birth, cell division in the nervous system stops. Apparently all the cells of the adult are present at this time. This means that when a nerve cell is destroyed, a new one cannot be formed to replace it. Individual cells and their processes, however, continue to grow and enlarge until after puberty.

The spinal cord in the embryo occupies the whole extent of the spinal canal. The vertebrae, however, grow at a much more rapid rate and for a longer time, so that the vertebral column soon surpasses the spinal cord in length. Consequently, the spinal cord ends at an increasingly higher level until, in the adult, it extends only to the level of the first or second lumbar vertebra. Since the spinal nerves leave the canal between the vertebrae, they are "dragged down," as it were, as the disproportion between vertebral and cord levels increases. This accounts for the fact that the spinal canal below the cord is filled with the roots of spinal nerves.

Congenital Defects of the Nervous System

Defects resulting from the maldevelopment of the nervous system are common. These may be as severe as the complete absence of cerebral hemispheres, or even of a head, or they may be as mild as the ordinary variations in the usual neuro-anatomical pattern. The more severe cases are usually monstrosities for whom there is no treatment.

One of the commoner defects is *spina bifida,* which is due to an interference with the normal process of formation and closure of the neural tube. The spinal cord may be affected, and there is usually an incomplete development or absence of some of the vertebral arches. In severe cases, either the meninges or spinal cord or both protrude to the surface, separated from the exterior only by skin and connective tissue. Most spinae bifidae are mild, without accompanying symptoms, and consist in a defect or absence of a vertebral arch, usually the fifth lumbar.

Summary

The structural unit in the body is the cell. Union of two specialized cells, the ovum and the spermatozoon, initiates the development of the embryo. Repetitive cell division leads to the formation of three cellular germ layers—ectoderm, mesoderm, and entoderm. The nervous system arises from ectoderm. A dorsal invagination of the ectoderm forms first a neural groove and then a neural tube. Rapid unequal growth of the cranial end of the neural tube forms three primary vesicles which give rise to five secondary vesicles from which the adult brain is derived. The remainder of the neural tube forms the spinal cord.

Cells in the neural tube form two types of cells: the spongioblasts, which give rise to the neuroglial cells, and the neuroblasts, most of which form nerve cells. Processes of the neuroblasts form the white matter. Some of the processes leave the brain and spinal cord to form fibers of cranial nerves and ventral roots of spinal nerves.

Most neural crest cells form unipolar cells which compose the dorsal root ganglia. The central processes form dorsal roots, and the peripheral ones enter spinal nerves. Some neural crest cells and cells from the mantle layer also migrate peripherally to form neurilemmal cells, sympathetic ganglion cells, and cells of the adrenal medullae.

Names in Neurology

Golgi, Camillo (1844–1926)

Golgi was an Italian anatomist who, in 1883, used silver nitrate to stain multipolar cells and all their processes. His studies and his stain, which was modified by later investigators, formed the basis for many important investigations of the nervous system. He was awarded the Nobel Prize in Physiology and Medicine in 1906, which he shared with S. Ramón y Cajal of Madrid (p. 92). His research was not confined to neuro-anatomy. He made important studies in malaria, especially the relation of fever to the development of parasites within the blood. It was by his staining method that the structures in cytoplasm which now bear his name were first demonstrated.

References

The following are recommended for those seeking further information regarding the development of the nervous system:

Arey, L. B.: Developmental Anatomy. 6th ed. Philadelphia, W. B. Saunders Company, 1954.

Child, C. M.: Origin and Development of the Nervous System. Chicago, University of Chicago Press, 1921. In spite of the lapse of time since it was written, this volume is valuable because of its discussion of the physiological factors in development.

Detwiler, S. R.: Neuroembryology. New York, Macmillan Company, 1936. An extremely valuable monograph on the experimental approach to neuroembryology, dealing particularly with the growth of peripheral nerves.

Gesell, A., and Amatruda, C.: Embryology of Behavior. New York, Harper & Brothers, 1945. A valuable and timely discussion of the early phases of mental and behavioral development.

Hamilton, W. J., Boyd, J. D., and Mossman, H. W.: Human Embryology. 2nd ed. Baltimore, Williams & Wilkins Company, 1952.

Patten, B. M.: Human Embryology. 2nd ed. Philadelphia, Blakiston Company, 1953.

Straus, W. L., Jr.: The concept of nerve-muscle specificity. Biol. Rev., *21*:75–91, 1946. An outstanding review of the relations of nerve and muscle, and of factors in early development.

CHAPTER 6

Microscopic Anatomy of the Nervous System

The Neuron

A STUDY of the minute anatomy of the adult nervous system reveals an extremely complex arrangement of cells. Physiological investigations show that these cells are specialized in that they exhibit to a great degree the phenomena of irritability and con-

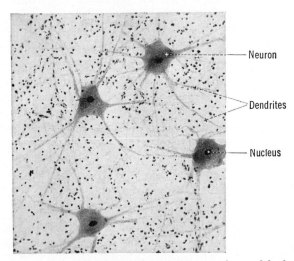

Figure 42. Photomicrograph of spinal motor neurons teased out of fresh material and stained. Note the extent of neural processes. The numerous small dots are nuclei of neuroglial cells.

Apical dendrite

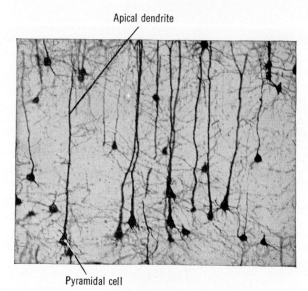

Pyramidal cell

Figure 43.   Photomicrograph of a section of cerebral cortex (rabbit) showing
neurons and their processes. Cox-Golgi stain.

ductivity. Despite their degree of specialization, however, nerve
cells have the fundamental structural characteristics of typical
cells, that is, cytoplasm, nuclei, Golgi bodies, mitochondria and so
forth. As indicated in the previous chapter, nerve cells have long,
protoplasmic processes (Figs. 42, 43). Microscopic and physiological studies show that these processes make possible the functional connections between different nerve cells. The nervous system is composed of billions of such cellular units, called neurons,
which are linked together to form conduction pathways and which
are supported or held together by a framework of specialized, nonconducting cells known collectively as neuroglia. (See Neuron
Theory, p. 91.)

Structure of the Cell Body

The bodies of nerve cells vary in diameter from 4 to 5 microns
up to 50 or even 100 microns. Their processes, on the other hand,
may be a few microns up to several feet in length. Neurons with
long processes are frequently called Golgi type 1 (Fig. 44), whereas
those whose processes are all short are Golgi type 2 (Fig. 45).

The cytoplasm of neuron bodies contains granules of a chromatin-like material which stain blue with such basic dyes as cresyl violet, toluidine blue or methylene blue (Fig. 46). This chromidial substance is often called *Nissl substance,* after Franz Nissl, who first described it (p. 92). The larger the cell, the more abundant is the Nissl substance.

Also characteristic of neurons are long, thin fibrils that extend throughout both the cytoplasm and the processes. These neuro-fibrils can be demonstrated only by a special staining process in which solutions of a silver salt are used. When the silver salt is absorbed by the tissue and then reduced in a manner similar to the development of a photographic plate, metallic silver is deposited in or on the neurofibrils.

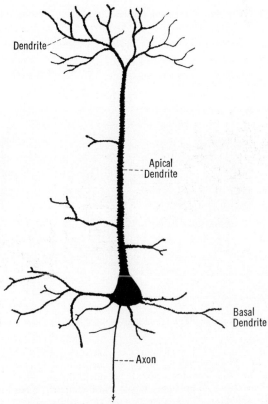

Figure 44.   Drawing of a pyramidal cell from the rabbit cortex illustrated in Fig. 43. This is a Golgi type 1 neuron. Note the surface irregularities of the dendrites. The axon of this type of cell in man may be several feet long.

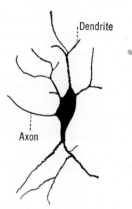

Figure 45. A spindle-shaped neuron from rabbit cortex (Fig. 43). This is a Golgi type 2 neuron. Only the first part of the axon is shown.

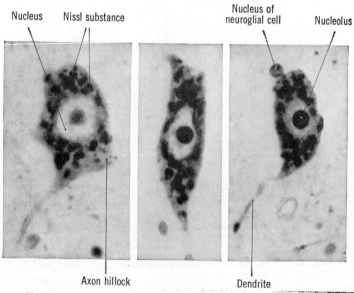

Figure 46. Photomicrographs of motor neurons of human spinal cord. Note the abundant Nissl substance, prominent nucleoli, and relative clearness of the nuclei. The sections do not show axons, and include the axon hillock in but one of the cells. Compare with Fig. 55 (p. 86). Cresyl violet stain.

The relatively little chromatin material in the nuclei of most neurons is condensed as a prominent nucleolus.

Pigment granules are frequently found in the cytoplasm. In certain areas of the brain, such as the substantia nigra, the cells normally contain large amounts of melanin pigment, thus accounting for the dark appearance of the region. Many neurons contain a yellow, lipochrome pigment which increases in amount with age. No pathological significance can be attached to such an increase.

Structure of the Cell Process

The processes of nerve cells differ according to the direction in which they conduct nerve impulses. Some are afferent in nature, conducting impulses toward the cell bodies; processes of this type are known as dendrites. Others are efferent, conducting impulses away from the cell bodies, and are known as axons or axis cylinders. This direction of conduction is determined, not by struc-

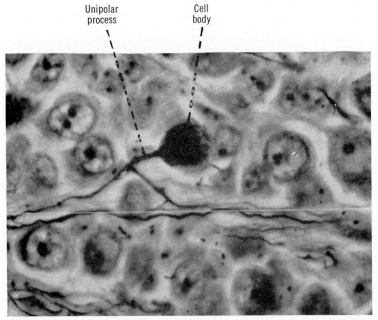

Figure 47.   Photomicrograph of a unipolar nerve cell in a dorsal root ganglion of a three-month's human fetus. Silver stain. The nucleus of this cell was not included in the section. Note how the single process divides a short distance from the cell body

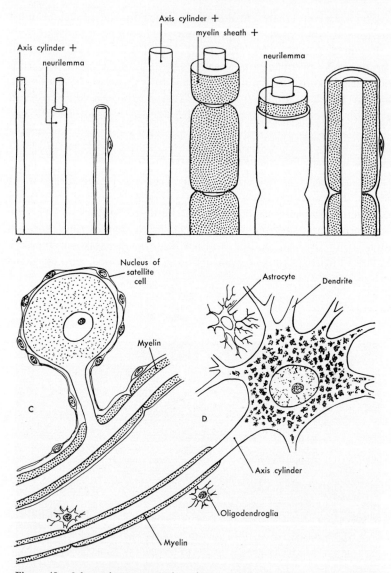

Figure 48.   Schematic representation of a nonmyelinated fiber, *A,* the right hand figure of the group showing the fiber cut longitudinally. *B* shows components of a myelinated fiber. *C* is a dorsal root ganglion cell with its unipolar process dividing into peripheral and central branches. *D* is a multipolar cell of the spinal cord, with associated neuroglial cells. The various layers of the nerve fibers are exaggerated in certain respects. This figure shows a single nonmyelinated fiber, but such fibers tend to occur in groups, with a common neurilemma (see Figure 52).

tural characteristics of the processes, but by a polarity set up at the points of functional connection between neurons.

Nerve cells usually have a single axon and at least one or more dendrites. The cells in cranial and spinal ganglia are exceptions to this rule. It was pointed out in Chap. 5 that the single processes of the unipolar cells in dorsal root ganglia divide into two branches, one projecting toward the central nervous system and the other toward the periphery (Figs. 47, 48). The cells of most of the cranial ganglia, such as the semilunar ganglia of the trigeminal nerves, are also unipolar. However, in the spiral and vestibular ganglia, in the olfactory mucous membrane, and in one of the layers of the retina, nerve cells retain their primitive bipolar characteristics. Except for these unipolar and bipolar varieties, all the cells in the nervous system are multipolar. Multipolar cells of the cerebral cortex are shown in Figs. 44 and 45, and one from the anterior gray matter of the cord in Fig. 48.

Structure of Dendrites. Dendrites usually extend but a short distance from the cell body, branch profusely, and contain Nissl substance. This arrangement increases the surface area of a neuron, so that large numbers of other neurons may be associated or linked with it.

Structure of Axons. Axons differ from dendrites in that they lack Nissl substance, often extend for long distances, and have relatively few branches until near their terminations. The area of the cell body from which they arise may also lack Nissl substance and is known as the *axon hillock* (Fig. 46). The axon is surrounded by a lipid membrane, the *myelin sheath* which is formed by neurilemmal or glial cells (p. 79). This sheath, with few exceptions, does not extend around the cell body, nor is it visible, with the optical microscope, around fibers less than 1 micron in diameter. The largest axons, with their myelin sheaths, may be 20 microns in diameter. Osmic acid, when used as a stain, colors the myelin black, leaving the axon unstained. Accordingly, osmicated fibers seen in cross section look like black rings. Osmic acid penetrates poorly, however, so that for large pieces of nerve tissue a different technique must be used to give the same result. After treatment with a chemical compound such as potassium dichromate or iron alum, the myelin sheaths stain blue or black with the dye hematoxylin. Fibers stained by such a method are shown in Fig. 49. This is the Weigert method of staining (p. 93), and its use shows that the

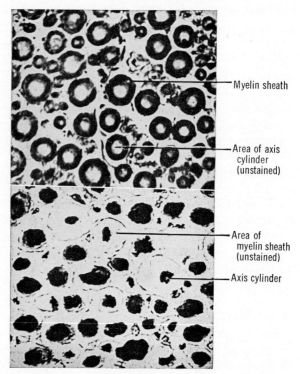

Figure 49.   Photomicrographs of cross sections of dorsal roots (rabbit). The fibers in the upper half of the figure are stained by the Weigert method to show myelin sheaths; those in the lower half by a silver method to demonstrate axis cylinders.

white matter of the central nervous system contains large numbers of myelinated fibers. Gray matter is gray by contrast because it is composed mainly of cell bodies and fibers which, for the most part, lack myelin. The same method also reveals that ventral and dorsal roots, cranial and other peripheral nerves contain large numbers of myelinated axons. In peripheral nerves and in the central nervous system the term "nerve fiber" is often used to specify a process and its covering sheaths.

Silver stains color axons rather than myelin sheaths; by using such methods, one can show that gray matter contains many fibers which are 1 micron or less in diameter and are, therefore, nonmyelinated. The white matter also contains many nonmyelinated fibers. This is also true of dorsal roots (but not ventral roots) and peripheral nerves. It should be emphasized that, while one of the two divisions of a unipolar process of a dorsal root ganglion cell is functionally an axon and the other functionally a dendrite, both are structurally like axons.

Axons Outside the Central Nervous System. All myelin sheaths, apparently, whether in the central nervous system or not, are interrupted at regular intervals. The interruptions are *nodes of Ranvier* (Fig. 48). These nodes may be several hundred microns or more apart. In addition, all axons outside the central nervous system, whether myelinated or not, have still another layer, the *neurilemma*. This is a thin, protoplasmic sheath wrapped around the axon or myelin sheath. In fact, the myelin is intimately related to and is probably a part of, the protoplasm of the neurilemmal layer. A single fiber with both myelin sheath and neurilemma is shown in Fig. 50. The neurilemma is a thin layer of flat cells so arranged that they form a tube enclosing the fiber. These are also called *cells of Schwann* (p. 93). Usually just one cell occurs between two successive nodes. The importance of the neurilemma will be discussed later (p. 89). It has a supportive role, is comparable to the neuroglia of the central nervous system, and is concerned in some way with the formation of myelin. The neurilemma of dorsal

Node of Ranvier

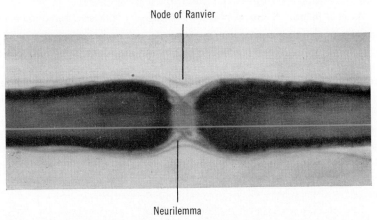

Neurilemma

Figure 50. Photomicrograph of a single myelinated fiber from frog sciatic nerve, stained with osmic acid. The myelin stains black and is interrupted at the node. The thin membrane external to the neurilemma represents endoneurium. The axis cylinder (stained grayish) continues through the node.

Vein

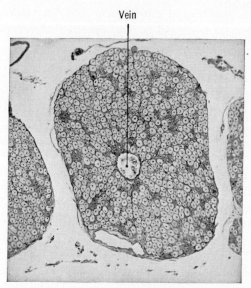

Figure 51.   Photomicrograph of a cross section of a human dorsal root. Each fiber is seen as a round, clear area, in the center of which is a dot. The clear area is myelin; the dot, an axis cylinder.

root ganglion cell processes is continuous with the layer of "satellite" cells that surrounds the ganglion cells (Fig. 48).

Axons in the Central Nervous System.   These axons may be either myelinated or nonmyelinated. The myelinated axons of the central nervous system have nodes of Ranvier, although they are difficult to demonstrate. In neither case, however, is a neurilemma present. Instead, neuroglial cells are found in comparable positions.

Spinal Roots, Spinal Nerves and Peripheral Nerves.   These structures are composed of large numbers of nerve fibers bound together by connective tissue, which is not present in the central nervous system except around blood vessels. The connective tissue contains small blood vessels that supply the nerves. The connective tissue of peripheral nerves is abundant enough to make them firm, tough and relatively easy to handle in dissection.

The dorsal roots are composed of central processes of dorsal root ganglion cells and contain thousands of myelinated and nonmyelinated fibers (Fig. 51). These range in diameter from less than 1 to about 20 microns. The nonmyelinated fibers are by far the most numerous.

The fibers in the ventral roots, that is, the axons of cells in the anterior gray matter of the spinal cord, are all myelinated. There is not, however, a continuous variation in size. If the fibers are grouped according to their diameters, there will be found one group of fibers which averages two to eight microns (with a peak of 2 to 3 microns), and another group which averages twelve to twenty microns.

Spinal nerves are mixed nerves, since they contain fibers of both

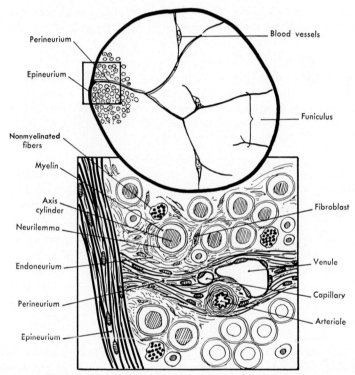

Figure 52. Schematic representation of peripheral nerve to show its general arrangement. The upper figure represents a whole nerve (nerve fibers are shown only in a small part of the nerve). The lower figure shows at a higher magnification that part of the whole nerve in the square. A nerve is surrounded by connective tissue, the epineurium, often called the sheath. Within the nerve, bundles of nerve fibers (funiculi) are surrounded by connective tissue, the perineurium. Generally, all fibers in a funiculus are destined for a specific region or muscle. Blood vessels supplying nerves run in epineurium and perineurium. Connective tissue fibers enclose individual nerve fibers, forming a sheath called endoneurium, immediately external to neurilemma. Nonmyelinated nerve fibers occur in groups, with a common neurilemmal sheath, the complicated arrangement of which is not shown.

ventral and dorsal roots. The small myelinated fibers of the ventral roots contribute to the formation of rami communicantes that extend to the paravertebral sympathetic trunks. Here they make functional connections with multipolar sympathetic ganglion cells. The axons of these cells are nonmyelinated. Many go directly to thoracic, abdominal and pelvic viscera. Others return to the spinal nerves by way of rami communicantes and thence are distributed by way of peripheral nerves.

The rami also contain afferent myelinated fibers derived from viscera. The cell bodies of these fibers are in dorsal root ganglia, and the central processes proceed to the cord by way of dorsal roots.

A major peripheral nerve, such as the sciatic, may contain over a million fibers of all types. The branches of such a nerve may contain fibers in which a group of one average diameter predominates. Branches to muscle, for instance, contain many large myelinated fibers, while those to skin and to subcutaneous tissues contain more of the smaller fibers and many nonmyelinated ones.

Neuronal Junctions

The dorsal root fibers that enter the spinal cord branch repeatedly. Some branches ascend in the posterior funiculi and end in the gray matter at higher levels of the spinal cord or medulla oblongata, others end in the gray matter at the level of entrance, and still others descend to end in gray matter at lower levels of the spinal cord. When they end, these branches form functional connections with cells whose axons in turn travel to other cells. These connections are of fundamental importance, and their arrangement will serve to illustrate neuronal junctions throughout the nervous system.

When an axon approaches another cell, it decreases in diameter and divides repeatedly, forming *telodendria*. Each small branch or telodendron ends by making contact with the surface of a dendrite (*axodendritic contact*) or of the cell body (*axosomatic contact*) of the succeeding cell. These contacts or junctional regions are generally called *synapses*. The cell membranes are in very close contact, but are not fused. Where the telodendron makes synaptic contact with the dendrite of a cell body it may end abruptly, sometimes forming a small swelling or having a ring-like appearance. Such endings are called *boutons terminaux* (end-feet or terminal buttons). The telodendron may, however, make synaptic contact (by a *bouton de passage*) and then continue to another part of the same cell or to another cell. Thus, an axon may have synaptic junctions with many cells (frequently hundreds with each cell). Conversely, any one cell may have hundreds or thousands of synaptic contacts on its surface, derived from many axons. Figure 53 illustrates some synaptic junctions.

Nerve impulses usually cross synaptic junctions in but one direction, from the axon of one cell to the dendrite or body of the next cell. The numbers and arrangements of synapses, and the electrical and chemical changes at such junctions when nerve impulses reach them, are of the utmost importance in determining whether or when a nerve cell can be activated.

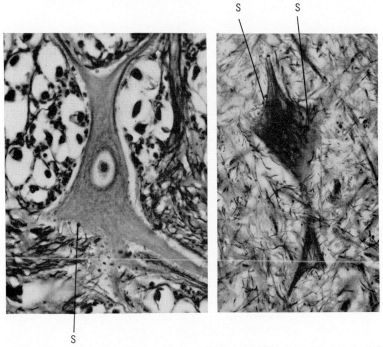

Figure 53. Photomicrographs of nerve cells stained with silver. That at the left is from medulla oblongata and shows synaptic endings, S, at the edge of the cell body and dendrites. The cell on the right, from spinal cord, is cut through the edge so that the nucleus is not included. Synaptic endings, S, occur on its surface. The left-hand leader ends between two synaptic endings.

Blood vessel   Astrocyte

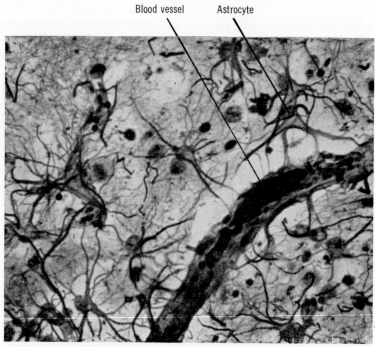

Figure 54. Photomicrograph of a section of human cerebral cortex stained for astrocytes. The cortex had been involved by an infection which had caused astrocytes to increase in number. The leader to the indicated astrocyte ends on the nucleus. Note how the extensions of this cell attach to the adjacent blood vessel.

Neuroglia

The supporting cells of the central nervous system are known collectively as neuroglia. Though glial cells differ in size and shape, they all have processes which weave around nerve cells and fibers and frequently attach to the walls of blood vessels (Fig. 54). Special stains are necessary to demonstrate neuroglial cells. Some have many processes and, because of their star shape, are called *astrocytes*. Other neuroglial cells with fewer and shorter processes are found along axons and around cell bodies. These are called *oligodendroglia*. Both types are derived originally from ectodermal cells of the neural tube. Still others, the *microglial* cells, are much smaller and probably originate from connective tissue of mesodermal origin that grows in with blood vessels. Our knowledge of the function of neuroglial cells is limited to a few facts. Microglial cells, for instance, can enlarge and become *phagocytes*, capable of removing degenerating nervous tissue after injury or destruction. Astrocytes proliferate in response to many types of infections and disorders of the nervous system. Neuroglial cells are particularly important because they are the most common source of primary tumors of the nervous system. Recent evidence indicates that glial cells are involved in the formation of myelin, and therefore are conceivably of considerable importance in diseases involving myelin.

Degeneration and Regeneration in the Nervous System

Adult nerve cells cannot divide mitotically and cannot, therefore, replace any that happen to be destroyed. For reasons that are not known, some nerve cells die during the normal lifetime of an individual. It has been estimated that up to a fourth of all the nerve cells in the brain, spinal cord and peripheral ganglia may be lost by the eighth or ninth decade. This loss is a major factor in the sensory changes that are common with advancing age—diminishing sensitivity to touch, taste and vision, for example.

If the processes of a nerve cell are destroyed, the cell body may survive, although it usually undergoes characteristic changes. For example, if an axon of an anterior horn cell is severed by cutting a peripheral nerve, the Nissl substance in the cell of origin slowly disappears (*chromatolysis*) and the nucleus shifts toward the periphery of the cell (Fig. 55). After several days or weeks there is a gradual reconstitution of the cell. These changes are more noticeable in large cells with abundant Nissl substance, and their severity is related to the distance of axonal section from the cell body, being more severe as the division is closer. Recovery is not invariable. Some cells die when axons are severed, and this is more likely to happen if the injury is near the cell body. Cells confined entirely to the central nervous system generally do not survive axonal section.

Cellular changes after axonal injury may be used to locate the cells of origin of axons in a peripheral nerve or in a pathway of the central nervous system. If a nerve or pathway is cut, and an appropriate interval allowed, the nervous system can be studied microscopically. Cells whose axons contribute to the nerve or tract that was sectioned undergo chromatolysis. Such experiments must

Nissl substance

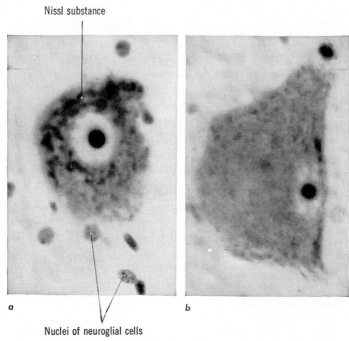

a   b

Nuclei of neuroglial cells

Figure 55.   Photomicrographs of giant pyramidal cells of human cerebral cortex. The cell on the left is normal. That on the right is undergoing chromatolysis. Note the swelling, the shifting of the nucleus, and the loss of Nissl substance. The magnification is the same as that of Fig. 46 (p. 74), which allows a comparison of relative sizes.

be carefully controlled by examination of similar areas in normal material because, in certain regions of the brain and spinal cord, there are cells that normally appear as if they were undergoing chromatolysis. Furthermore, if the tissues being examined are not fixed promptly after death, postmortem disintegration causes cellular changes that may, in their early stages, resemble chromatolysis.

An axon that has been severed from its cell body undergoes changes that collectively constitute *wallerian degeneration* (Fig. 56). The terminal parts of the axis cylinder (at the end organ or at synaptic junctions) begin to swell (within a day or so after section). The terminal axis cylinder then begins to disintegrate. The process of swelling and disintegration proceeds proximally, toward the cell body. If the axon is myelinated, the myelin begins

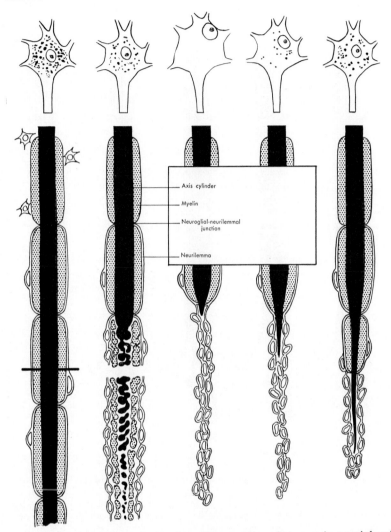

Figure 56. Schematic representation of degeneration of an axon in a peripheral nerve. The upper row shows the cell body, the normal one being at the left. After section, Nissl substance disappears and the nucleus shifts peripherally. The Nissl substance then reappears and the nucleus regains its central position. The lower row shows the axon (at a higher magnification), the line representing the level of section outside the spinal cord. The axis cylinder and myelin begin to disintegrate and are removed by phagocytosis. A cord of proliferating neurilemmal cells remains, into which the axis cylinder begins to grow. The growing axon may have multiple sprouts (not shown).

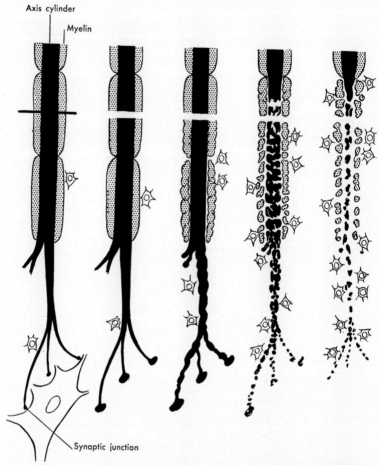

Figure 57. Schematic representation of degeneration of an axon in the central nervous system (cell body not shown). After section at the level indicated on the left, the synaptic junctions begin to swell, then the axis cylinder, these degenerative processes extending toward the cell body. Neuroglial cells proliferate and phagocytize the fragmenting axis cylinder and myelin.

to break down (within a few days). Neurilemmal cells proliferate and become scavengers or phagocytes that ingest the disintegrating axis cylinder and myelin. Proliferating connective tissue cells may also aid in the phagocytosis. Eventually, all remains of axis cylinder and myelin are removed and only cords of neurilemmal cells are left. Similar changes may be found for a short distance proximal to the point of axon section (*retrograde degeneration*).

Similar axonal changes are found in the central nervous system except that neuroglial cells proliferate (gliosis) and act as phagocytes (Fig. 57). In man phagocytosis may not be completed for several months or longer. If many nerve fibers are severed, the proliferating glial cells that replace the nerve fibers form a rather dense glial scar.

Degenerating myelin differs chemically from normal myelin. Degenerating myelin, after chemical treatment with a compound such as potassium dichromate, will stain black with osmic acid (Fig. 97); normal myelin will not stain in this way if similarly pretreated. This reaction forms the basis of the *Marchi* method (p. 92) for staining degenerating myelinated fibers, and enables one to trace such fibers in microscopic sections.

In the peripheral nervous system, very shortly after an axon has been severed, the severed axon tip begins to grow distally, through the neurilemmal cord, by ameboid extension. There is a marked tendency for each such tip to branch or sprout, but generally only one of these branches continues distally for any distance. Such distal growth does not occur unless the cell body survives and begins to reverse the chromatolytic process. The axon regenerates at the rate of a few millimeters a day, at least initially. The rate of growth later becomes considerably less. With regeneration, myelin begins to form. Eventually, the axon re-establishes contact with whatever structure it had previously innervated. The contact may not be normal at first, or the axon may be misdirected during its growth, and functional recovery may be delayed.

Practically speaking, the neurilemmal cords might be regarded as tubes that conduct or direct the growing axon, although the interrelationship is much more complicated. The neurilemmal cells are necessary for, and are probably directly responsible for, the formation of myelin.

Regeneration does not occur in the brain and spinal cord, at least to any significant degree. In very young animals, however, neuroblasts may still be present and these may enable some regeneration to occur. Abortive attempts at regeneration have been observed in the adult (axonal sprouting in the vicinity of the injury), but without evidence of significant regrowth. Apparently the dense glial and collagenous scars that are characteristic of central nervous system injuries are major factors that prevent regeneration. Other, unknown factors are also important, related to differences between warm- and cold-blooded animals. The amazing capacity for regeneration in lower forms of life is familiar to all. Such capacity is retained to a considerable extent in fishes and amphibians, but is less evident in reptiles, and, so far as the nervous system is concerned, is practically restricted to the peripheral nervous system in birds and mammals. If recovery of function in the central nervous system does occur, it is either because the cells were not actually killed or their fibers severed, or because other cells or areas take over their functions.

Figure 56 illustrates the various changes in degeneration and regeneration of a single fiber. Widely different agents may produce almost identical changes in nerve cells and fibers. Chromatolysis, which was discussed as a consequence of axonal injury, may follow a direct attack on nerve cells by poisons, bacterial toxins, viruses, and the like, although in such cases, recovery is certainly less common. With such direct attacks, chromatolysis is more likely to be followed by cellular disintegration and phagocytosis. Metabolic disorders, or diminution or loss of blood supply, may cause chromatolysis followed by cell shrinkage and disappearance. Some diseases and poisons affect only the axonal processes, either axis cylinder or myelin sheath, or both, and may produce swelling, demyelination or disintegration. Any injurious change may be initially irritative and later destructive, so that the functions of involved neurons may be at first enhanced or exaggerated, and later lost.

Under most circumstances the degeneration of an axon does not involve the succeeding cell with which that axon may be functionally connected. This is another example of data supporting the theory that functional units or cells of the nervous system are entities that are not morphologically continuous.

When a peripheral nerve is cut, hundreds or thousands of fibers are separated from their cell bodies. Function is immediately lost, and degenerative changes go on almost simultaneously in each fiber of that nerve. When recovery begins, however, it proceeds at different rates for nonmyelinated (faster rate of regeneration) and myelinated fibers. Recovery is also affected by the manner in which the cut ends of the nerve are united. A close union, without scar formation, favors recovery. Scar tissue prevents proper growth and as a consequence the multiple growing tips often form a swelling or *neuroma* above the scar. Similarly, the loss of a long stretch of nerve prevents recovery unless the gap is bridged in some way.

Growth is not limited to regenerating nerve fibers. When an area of skin, for example, is deprived of its nerve supply, branches of the fibers that supply adjacent normal skin may grow into the denervated area and will, of course, reach it before the severed axons can regenerate. Consequently, some return of sensory function may occur long before that calculated on the basis of rate of regeneration.

The Neuron Theory

Even today there are remnants of the great debate of past years on the existence of functional entities of the nervous system, the neurons. It has taken at least sixty years to place the neuron theory on a firm basis. The crux of the debate was the question of protoplasmic continuity at the synapse. The facts which support the neuron theory are as follows: It was established in the latter part of the last century that each neuroblast in the embryo formed a single adult nerve cell. Later it was shown that synaptic junctions were actually present and that neurofibrils did not pass from one cell to another. If cells were actually continuous, it would be difficult to explain how nerve impulses subserving a particular function could be conducted within a chain of neurons without spreading haphazardly to other chains.

Studies of degeneration and regeneration offered further substantiation. In most cases, neither chromatolysis nor degeneration involves other neurons. There is no evidence that any structures other than neurons (such as neuroglia) are concerned in the actual transmission of nerve impulses.

The final evidence was provided by the experimental method. In tissue cultures of neuroblasts it was observed that nerve processes arose by direct growth from parent cells and not by differentiation from intercellular material. The evidence is overwhelmingly in favor of the neuron as a cellular entity and of conduction occurring over chains of such neurons.

Summary

The adult nervous system is composed of specialized cellular units called neurons that are linked together by synaptic junctions to form conduction pathways for nerve impulses. Dendrites are usually protoplasmic extensions of the neuron; they conduct toward the cell body. Axons lack Nissl substance, have fewer branches, are usually longer, and conduct away from the cell body. They may be either nonmyelinated or myelinated, the myelin being interrupted by nodes of Ranvier. Axons in the peripheral nervous system have a protoplasmic layer, the neurilemma, which is external to any myelin present. The white matter of the nervous system contains myelinated and nonmyelinated fibers; the gray matter has cell bodies and nonmyelinated and a few myelinated fibers. Dorsal roots, spinal nerves and peripheral nerves contain both types of fibers; the ventral roots contain only myelinated fibers.

In the central nervous system there is a supporting framework formed by a system of neuroglial cells.

New nerve cells cannot be formed in the adult nervous system. If processes such as axons are destroyed, the cells of origin undergo chromatolysis. If the axonal injury has occurred outside the central nervous system, regeneration is possible, seemingly because of the presence of neurilemmal cells which form cords along which the regenerating fibers grow.

Names in Neurology

Marchi, Vittorio (1851–1908)

Marchi was an Italian physician who contributed to the establishment of the neuron theory by developing a method for staining degenerating fibers and applying it to experimentally produced lesions.

Nissl, Franz (1860–1919)

Nissl was a German neuropathologist and psychiatrist who developed a method of staining nerve cells with aniline dyes. He discovered the chromidial substance in the cytoplasm of nerve cells. He also studied pathological lesions of the nervous system resulting from syphilis.

Ramón y Cajal, Santiago (1852–1934)

Ramón y Cajal was the greatest of all neuro-anatomists. He did so much that is fundamental to present day knowledge that it is difficult to list his accomplishments. When he was professor of anatomy at the University of Valencia, he learned of Golgi's method for staining nerve tissue. The stain, however, was capricious and undependable. After two years of vain attempts to use it, he conceived the use of embryos in which myelin sheaths are not fully developed and, therefore, less liable to interfere with the impregnation of processes by silver. Because of this, and because of certain modifications of the stain, he demonstrated nerve cells in their entirety, their relationships to other neurons and the presence of synaptic junctions. With this method and with others which he subsequently developed he studied almost every portion of the nervous system. He described the fundamental structures of cerebral cortex, cerebellum, retina, spinal cord, peripheral nerves, and so forth. His account of degeneration and regeneration is a masterpiece. He demonstrated neuroglial cells in all their detail. In 1906 he shared the Nobel Prize for the Section on Physiology and Medicine with Camillo Golgi. During the latter part of his life, he was professor of normal histology and pathological anatomy at the University of Madrid.

Ranvier, Louis Antoine (1835–1922)

Ranvier was a French histologist, best known for his description in 1878 of the interruptions of peripheral myelin sheaths which now bear his name.

Schwann, Theodore (1810–1882)

Schwann, a German physician, is best known for the studies by which he concluded that fundamental units in animal and vegetable tissues are cells. He also demonstrated the influence of organisms and lower fungi on fermentation and putrefaction; he investigated muscular contractions and first described neurilemma.

Waller, Augustus (1816–1870)

Waller, an English physician, contributed to the neuron theory through his studies of degenerating nerve fibers. He traced the degeneration which resulted from section of various cranial nerves and spinal roots. He established the direction and, thereby, the source of the process which is now frequently termed Wallerian degeneration.

Weigert, Carl (1845–1904)

Weigert was a German pathologist who contributed immensely to our knowledge of the nervous system by his development of various staining methods. The one applied to myelin sheaths, somewhat modified today, is still the most important single stain for nervous tissue. He also stained neuroglia. He was the first to stain bacteria, and he studied the pathological anatomy of small-pox and of Bright's disease.

References

The neuro-anatomy textbooks cited in previous chapters contain chapters on the minute anatomy of the nervous system. The following two textbooks of histology contain similar sections:

Ham, A. W.: Histology. 3rd ed. Philadelphia, J. B. Lippincott Co., 1957.
Maximow, A., and Bloom, W.: Textbook of Histology. 7th ed. Philadelphia, W. B. Saunders Company, 1957.

The following references deal with experimental and clinical aspects of degeneration and regeneration.

Guth, L.: Regeneration in the mammalian peripheral nervous system. Physiol. Rev., 36:441–478, 1956.
Seddon, H. J., ed.: Peripheral nerve injuries. Med. Res. Council. Spec. Rep. Ser. No. 282. London, Her Majesty's Stationery Office, 1954.
Sperry, R. W.: The problem of central nervous reorganization after nerve regeneration and muscle transposition. Quart. Rev. Biol., 20:311–369, 1945.
Windle, W. F.: Regeneration of axons in the vertebrate central nervous system. Physiol. Rev., 36:427–440, 1956.

CHAPTER 7

Excitation and Conduction

A FUNDAMENTAL property of living organisms is excitability, the ability to respond or react to a *stimulus,* that is, to some change in external surroundings or internal medium. The response is a change in state of activity of the organism. Excitability is also a property of cellular units of organisms. The reactions of such units are often specific. For example, gland cells may secrete (or a secreting cell may stop secreting); muscles may contract. In many, if not all, cells the change initiated by the stimulus spreads throughout the cell and, once initiated, is independent of the stimulus. This spread is spoken of as *conduction;* in some cells, such as muscle and nerve, it is rapid. Nerve cells are peculiarly adapted for controlling and directing such spread of activity, and the physicochemical reactions which constitute the conducted response are spoken of as the *nerve impulse.* The reactions are accompanied by such phenomena as the utilization of oxygen, the formation of carbon dioxide, the production of heat, ion transfer across the cell membrane, and the appearance of certain electrical changes.

Methods of Study

One of the problems in studying excitation and conduction is how to detect and record such activity. One method is to use the end result, such as muscular contraction or glandular secretion. Another is to estimate activity by measuring such things as the uptake of oxygen during conduction. A common method is to gauge activity by measuring electrical changes during conduc-

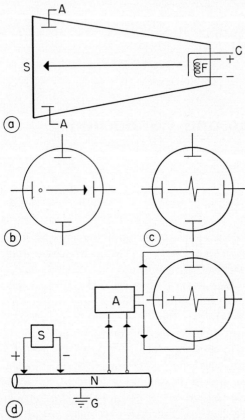

Figure 58. Simplified schematic representation of recording arrangement with cathode-ray oscillograph. In *a*, the cathode ray tube is shown in side view. A current heats the filament, *F*, and this in turn heats a cathode, *C*. Electrons from the heated cathode stream to the front of the tube, attracted by anodes, *A*, with a positive voltage. Between cathode and anode are plates with negative voltages (not shown). These repel electrons, and are so arranged that electrons are concentrated into a narrow beam. The front of the tube (screen, S) has a material that fluoresces where electrons strike it. When viewed from the front (*b*) a single glowing spot is seen. There are four plates at the front of the tube. If a positive voltage is placed on the right-hand plate, and if this voltage is increased, the electrons will move across the screen toward the right-hand plate. If, on reaching the right-hand side, the voltage abruptly stops and is applied to the left-hand plate, the spot returns to the left. If, while the spot is moving across the screen, voltages are applied to upper or lower plates, the spot will move up or down according to the rate and nature of voltage change, *c*. If the electron spot moves fast enough, fluorescence persists so as to give the impression of a line. In actual recording, an oscillating voltage is applied to right- and left-hand plates. In *d*, a nerve, *N*, is stimulated by a brief shock from a stimulator, *S*. The nerve impulse is picked up by electrodes and led into the

tion. Electrical currents applied to nerve are effective stimuli and, since they are easily measured and controlled, are the most commonly used artificial stimuli. Physiological stimuli may also be used and, in some instances, may be precisely applied and controlled, as for example, stimulation of the retina by light and the ear by sound.

The Inactive Nerve Cell

The surfaces of neurons are particularly important in all phases of excitation and conduction. A simplified concept of these changes postulates an *electrical polarity*, with opposite electrical charges on either side of the surface of the axis cylinder. This surface constitutes a membrane, commonly assumed to be a lipoid-protein structure of about 50 to 100 Ångstrom units thick and thus not visible with the optical microscope. This membrane has special electrical properties and selective permeability to various ions. The interior of the axis cylinder contains neurofibrils within a watery medium of special composition, the axoplasm. The outside of the axis cylinder is bathed in tissue fluid, an ultrafiltrate of blood, and of different composition than the axoplasm, due to the selective permeability of the membrane. The resting membrane is readily permeable to potassium and chloride, but not to sodium. As a consequence, sodium is about 10 times more concentrated outside than inside the axis cylinder. There is also a high internal concentration of impermeable anions. As a consequence, in the resulting Donnan equilibrium, potassium is about 20 to 50 times more concentrated inside, and chloride the converse. The total distribution of ions is such that the outside of the axis cylinder is positive to the interior by about 75 to 100 millivolts. The recorded potential difference may, however, be lower, according to the recording method used and the conditions of the experiment (Fig. 59).

This *resting* or *membrane potential* can be demonstrated and measured. If a suitable small electrode is thrust into the interior of

---

amplifier, *A*. Amplifiers are necessary because high voltages are needed to operate the cathode-ray tube. The output of the amplifier feeds to upper and lower plates of the tube, producing the vertical deflection characteristic of the nerve impulse as the spot moves across. The initial small deflection after the spot starts moving is the shock artifact, which signals the moment of stimulation. Some of the stimulating current leaks down the nerve to pick-up electrodes, most, however, leaking off to ground at *G*. The recorded deflection of the tube can be photographed for permanent records.

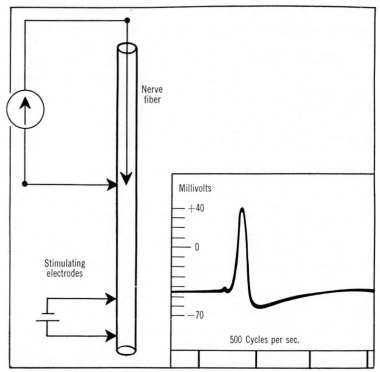

Figure 59. Diagram of recording from a single nerve fiber. At the left, a single nerve fiber is represented as a tube. One electrode is placed inside the fiber and the other on the surface so that the electrodes are across the membrane. These two electrodes are connected to a recording instrument. The two stimulating electrodes are indicated on the lower part of the fiber. The recording electrodes are so connected that when the internal electrode becomes more positive, the recording instrument gives an upward deflection. To the right is a figure indicating that when the electrodes are placed as indicated, the internal electrode is constantly between 40 and 50 millivolts negative. When a nerve impulse is initiated (the small initial deflection is the shock artifact), the resting potential is not only abolished, but is reversed, so that the internal electrode becomes positive with respect to the external electrode. (Modified from Hodgkin and Huxley.)

a single nerve fiber, and another is placed on the surface of the fiber, and if these two electrodes are connected to a sensitive measuring instrument such as a galvanometer, a current can be measured as it flows from the positive to the negative side. Of course, current flows only when there is a potential difference. If one connects the electrodes to a voltage-measuring instrument, a potential difference can be measured (Fig. 59). This indicates the membrane polarization mentioned above. If one places both electrodes on the surface of the fiber, no current flow or potential difference can be detected. The surface is said to be everywhere equipotential.

Measurements of this type dealing with single fibers have for the most part been carried out on giant nerve fibers, mainly in invertebrate animals. Available experimental evidence indicates that there are similar properties for nerve fibers in all vertebrate forms.

The Active Nerve Cell

If an adequate stimulus, physiological or artificial, is applied to a nerve fiber, the surface membrane of several centimeters of nerve fiber develops a high, specific permeability to sodium such that sodium enters the interior of the fiber at a very rapid rate. In less than a millisecond, the resting potential is not only abolished, it is reversed. The external surface becomes negative to the interior. The membrane is said to be depolarized. The accompanying change in potential difference can be recorded as what is usually called a *spike* or *spike potential*. What is further characteristic is that the depolarization, once started, spreads along the fibers independently of the stimulus, much as a bullet travels independently of the pull on the trigger.

At the peak of the action potential, the sodium entry lessens Potassium permeability increases, and potassium leaves the fiber. Thus, the original membrane potential begins to be restored. It has been suggested that there is in the membrane a "sodium pump," deriving its energy from metabolic processes in the interior, this pump serving to maintain sodium at a high concentration outside the fiber. It is further suggested that after the sodium entry and potassium departure during the spike potential, the sodium pump slowly restores the original differences in sodium concentration, and potassium slowly diffuses back into the interior.

The explanations of nerve activity in terms of ionic exchanges are collectively termed the ionic hypothesis and satisfactorily explain many phases of nerve activity. Nevertheless, our knowledge of nerve activity is still very elementary. Nothing is known of the nature of the sodium pump, if it exists, and the rate and nature of metabolic processes remain to be determined. Certain chemicals, such as acetylcholine, have been implicated as having vital roles in nerve conduction, but the evidence is not entirely satisfactory.

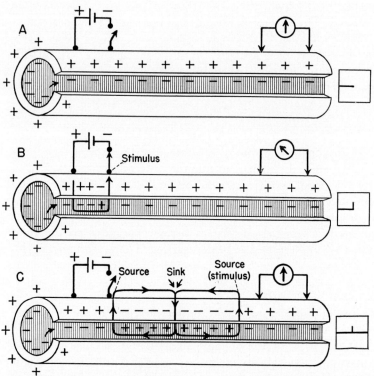

Figure 60. Diagram illustrating the initial changes following application of a stimulus to a nerve fiber. *A*, The fiber is represented as a tube with a strip cut away so as to expose the interior. The stimulating electrodes, indicated by + and −, are at one end and the recording electrodes at the other. The electrical charges internal and external to the membrane are also indicated. *B*, When the switch is closed, a current flows from the positive electrode into the fiber and out through the membrane back to the negative electrode (cathode). This current is derived entirely from the battery. Some of it leaks down the nerve, instantaneously for all practical purposes, and is recorded as a small deflection (inset at right). This is the shock artifact and indicates the moment of stimulation. *C*, The effect of current flow out through the membrane is to initiate the conduction of a nerve impulse. The impulse is represented as two dipoles, each consisting of current flow (not the stimulating current from the battery) within a region indicated by the reversal of electrical charges. The current flow out through the membrane in the leading dipole acts as a stimulus, just as did the artificial current from the battery. According to conventional methods, the recording instrument will not show a deflection until the region of negativity passes under the first electrode.

As mentioned above, the depolarization, once started, spreads along the fiber independently of the stimulus. This spread constitutes a nerve impulse, which may be defined as a wave of depolarization or electrical negativity that travels without decrement along a nerve fiber. A nerve impulse is ordinarily studied by recording the electrical activity that accompanies the impulse. For example, one can remove a nerve, suspend it on electrodes in a moist atmosphere, stimulate it electrically and record the conducted potential changes. In studying many nerve fibers in this manner, certain changes other than spike potential are more easily demonstrated. These are *after-potentials* (see p. 108). Together with the spike they form what is often termed the *action potential*. This is accompanied by the uptake of a very small amount of oxygen, formation of carbon dioxide, and production of a very small amount of heat.

Figure 60 illustrates the initiation of a nerve impulse by an artificial stimulus, the application of a brief electrical shock. When the switch is closed, current flows from positive to negative. The region where the current is flowing out of the membrane to the negative electrode or *cathode* is the region where depolarization begins and the nerve impulse starts.

Figure 61 illustrates the conventional method of indicating the recorded electrical response. With two electrodes on a fiber (or on a nerve with many fibers) a diphasic response is recorded. If one electrode is on the killed end, the impulse cannot travel past that electrode, and a monophasic response would be recorded.

What is actually being recorded in these circumstances? Is there anything more than the reversal of membrane potential? Actually, the ionic movement or current flow inward through the depolarized region is continued as a current flow longitudinally inside each fiber. (The term *current* is used here for want of anything more satisfactory; it refers to the total process, the movement of ions or whatever chemical and physicochemical changes take place. It is not the current of the stimulating circuit.) The current flows inside the fiber to intact (polarized) regions ahead of the depolarized zone, and also behind to repolarizing regions. In each instance it flows out through the membrane in the fluid surrounding the fiber and by way of this fluid returns to the depolarized region. The latter, where current flows inward, is spoken of as a *sink*. The area where current flows out constitutes a *source*. Just what part the axoplasm (the interior of a fiber) plays is uncertain. Axoplasm has been re-

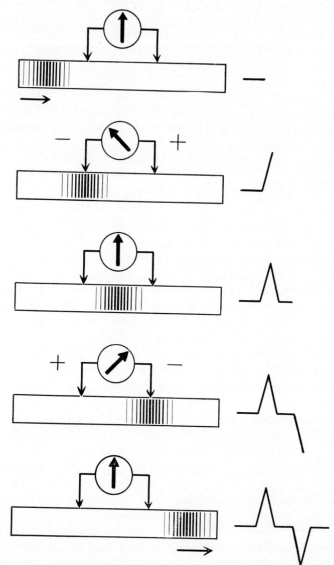

Figure 61. Conventional schematic representation of recording conducted activity. The long rectangle is a nerve on the surface of which are two electrodes (arrows) connected to a galvanometer in which the direction of conduction is indicated by an arrow. As an excitatory or negative change (vertical lines) comes under the first electrode, current flows from positive to negative, as indicated. When the impulse is between the electrodes, no current flows and the record returns to the base line. When it reaches the second electrode, current again flows from positive to negative, but in a direction opposite to that recorded first. When the impulse is past the electrode, no current flows. Thus a diphasic record is obtained.

moved from single giant fibers. In such cases the remaining tube, composed mainly of membrane, conducts like a normal fiber. In effect, a nerve fiber behaves like a *core conductor*.

It is believed that current flow out through the membrane acts as a stimulus (just as the current of the artificial stimulating circuit does) and that when the density of such flow is great enough, resistance breaks down and membrane potential reverses. In other words, an impulse, once started, is self-propagating because the current flow created by the membrane reversal acts as a stimulus for preceding portions of the fiber; when these break down, the process is repeated and thereby spreads. The energy for these changes is derived from metabolic processes, during the course of which oxygen is utilized and carbon dioxide is given off.

One might suppose that if a region where current is flowing inward is negative, then a region where it is flowing outward should be relatively positive. Accordingly, in Fig. 62 the first change to be detected by the nearest electrode should really be positive, representing current flow outward through the membrane ahead of the nerve impulse. This should be followed by what is usually thought of as the nerve impulse, represented by a negative change, the inward current flow at the depolarized region. This should in turn be succeeded by positivity, representing outward current flow behind the impulse. With both electrodes relatively near the tissue under study, one should record this triphasic process twice. With one electrode relatively far away, only a single triphasic response would be detected.

These types of changes are not readily demonstrable in isolated conducting tissue, because the fluid surrounding nerve fibers is probably decreased from normal, thereby altering or impeding the longitudinal flow of current. This can be demonstrated by replacing this fluid with a nonconducting medium, such as mineral oil The external resistance is thereby so increased that the rate of conduction decreases.

These complicated electrical changes are more easily demonstrated when the conducting tissue is in its normal situation, that is, in the body and surrounded by electrolytic fluid or other conducting tissue. Since they spread in all directions and since their interpretation involves geometry in three dimensions, the conduction is often called *volume conduction*. The contraction of a muscle is preceded by electrical activity which can easily be de-

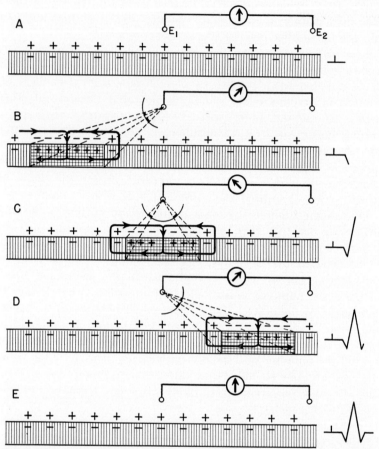

Figure 62. Diagram indicating recording from a volume conductor. *A,* Nerve fiber with electrical charges. At some distance from the nerve, separated by body fluid and tissue, are two electrodes, E_1 and E_2, connected to a recording instrument. E_2 is considered to be far enough away so that it can be neglected in this discussion. At some distance away a stimulus has been applied (not shown), and the shock artifact is shown at the right. *B,* The nerve impulse is conducting toward E_1, and the leading dipole is indicated completely. In order to determine the sign of any recorded potential, lines are drawn from E_1 to each end of the planes separating depolarized from polarized regions. With E_1 as a center, part of a circle is drawn. The length of arc included between each pair of lines as an indication of sign, in the following manner: The pair of lines to the right occupies a longer arc than does the other pair, and the surface of the fiber included by these two lines is positive, whereas that included between the other two is negative. Therefore, E_1 is "looking at more positivity than negativity," and a small positive deflection will be recorded. *C,* Both dipoles are under E_1, and the surfaces included by the lines are both negative; therefore a large negative deflection is recorded. *D,* Both dipoles

tected by electrodes on overlying skin. The spread of excitation over the heart is accompanied by characteristic electrical changes, the recorded form of which constitutes the *electrocardiogram*. This can be detected by electrodes from many different positions, a few of which are usually selected as standard leads. An electrode on each wrist, for example, picks up the electrical activity of the heart without ever being in actual contact with the heart.

So far as nerve fibers are concerned, then, one can consider conduction as if two whirlpools were moving down a fiber (Fig. 62). Each whirlpool or *dipole* consists of lines of current flow inside a fiber, out through the membrane (source), back through extracellular fluid and into the fiber through the membrane (sink). The place where the entering lines of both dipoles converge is the active region (sink), the region of membrane potential reversal. The leading dipole is associated with propagation, since its current, on flowing outward, acts as a stimulus. The trailing dipole is associated with recovery processes. If a whole nerve is being studied, then the recorded response can be very complicated and will be determined by the time relationships of the changes in each fiber of the nerve. If the fibers are conducting together, that is, have the same time relationships, then the form of the recorded change may approach the theoretical triphasic type. This, however, is to be expected only when dealing with parallel elements, such as nerve fibers lying side by side. Otherwise it may be difficult, if not impossible, to interpret electrical changes. This is true in the central nervous system, where in a given area great numbers of fibers and cell bodies are crowded together. Little is known about electrical activity in cells, and at the present time electrical activity of the central nervous system cannot be interpreted with any degree of certainty.

One might ask, if current flows through extracellular fluid, could it not flow through adjacent nerve fibers and affect them? Recent evidence indicates that it does and that it probably changes the local excitatory state (p. 110) of the inactive fiber, that is, makes it more susceptible to a stimulus. One may block conduction in a nerve, for example, with cold, and yet the current flow can spread beyond the block. On flowing out through the membrane beyond

---

are past E_1, which is again "looking" at positivity, and a small positive change is again recorded. *E,* The dipoles are relatively far away, and the triphasic change is completed. If E_2 were now represented as being affected, another triphasic change would be recorded, but with opposite signs.

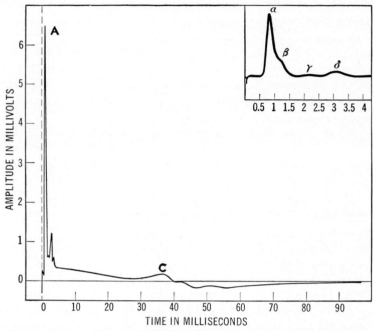

Figure 63.   Potentials recorded from mammalian saphenous nerve several centimeters from the point of stimulation. Rapidly traveling nerve impulses reach the electrodes first and are recorded as the *A* elevation, the fastest component of which has a velocity of about 80 meters per second. Its other components have maximum velocities of 25, 20 and 15 meters per second. The saphenous nerve, supplying skin, lacks the large fibers of muscle nerves which conduct at rates up to 120 meters per second. Following the *A* elevation by a considerable interval is the *C* elevation with components having velocities of 2 to 0.9 meters per second, these representing nonmyelinated fibers. The inset shows the *A* elevation recorded from the cat saphenous nerve 6 cm. from the point of stimulation. Since the recording rate is faster, the *A* components, *alpha, beta, gamma* and *delta*, are dispersed to a greater degree and represent the algebraic summation of potentials recorded from fibers varying from 2 to 16 microns in diameter. An intermediate or *B* elevation is recorded only from nerves containing preganglionic autonomic fibers. These fibers are myelinated, but differ considerably from *A* fibers in duration of spike potential and type of after-potential. (From Gasser, H. S.: Classification of Nerve Fibers. Ohio J. Sci., *41*:145–159, 1941; and Gasser, H. S.: Pain-Producing Impulses in Peripheral Nerves. Proc. A. Res. Nerv. & Ment. Dis., *23*:44–62, 1943.)

the block it may actually stimulate (and in effect cause the nerve impulse to jump the block), or it may simply render the nerve beyond the block more susceptible to stimulation.

Rates of Conduction.   Rates of conduction in nerve fibers vary according to fiber diameter. That is, a large fiber conducts at a faster rate than a small one. The ratio is such that for myelinated fibers in warm-blooded animals, multiplying the diameter by 6 gives the approximate conduction rate in meters per second. An axon 20 microns in diameter conducts about 120 meters per second (in cats; available evidence indicates that fibers of comparable size in man conduct more slowly). Nonmyelinated fibers conduct much more slowly (Fig. 63).

Nerve fibers conduct without decrement; that is, the impulses travel without decreasing in magnitude. Transmission in other tissues is fundamentally similar, but the intensity of the impulses frequently decreases in magnitude as the distance from the source increases.

Not all the factors responsible for differences in conduction rates are known. It has been suggested that myelin has an insulating function and that its association with faster conduction rates is coincidental. The smallest fibers, however, have no myelin and yet seem effectively insulated; impulses traversing them do not jump to other fibers. Recent evidence indicates that myelin prevents an outward flow of current, so that only at breaks in the myelin, such as nodes of Ranvier, can current flow out. It therefore concentrates at the first node ahead of an active region, the fiber is stimulated here, and current then flows out through the membrane at the next node. Thus the rate of conduction is greatly increased and the impulse actually proceeds in a *saltatory* fashion, from node to node.

Refractory Periods. In shooting a rifle, another shot will not result until another bullet is in place and the firing pin drops again. This has something of a counterpart in the nerve impulse. There is a short period following the initiation of an impulse in which another one cannot be set off, no matter how strong the stimulus. This is the *absolute refractory period.* In larger fibers, it lasts about 0.5 millisecond and probably corresponds to most of the time a given region is occupied by the active process. This continues into the *relative refractory period,* in which nerve impulses can be initiated but the stimuli have to be stronger than usual; that is to say, the threshold is higher. The total refractory period corresponds approximately to the duration of the spike potential. The threshold returns to normal in 0.5 to 2 milliseconds, depending upon fiber size, but then is lowered as fibers enter a *supernormal phase,* and finally raised in a *subnormal phase.* Threshold variations cease after about 80 milliseconds.

The fact that during the passage of a spike potential a fiber is refractory to stimuli limits the number of impulses per unit time in any one fiber. Nerve impulses, then, are not like a stream of water, but more like a succession of shots from a machine gun.

After-Potentials. The action potential is compounded of the spike and the negative and positive after-potentials. The negative after-potential begins before the spike is through and consists in a relatively prolonged negative electrical change which may last 15 milliseconds and is related in time to the supernormal phase of nerve. The positive after-potential is a positive electrical change succeeding the negative. It is of longer duration and is associated in time with the subnormal phase of nerve. These after-potentials are probably associated with processes of recovery following the passage of nerve impulses. The total time of all the changes produced by a stimulus may amount to as much as 80 milliseconds. The spike potential accounts for less than 1 millisecond.

The after-potentials are very variable, and are easily affected by changes in ionic environment. Certain drugs also have profound effects. Veratrine, for example, increases and prolongs the negative after-potential.

Nerve Impulses and Stimuli

A nerve impulse derives no energy from an initiating stimulus. If the stimulus reaches a threshold value, one just strong enough to initiate activity, then the nerve fiber responds to the maximum of its ability. A stronger stimulus to the same fiber can accomplish no more. The magnitude of the impulse remains the same. This is known as the *all-or-none law,* and the process may be compared to the firing of a gun. If the pull on the trigger is just strong enough to drop the firing pin (threshold value), the gun will be fired. Pulling harder on the trigger will not change subsequent events. It is the powder charge of the bullet and not the pull on the trigger which determines the response. Nerve fibers, however, differ in their excitability, and any one fiber may change in excitability. Larger and faster conducting fibers are more easily stimulated. An impulse may be initiated in them by a stimulus many times weaker than that necessary to stimulate a nonmyelinated fiber. Furthermore, the spike potentials of larger fibers rise to higher momentary values than do those of smaller fibers. An analogous condition would be the difference between a high-powered rifle with a hair trigger and a .22 caliber rifle in which the trigger pull was great.

Ideally, in studying the events characterizing stimulation, one would use normal physiological stimuli. Light falling on the retina can be controlled in wavelength, intensity and duration. Other stimuli, such as sound, can likewise be controlled. But for nerves coming from regions containing a variety of endings, each sensitive to different types of stimuli, it is difficult to control or measure physiological stimuli. Consequently, artificial stimuli such as electric currents are used. These are usually applied by connecting a current source, such as a battery, to electrodes on the nerve (Fig. 60). The electrode connected to the negative pole of the battery is the *cathode.* That connected to the positive pole is the *anode.* When a current is allowed to flow under such conditions, it is found that the permeability of the membrane is changed, and that it is increased at the cathode where current is flowing out through the membrane back to the negative pole of the battery. If the current is strong enough, then the membrane potential reverses, and an active, self-propagating locus is started; the nerve is stimulated. The cathode, therefore, is the stimulating electrode.

Stimulation takes place primarily during rate of change. That is, if the current is turned on and left on, so that a constant current is said to flow, then stimulation takes place at the *make,* when the current is turned on, and at the *break,* when the current is turned off.

When a constant current is applied, it is found that that part of the nerve under the cathode increases in excitability, and also that this excitability later decreases as the current is left on. The converse occurs at the anode. This decline from maximum excitability during the period of constant current is *accommodation,* and the various changes are summarized in Fig. 64.

Current has to flow for a certain finite period of time in order to be effective. For example, if one uses brief shocks, that is, currents turned on and off rapidly, then it is found that if the time each stimulus lasts is made shorter and shorter, there is produced a current which lasts such a short time that it will not stimulate, no matter how strong it is. This accounts for the fact that high frequency currents, even though they may be thousands or millions of volts, may not stimulate. Conversely, a subthreshold current may not stimulate, no matter how long it is allowed to flow.

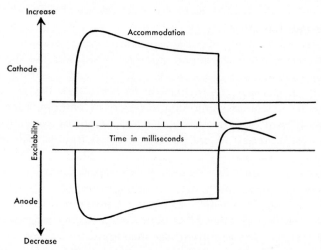

Figure 64. Diagram of excitability changes in nerve during the passage of a current for a short period of time. Note that the nerve under the negative electrode (cathode) increases in excitability very quickly, but that this excitability slowly decreases (accommodation) as the current continues to flow, and drops very abruptly when the current is turned off. In fact, the nerve momentarily becomes less sensitive to stimuli than it was before the current was applied. Converse changes occur in that part of the nerve under the positive electrode (anode). (Based on Erlanger and Blair, Am. J. Physiol., vol. 99, 1931, and Lloyd, in Fulton: Physiology.)

The curve illustrated in Fig. 65 is a *strength-duration curve,* showing the relationship of the strength of the stimulus to the time during which it acts. That strength of current which, when acting over an infinite time, is just sufficient to stimulate is known as the *rheobase.* If a current of twice the rheobase is chosen and the shortest time during which this can flow and still stimulate is measured, then this time is known as the *chronaxie* or *excitation time.* Chronaxie is an arbitrary but useful measure of excitability which has rather characteristic values for different tissues. More useful, however, are strength-duration curves, whose applications are discussed on p. 147.

Subthreshold Stimuli. It should not be supposed that a stimulus too weak to produce a nerve impulse has no effect on a fiber. On the contrary, a weak (subthreshold) stimulus causes a change known as a *local excitatory state.* At the stimulating electrode (the cathode), there is a momentary increase in excitation (already mentioned in connection with accommodation), which can be recorded as a momentary increase in electronegativity. This change is not propagated; that is, no such change can be recorded elsewhere than under the cathode. But if another subthreshold stimulus is applied to the same area before the local change dies away, the second local change summates with the first, and the combined effect may result in an excitation of threshold magnitude. In this event it becomes propagated and can be recorded elsewhere as it traverses the fiber. In other words, the first stimulus has *facilitated* the fiber. It is as if in using a gun one had pulled the trigger halfway back. This is a subthreshold stimulus, and the addition of another one causes the trigger to reach the point where the firing pin falls and detonates the cartridge.

Conduction in Dendrites. The properties of dendrites are different from those of cell bodies and axons. Conduction is often antidromic, that is, along the dendrite away from the cell body. For example, when a cell body is activated, the depolarization spreads along the axon as a nerve impulse, and antidromically

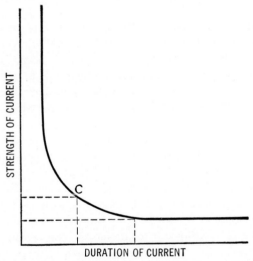

Figure 65. Graph illustrating relationship of current strength and duration. The horizontal portion of the curve indicates the rheobase, the least strength of current which, if flowing an infinite time, is just sufficient to stimulate. A current of less strength will never stimulate, no matter how long it flows. A current of twice rheobase strength reaches threshold after a time interval known as chronaxie, C. The vertical portion of the curve indicates that the stronger a current, the shorter its excitation time. Currents of high frequency act over such short times that they may never stimulate, no matter what their intensity.

along the dendrites. Conduction over dendrites is slow, it may be decremental, and there is evidence that the depolarization may persist for long periods of time. There is also evidence that local current flow from depolarized dendrites may depolarize cell bodies and cause them to discharge. Maintained dendritic depolarization may, therefore, serve as a constant stimulus to the cell body and be a factor in repetitive activity in the nervous system. The apical dendrites of cortical neurons have been most extensively studied with regard to these phenomena.

The Impulse and the Synaptic Junction

When a fiber is stimulated at some intermediate point, the nerve impulse spreads in both directions. Under most conditions, however, conduction in nerves is in one direction, because an impulse initiated at the distal end of a fiber has but one direction in which to go. An impulse starting in a cell body spreads in two directions, (a) along its axon and (b) along its dendrites through synaptic junctions to the telodendria of other axons. There is, however, a functional polarity imposed by the synaptic junctions so that a truly conducted impulse involves only the axon. Just how this is accomplished is not known. It is known only that, under most conditions, impulses pass from axon to dendrite or to cell body surface. Impulses initiated at axodendritic contacts spread in the dendrite away from the cell (see above). Impulses initiated at axosomatic contacts activate the cell with resulting conduction along the axon, and antidromic spread along dendrites.

Unipolar and bipolar cells pose some puzzling questions. Both processes are structurally like axons, and there is some question as to the functions of the cell bodies in transmission of nerve impulses. Furthermore, there is some evidence that these cells may conduct in either direction under normal conditions.

An impulse arriving at a synaptic junction does not automatically cause the succeeding cell to discharge. The factors governing events at synaptic junctions are not known with certainty, but apparently the manner in which the synaptic junctions are arranged is important. For instance, if the telodendria of an axon form synaptic junctions widely over the surface of a cell and the impulse is transmitted through each telodendron, then a number of impulses arrive at scattered points on the surface of the cell. The accompanying flow of current at any one point, however, may not be a threshold stimulus for that cell. If, therefore, a number of impulses arrive at scattered points on the cell surface, they may still not be able to cause the cell to discharge. If, however, synaptic junctions from a single axon are grouped closely in a discrete zone of a cell surface, then the impulses may be effective. If impulses from two different axons arrive simultaneously at the same zone on the cell surface, summation may result in a discharge.

The events at synaptic junctions are complex and not well understood. As impulses in terminal fibers (telodendria) approach synaptic junctions, current flow becomes dense, crosses synaptic junctions to invade the cell body, and produces a local depolarization. Depending on circumstances, this local change may suffice, or summation with a similar adjacent change may be necessary to cause the cell to conduct. It is also held that chemical substances are mediators at synaptic junctions (acetylcholine has been held to be the most likely), but the problem is still very controversial. An important factor is the orientation of telodendria with respect to cell bodies and dendrites. The degree or angle made by one fiber with respect to another determines the effect of current flow. One has only to consider the vast tangle of fibers and cells in gray matter to realize how complicated the problem is.

The foregoing discussion has dealt with excitation at synaptic junctions. Some fibers, however, are *inhibitory,* that is, nerve impulses over them prevent cells from discharging or stop existing activity. It is held that in such instances a transmitter is released at synaptic junctions with dendrites, this transmitter having a specific effect on membrane permeability such that the membrane is made more stable. In other words, the inhibitory mechanism, whatever it may be, tends to restore the resting potential and thereby to prevent current flow from dendrites from activating the cell body. It is also held that strychnine blocks this inhibitory mechanism and thereby indirectly has an excitatory effect. The details of this very important inhibitory mechanism are still very obscure.

The total delay in the passage of an impulse across a synaptic junction probably occupies no more than a fraction of a millisecond. When a cell discharges, it undergoes refractory periods as do the axons, and the time relationships may be approximately the same.

When a motor nerve fiber makes contact with a skeletal muscle fiber, the junctional region is called an endplate. This region is comparable to a synaptic junction, and the electrical events that occur there are similar to those at synapses (p. 144).

Summary

Nerve fibers are polarized in such a way that the interior of a fiber is negative to the exterior. The potential difference between the two is the membrane potential. An adequate stimulus to a fiber greatly alters the permeability of the membrane to many ions. The potential difference reverses as the interior becomes positive to the exterior. The resulting current flow spreads inside the fiber and, on flowing out through the membrane ahead of the altered membrane, acts as a stimulus. A self-propagating change thus results. This is the nerve impulse. The potential change constitutes the spike potential. Its form depends upon methods of recording, and is complicated when recorded from intact conducting tissue.

Nerves conduct at rates which depend upon fiber diameter. The maximum rate is about 120 meters per second. After the passage of a nerve impulse there are absolute and relative refractory periods as well as negative and positive after-potentials. There are changes in excitability of the nerve, the supernormal and subnormal periods, which correspond to the after-potentials and are associated with recovery processes in the nerve.

A subthreshold stimulus produces a local excitatory state in a fiber; as a result, another subthreshold stimulus may raise the local excitation to a threshold value and thereby set off a nerve impulse. The time during which the stimulus current flows is important. If it is too short, the current will not stimulate. A measure of excitability is chronaxie, the shortest time during which a current of twice rheobase strength must flow in order to stimulate.

References

Brazier, Mary A. B.: Electrical Activity of the Nervous System. London, Sir Isaac Pitman & Sons, Ltd., 1951. This is an excellent, generalized account of the subject. Both peripheral and central nervous systems are treated, and the conciseness and clearness of the text make it suitable for beginning and advanced students.

The following two textbooks deal primarily with mammalian physiology, are quite detailed, and contain excellent and in many ways advanced sections on neurophysiology. The relation of the latter to the human nervous system, however, is often minimal.

Fulton, J. F., ed.: Textbook of Physiology. 17th ed. Philadelphia, W. B. Saunders Company, 1955.

Bard, P., ed.: Medical Physiology. St. Louis, C. V. Mosby Company, 1956.

The following three textbooks also deal primarily with mammalian physiology, but emphasize human physiology and clinical applications.

Best, C. H., and Taylor, N. B.: Physiological Basis of Medical Practice. 6th ed. Baltimore, Williams and Wilkins Company, 1955.

Guyton, A. C.: Textbook of Medical Physiology. Philadelphia, W. B. Saunders Co., 1956.

Wright, S.: Applied Physiology. 9th ed. London, Geoffrey Cumberledge, Oxford University Press, 1952.

The following are reviews, monographs and books of an advanced nature, also containing valuable bibliographies.

Bishop, G. H.: Natural history of the nerve impulse. Physiol. Rev., 36:376–399, 1956.

Eccles, J. C.: The Neurophysiological Basis of Mind. Oxford, Clarendon Press, 1953.

Eccles, J. C.: The Physiology of Nerve Cells. Baltimore, The Johns Hopkins Press, 1957.

Hodgkin, A. L.: The ionic basis of electrical activity in nerve and muscle. Biol. Rev., 26:339–409, 1951.

The following two works are clearly written, concise accounts of some of the early studies of nerve conduction and function. All three men were awarded the Nobel Prize in recognition of their work in neurophysiology.

Adrian, E. D.: Mechanism of Nervous Action. Philadelphia, University of Pennsylvania Press, 1932.

Erlanger, J., and Gasser, H. S.: Electrical Signs of Nervous Activity. Philadelphia, University of Pennsylvania Press, 1937.

CHAPTER 8

General Properties of the
Reflex Arc

A REFLEX act may be defined as a relatively fixed pattern of response or behavior that is similar for any given stimulus. The pupil of the eye gets smaller when a light is flashed in the eye. A hand inadvertently set on a hot object is immediately jerked away; the withdrawal is partially completed before pain is felt. A few drops of a weak acid may be placed on the skin of a frog that has had its brain destroyed. The animal attempts to get rid of the irritating agent by making active, coordinated limb movements. These movements do not take place if the spinal cord is destroyed or if the nerves between the cord and the leg have been cut. The pathway consists of afferent nerves by which impulses initiated by the stimulus reach the spinal cord; synaptic connections are made within the cord so that impulses leave by way of efferent nerves which transmit them to the proper skeletal muscles. The total pathway is termed a *reflex path* or *reflex arc* and can function independently of higher centers. This independence, however, is rarely characteristic of normal activity.

Receptors, Neuro-effector Junctions and Effectors. These are the structures that receive stimuli and produce responses. They are discussed in more detail in Chapter 9. *Receptors* are either specialized terminations of the peripheral processes of unipolar cells, or they are nerve endings associated with special sense organs. *Neuro-effector junctions* are specialized terminals of efferent fibers arising from cells in the central nervous system or from cells in

116

autonomic ganglia. *Effectors* are structures which carry out the actual responses. In the higher animals, including man, they are muscles and glands.

Types of Reflexes

Reflexes are often classified according to the smallest number of neurons by which their pathways can be represented. Such paths are abstractions only; functionally, they rarely, if ever, operate in such isolated form.

Three-Neuron Reflex Arcs. There are a variety of such reflexes, perhaps best exemplified by reflex withdrawal of a limb in response to a painful stimulus. The impulses travel centrally and are widely distributed within the spinal cord so that, after passage through *intercalated* or *internuncial neurons* (*interneurons*), they activate many motor cells. Thus, reflex flexion at several joints may follow a painful stimulus to a relatively small area of skin. Figure 66 illustrates the simplest abstraction of such a reflex. Three-neuron reflexes may also be initiated by stimulation of receptors in deep tissues (in reflex components of walking) and are the most common type of reflex involving skeletal muscle.

Two-Neuron Reflex Arcs. Certain reflexes may be represented by a pathway of two neurons (Fig. 67). Nearly everyone is familiar with the knee jerk, which is elicited by tapping the tendon of the quadriceps femoris muscle just below the patella (knee cap). This stretches the muscle, and the receptors stimulated include *neuromuscular spindles* (described on p. 133). The resulting nerve im-

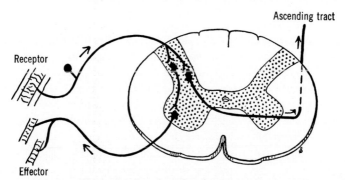

Figure 66. Diagram illustrating how impulses from a cutaneous receptor reach an effector (skeletal muscle), by a three-neuron arc at the level of entrance. Impulses also reach the cerebral hemisphere by way of an ascending tract. Arrows indicate direction of conduction.

Neuromuscular spindle

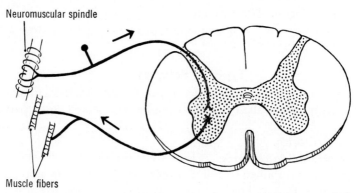

Muscle fibers

Figure 67. Diagram of a two-neuron reflex, from a spindle in a muscle back to other fibers of the same muscle. Arrows indicate direction of conduction.

pulses reach the spinal cord over fibers which synapse with cells in the ventral gray matter. These are large multipolar cells called ventral horn cells, or *motor neurons*. The axons of these cells transmit impulses to the muscle originally lengthened, which then contracts and regains its former length.

This *stretch* or *myotatic reflex* is a rather restricted or local type of response. In its simplest form, it involves two neurons and, therefore, one area of synaptic junctions. The nerve fibers concerned are large and conduct rapidly. Since there is also a minimum of synaptic delay, the resulting reflexes are among the fastest known. Myotatic reflexes are further characterized by the fact that the motor discharge is mainly restricted to the muscle which was stretched.

The knee jerk is also called a *phasic* type of stretch reflex. The muscle is stretched quickly, and the spindles within it are stimulated at the same time. Consequently, the resulting nerve impulses travel centrally as a synchronous volley, much like a volley from a rifle squad when the rifles are fired simultaneously. The reflex discharges from the spinal cord are likewise in phase, so that muscle fibers are activated at the same time. The result is a quick, reflex muscular contraction, lasting but a short time; hence the term "jerk." There are also *static* types of stretch reflexes. If a muscle is slowly stretched, varying numbers of spindles are stimulated, some at first and some later as the stretch increases or is maintained. The result is an irregular, or asynchronous, discharge from these endings, much as if the members of a rifle squad were firing in sequence or at random. The reflex motor discharge is likewise asynchronous, and muscle fibers are activated at different times. The result is a more sustained contraction, but one in which at any one time only a relatively few muscle fibers may be in action.

Muscles are stretched when their antagonists are contracting and also when joints flex as a result of the effect of gravity upon a limb. It is ordinarily held that antigravity muscles are so sensitive to the latter situation that they always exhibit static stretch reflexes, to the extent that they have what is called *tone* or *postural contraction*. It is also held that tone may be present in muscles which are not strictly postural. While tone is undoubtedly present in lower animals, its presence in man under all postural conditions is debatable. A muscle can be so relaxed that no electrical or mechanical activity can be detected. What tone it now possesses is due to its inherent elasticity, not to neurological mechanisms. Furthermore, in an upright, comfortable position, with feet fairly well apart, there is little if any electrical or mechanical activity in the antigravity muscles until there is a fairly considerable deviation or flexion. In other words, the structure and arrangement of human joints are such that in an upright static position they provide maximum stability. Little if any muscular effort is needed. In other types of positions tone is undoubtedly present, and reflex mechanisms are of course easily demonstrated upon deviation from the mechanically stable situation. It should be emphasized that most experimental work on stretch reflexes has been carried out on lower animals, such as cats.

Coordination of Reflex Arcs

Reflex arcs are not limited to the spinal cord, but occur over brain stem areas as well. In an intact organism, the initiating impulses may also traverse fibers which reach the cerebral cortex, where they may be interpreted as sensations. But reflexes are not dependent upon this. A painful stimulus may be followed by a reflex response before the subject experiences pain or even without the knowledge of pain. Responses may occur after the spinal cord has been severed above the level over which the reflex takes place. Although a subject under general anesthesia feels no pain, reflexes can be elicited by appropriate stimuli.

To the casual observer a reflex is an apparently simple and relatively isolated mechanism of which the knee jerk is a splendid

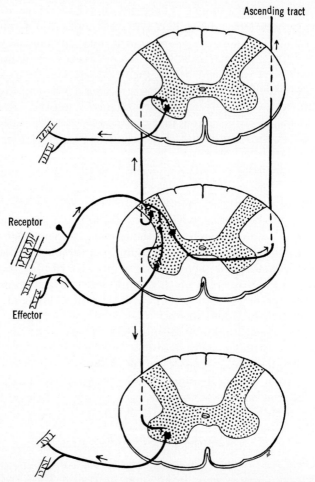

Figure 68.   Diagram of the connections by which impulses from a receptor reach motor neurons at different cord levels. This accounts for multisegmental, ipsilateral responses. Arrows indicate direction of conduction.

example. The response is an extension of the leg. But is it so simple? In order for this to happen, the opposing muscles (flexors of the leg) must give way to a degree corresponding to the extension. The muscles are said to relax, and the production of this relaxation is a function of the gray matter of the cord—a central mechanism. Impulses from the receptors in the muscle are carried by dorsal root fibers into the cord. Here the fibers reach the motor neurons supplying the extensors. But branches also reach those supplying flexor muscles, and the reflex or tonic activity of these neurons is decreased or *inhibited* by the impulses arriving from the stretch reflex arc. Although little is known about the actual mechanism of inhibition, it is nevertheless an important factor in muscular activity. When muscles contract, those which oppose them must be coordinated in some way. They either contract and

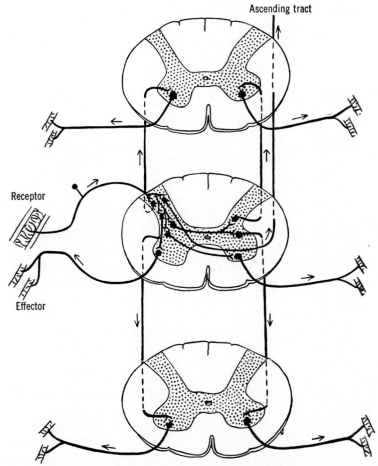

Figure 69.   Diagram of the connections by which impulses from a receptor reach motor neurons at various levels of both sides of the spinal cord. This accounts for multisegmental, ipsilateral and contralateral responses. Arrows indicate direction of conduction.

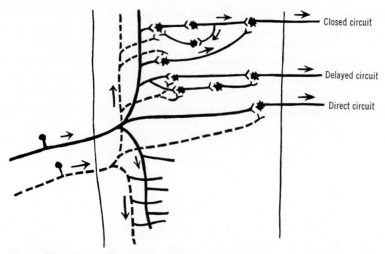

Closed circuit

Delayed circuit

Direct circuit

Figure 70. The fundamental neuronal arrangements in gray matter. Entering dorsal root fibers give off horizontal, ascending and descending branches. Some go directly to motor neurons (for two-neuron reflexes). Others synapse with interneurons so that impulses reach motor neurons by delayed and closed circuits. Tracts ascending to the brain may be continuations of ascending fibers, or may arise from interneurons (Fig. 98, p. 181). Arrows indicate direction of conduction.

a fixed position results, or they relax and a movement occurs. The causative inhibition in the latter case is frequently termed *Sherrington's inhibition* (p. 128).

Let us return to the protective reflex, cited on p. 116, brought about in a frog by placing a few drops of a weak acid on the skin of its leg. The reflex is complex because a number of muscles are involved in the withdrawal movement. These are supplied by efferent fibers from more than one segment of the cord. Therefore, the cells with which the entering dorsal root fibers synapse connect with motor neurons at the same level and also send axons up and down the cord to motor neurons at other levels (Fig. 68). These *ipsilateral* connections provide for widespread reciprocal responses.

These responses are further complicated by the necessity, in many cases, of *contralateral responses*. Suppose that a painful stimulus is applied to the bottom of the foot. The entire lower limb may be withdrawn or jerked away. The weight of the body must then be supported by the opposite lower limb whose muscles, therefore, contract strongly. There is an anatomic basis for such a response. In addition to the connections of internuncial neurons cited earlier, axons cross the midline of the spinal cord and reach motor neurons at many levels (Fig. 69). Motor impulses thus reach muscles in the opposite extremity; this again is accompanied by the necessary reciprocal inhibition.

These examples illustrate admirably the remarkable degree of coordination of two equally significant interacting mechanisms, namely, excitation and inhibition. When one group of muscles contracts, certain other muscles must either contract or relax to a like degree. This may be a reflex activity or, as will be shown later, a result of voluntary mechanisms.

Reflexes are not so invariable as the definition of a reflex would indicate. For instance, an afferent nerve may be stimulated and a muscle reflexly contracts. But when the stimulation stops and impulses can no longer be recorded from the afferent nerve, the muscle may continue to contract for many milliseconds during which time impulses can be recorded from the efferent nerve. This is an *after-discharge.* Not all the factors are known, but Fig. 70

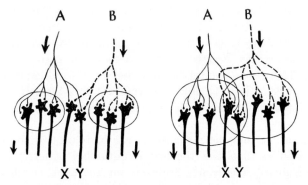

Figure 71. Diagram illustrating facilitation (*left*) and occlusion (*right*). It is arbitrarily assumed that impulses at two synaptic junctions are necessary to stimulate a motor neuron. *Left:* Afferent fiber *A* forms two junctions with each motor neuron in the encircled field, but only one each with motor neurons *X* and *Y*. An impulse over *A* therefore causes three neurons to discharge. The same situation obtains for *B.* But if impulses arrive over *A* and *B* simultaneously, not only will the six encircled neurons discharge, but also *X* and *Y,* since these will have two active junctions each. The reflex response will be greater than could be postulated from the result of stimulating *A* or *B* separately. *Right:* Afferent fiber *A* forms two junctions with each of five motor neurons, as does *B.* But *X* and *Y* are common to both, so that impulses over *A* and *B* simultaneously cause eight, and not ten, neurons to discharge. The reflex response is less than could be postulated from the result of stimulating *A* or *B* separately.

illustrates some of the anatomic features. The branching of an entering fiber allows an impulse to traverse paths containing varying numbers of interneurons and thus to reach a motor neuron at different times, providing for a succession of discharges from it. Furthermore, some of the interneurons in the gray matter form closed circuits which can continue to excite a motor neuron after impulses have ceased entering the cord. The multiple and closed circuits are characteristic of gray matter throughout the central nervous system.

The degree to which afferent fibers overlap in making functional connections with interneurons and motor neurons provides another basis for variability. Figure 71 illustrates how reflexes elicited by stimulation of different afferent fibers may either summate or become occluded.

Reflexes and Behavior

It would seem justified to consider the reflex arc a basic unit of the nervous system. The isolation and study of clear-cut reflexes would support the conception of a nervous system composed of racks of such arcs, integrated and controlled by higher centers. Indeed, such a conception is commonly encountered. But is such the case? Do the facts support it? Can we really conceive of the nervous system as a mass of such stereotyped patterns? No, we cannot. The reflex should be regarded as a local, highly differentiated mechanism the study of which affords little insight into those higher functions which are characterized by extreme variability.

The concept that the reflex arc is the basic unit of the nervous system implies that it is the first recognizable pattern to appear in the embryo. There are, however, no anatomic or physiologic data which adequately support this hypothesis. The admirable work of Coghill on the spotted salamander, *Ambystoma punctatum,* established the development of behavior as follows:

First of all, in the development of the nervous system, there is a physiologic gradient in a cephalocaudal direction. Metabolic activity is highest in the head or cephalic region, and from here the growth of neuroblast processes is caudally, that is, longitudinally. Motor chains are formed from which axons grow out into developing muscles (p. 64). This is illustrated by the following observations: The first movement executed by Ambystoma is a bending of the head to one side. As the paths continue to develop and branches are given to trunk musculature, the entire trunk may coil. With increasing differentiation of the nervous system, the animal can perform two flexures instead of a simple coil, the flexures progressing in the shape of an S. As this performance improves, the animal becomes capable of locomotion, and thus the initial independence of environment is attained.

In the early but nonmotile stage, muscles are contractile, but the animal cannot respond to the stimulus of a light touch on the skin. Yet at this stage there are nerve fibers supplying the skin. There are, however, no commissural neurons or interneurons within the cord at this stage, and impulses cannot pass from the sensory to the motor paths. As soon as commissural neurons appear in the brain stem, muscular contraction follows tactile stimulation. The afferent impulses must go up to the brain stem, where connections are made with motor tracts. Interneurons then begin to appear in greater numbers in a cephalocaudal manner.

When the limb buds appear, their movements are at first associated with trunk movements. This is because the nerves to trunk muscles send branches to limb muscles, and movements of one without the other are not possible. The subsequent occurrence of separate limb movements is correlated with an increasing independence of nerve supply. Some local reflexes are secondary and are derived from a total pattern by differentiation.

It is evident that the pattern of skin and muscle innervation is laid down *before* the animal can reflexly respond to changes in the external environment. Therefore, experience with such changes cannot influence the development of structural foundations of response. The weight of evidence is in favor of similar processes in higher animals, including man.

Clinical Value of Reflexes

Reflexes are important, because an examination of them may yield information about the nature and location of neurological disorders. Clinically, reflexes may be classified as superficial, deep, special and abnormal.

Superficial reflexes are those elicited by cutaneous stimulation. If the skin of the abdominal wall is scratched, the abdominal muscles contract. The toes flex if the sole of the foot is scratched. These responses are of the three-neuron or flexor type.

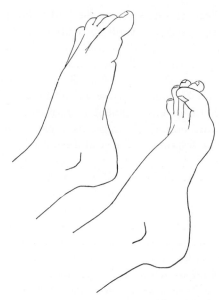

Figure 72.   *Upper:* The normal response to scratching the sole of the foot. *Lower:* Pathological or Babinski response.

Deep reflexes are those elicited by tapping a tendon and are of the stretch or myotatic type. Those commonly tested are the *ankle jerk,* by tapping the Achilles tendon (tendon of the triceps surae) (p. 127), with resulting plantar flexion of the foot; the *knee jerk,* by tapping the quadriceps femoris tendon just below the patella, the leg extending; the *biceps jerk,* by tapping the biceps brachii tendon and obtaining a flexion of the forearm; and the *triceps jerk,* by tapping the tendon of the triceps brachii muscle, the forearm extending.

Special reflexes involve structures other than skeletal muscles. When a light is flashed upon the eye, the diameter of the pupil lessens, thus restricting the amount of light which can enter the organ. Some of the more important special reflexes will be discussed in Chaps. 13 and 15.

Abnormal or *pathological reflexes* are those not present normally or are exaggerations of normal ones. Disorders of the spinal cord or higher centers are the common causes, and the reasons for them are discussed in Chap. 10. The most important pathological reflex is the *Babinski response* (p. 128). This is a dorsiflexion of the big toe and often a fanning of the other toes, rather than plantar flexion, when the sole of the foot is stimulated (Fig. 72).

The usefulness of such examinations is shown as follows: If a knee jerk is absent and cutaneous sensation is absent over the knee and thigh, but the patient can voluntarily extend his leg, an action which cannot be produced reflexly, then dorsal roots must be involved. This interrupts afferent impulses of reflex and sensory pathways. But if cutaneous sensation is normal and leg extension cannot be produced either reflexly or voluntarily, the involvement is of ventral horn cells or ventral roots, that is, the efferent pathway. If the first two instances are combined, however, the disorder must affect spinal or peripheral nerves in which both efferent and afferent fibers are present.

Summary

In reflex mechanisms, nerve impulses from the periphery reach the central nervous system and are then directed back to the periphery, where a response occurs. Receptors, central connections, neuro-effector junctions, and effectors are parts of reflex arcs.

The simplest of these are two-neuron arcs for stretch or myotatic reflexes, and three-neuron arcs for flexor or superficial reflexes.

Reflex responses involve not only contractions, but also relaxations, of opposing muscles. A number of muscles may be involved in or be subsidiary to a reflex. Ipsilateral and contralateral connections within the cord provide for these.

Reflexes are to be regarded as highly differentiated mechanisms which arise secondarily from a total response pattern. They are not to be regarded as the basic units of the nervous system.

The clinical examination of reflexes may enable one to determine the nature and location of neurological disorders.

Names in Neurology

Achilles, son of Peleus and Thetis

After Thetis dipped the child in the waters of the River Styx, he became invulnerable except in that part of the heel by which she held him. From this arises the proverbial term, "heel of Achilles." It was here he later received a mortal wound. The tendon by which the calf muscles attach to the calcaneus or heel bone is termed the Achilles tendon, and the reflex elicited by tapping this tendon is the Achilles reflex.

Babinski, Josef (1857–1932)

Babinski was a physician in Paris who is best known for his description of the pathological reflex of the toes which occurs in central nervous system disorders.

Sherrington, Sir Charles Scott (1859–1952)

There is scarcely a phase of neurophysiology in which this noted English physiologist was not a pioneer or a leading investigator. A few of his most important contributions are studies of muscular rigidity, reciprocal innervation, physiology of synapses, many types of reflexes, the activity of the cerebral cortex, and functions of the inner ear. In all his work, he stressed the integrative actions and coordinating mechanisms of the nervous system. It is difficult to do justice to the extent of his contributions to our understanding of the nervous system. So much that is known today can be traced to an original work by Sir Charles that one can do no more than state that this is the situation. He was as pre-eminent in neurophysiology as Jackson was in clinical neurology and Ramón y Cajal in neuroanatomy.

References

For discussions of structures and function of reflex arcs, refer to the histology, neuroanatomy and physiology textbooks cited in previous chapters.

Coghill, G. E.: Anatomy and the Problem of Behavior. Cambridge, Cambridge University Press, 1929. This is a "must" for all biology students. It summarizes a series of classic investigations of nervous structure and behavior.

Fulton, J. F.: Physiology of the Nervous System. 3rd ed. London, Oxford University Press, 1949. The first eight chapters contain excellent discussions of various reflex mechanisms.

Wartenberg, R.: Diagnostic Tests in Neurology. Chicago, The Year Book Publishers, Inc., 1953. A small, clearly written, accurate and practical book; one of the finest of its kind, by an outstanding clinician.

CHAPTER 9

Structures Mediating

Reception and Response

A HAND touching a hot light globe is pulled away; the patellar tendon is tapped and the leg extends; an object moves suddenly into the field of vision and the eye blinks; one is thirsty and takes a drink of water; a symphony orchestra provides a pleasurable background to a session in the easy chair. These are responses to changes in the environment. How are such changes recorded, and how is one type of change differentiated from another? What structures carry out the responses? The environmental changes are detected by *receptors,* and the responses are carried out by *effectors.* These structures and their connections will be the subject of this and succeeding chapters.

Environmental changes may affect the skin and underlying tissues; the receptors sensitive to such stimuli are *exteroceptive receptors.* A special category includes receptors sensitive to stimuli originating at a distance; these are associated with the eye, ear and nose, and will be discussed in Chap. 12. Changes in tension of muscles or tendons, or in the position of a limb, are stimuli arising within the body that affect *proprioceptive receptors.* A special category of these includes certain receptors in the inner ear which are discussed in Chap. 12. *Interoceptive receptors* are sensitive to stimuli arising within the body in connection with such visceral changes as distention of the bladder, drying of the throat, variations in blood pressure, and so forth.

Neuro-effector junctions are specialized associations of nerve fibers and effectors. Effectors include skeletal or voluntary muscle, smooth or involuntary muscle, cardiac or heart muscle, and glands. In lower forms of life such structures as *electric organs* (electric eel) and *luminescent organs* (firefly) are also effectors.

Receptors

Exteroceptive Receptors of the Skin. When the skin of a normal subject is lightly stroked with a wisp of cotton, touched with a fine hair, or lightly stroked with the fingers, the sensation perceived is *touch* (often termed *light touch*). This type of stimulus activates several types of receptors, depending on the type of skin touched. In skin without hair there are specialized, encapsulated endings (*Meissner's corpuscles*) in the dermis, and *free endings* in dermis and epidermis (in the latter location the endings are sometimes called tactile disks). Hairy skin lacks encapsulated endings (although skin with sparse hair may have a few). Free endings are found in dermis and epidermis, and relatively large fibers form complex plexuses around hair follicles (roots of hairs). The various cutaneous endings are illustrated in a combined drawing (Fig. 73). The tactile endings are derived from myelinated and nonmyelinated fibers that enter the deeper skin (dermis), where they form an extensive plexus. The fibers branch as they approach the outer skin (epidermis), and the endings arise from these branches.

Tactile endings are examples of what are often called mechanoreceptors. Endings sensitive to mechanical deformation are common in the animal kingdom. A deformation of any of the tactile endings initiates nerve impulses which, if they reach the cerebral cortex, are interpreted as light touch. These receptors, and all others, are functionally specific in that they are more sensitive to one type of stimulus than another.

Tactile receptors are not distributed evenly throughout the skin, but occur in groups. Only by a stimulation of one of these groups (a *touch spot*) can the sensation of touch be aroused. Between the spots, tactile sensation is decreased or absent. Tactile groups are numerous in the finger tips, but relatively scarce in such areas as the skin of the back.

If the skin is pricked with a pin, cut with a knife, or bruised, the resulting sensation is *pain*. The receptors sensitive to painful stimuli are free nerve endings, derived from myelinated and nonmyelinated fibers in the plexus of the dermis. The endings derived from myelinated fibers are found mainly within the epidermis, although the myelin is lost before the fibers end, while free nerve endings in the dermis arise mainly from nonmyelinated fibers. Free nerve endings are also found near encapsulated terminals, such as pacinian corpuscles (Fig. 74).

Changes in temperature above or below the normal body variations activate endings in the dermis near blood vessels. No specific

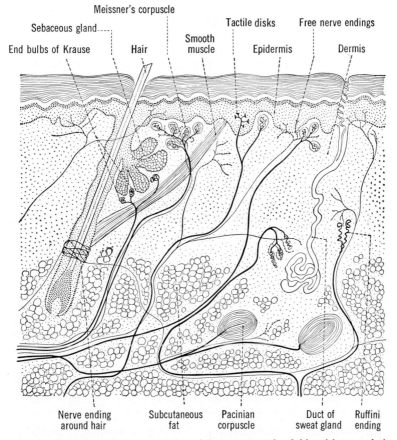

Figure 73.   Schematic representation of the nerve supply of skin with sparse hair. Not all the endings shown are to be found in any one skin area. The heavy lines are myelinated fibers, the light lines, nonmyelinated fibers. (Modified after Woollard et al.: J. Anat., Vol. 74.)

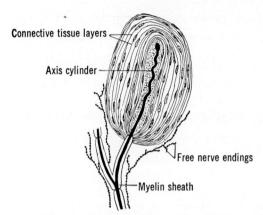

Connective tissue layers

Axis cylinder

Free nerve endings

Myelin sheath

Figure 74. Simplified representation of a pacinian corpuscle. Note that the connective tissue layers are separated from the axis cylinder by a central space. Note also the accessory fibers forming free endings, similar to those of Fig. 73. The myelin may persist into the interior, and the axis cylinder commonly divides into a complex network in the central space.

kind of receptor can be related to temperature, however, at least with any certainty.

In spite of the fact that in skin lacking hair, as in the palm of the hand, there are various kinds of encapsulated endings, one cannot be sure of the functional specificity of these endings. And in hairy skin, where only free endings and plexuses around hair follicles are found, all types of skin sensations can be aroused, just as in the hand. It may be that sensation depends more on frequency and timing of impulses than on the type of receptor stimulated.

Exteroceptive Receptors in the Deeper Tissues. There are a variety of receptors in the subcutaneous tissues, in the connective tissue of fascial planes, and in the connective tissue of muscles, tendons and joints, some sensitive to painful stimuli, others to *pressure.* Those excited by painful stimuli are free nerve endings similar to those in the skin. Those sensitive to pressure are encapsulated and are known as *pacinian corpuscles* (p. 149). Ruffini endings may serve a similar function. If the skin is pressed with the finger or with a blunt instrument, the pressure transmitted through the skin deforms these endings, yielding a quality of sensation known usually as pressure and occasionally as *deep touch.* Pacinian corpuscles are a type of mechanoreceptor. Many varieties have been described, according to size, shape and location. The classical pacinian corpuscle is formed by numerous, thin laminae of connective tissue arranged like the layers of onion skin which surround the end of a large myelinated fiber (Fig. 74). These receptors are often large enough (1 to 2 mm. long) to be seen with the naked eye during dissections.

Proprioceptive Receptors. These occur in muscles, tendons and joints. There are several types in muscle. Those best known and most widely studied are *neuromuscular spindles,* found in nearly all muscles, generally near musculotendinous junctions. Each spindle, which may be a millimeter or more in length, consists of one or more muscle fibers, each supplied by small motor nerve fibers (*gamma* efferents), and one or more large sensory nerve fibers that form annulospiral or primary endings and flower-spray or secondary endings on the spindle muscle fibers (Fig. 75). These muscle and nerve fibers are enclosed by a connective tissue capsule and surrounded by fluid. Neuromuscular spindles are sensitive to changes in tension caused by increase in muscle length, that is, by stretch, and are therefore often called stretch receptors. An additional means of stimulation is also available. Nerve impulses over *gamma* efferents cause the spindle muscle fibers to contract. The resulting shortening stimulates the sensory endings on the spindle muscle fibers, causing the endings to discharge. Little is known about other sensory receptors in muscle. The nerve supply of muscle is diagrammatically represented in Fig. 81.

Encapsulated endings in tendons are *neurotendinous spindles* or *endings* (often called Golgi tendon organs). They are stimulated by the tension produced in the tendon during either contraction or stretching of its attached muscle.

Proprioceptive endings are found in the connective tissue around muscles and bones, and in the connective tissue that forms the capsules of movable joints. The most common joint ending is the Ruffini type ending (Fig. 77). It is a slowly adapting ending that records the position of joints and movement at joints.

Interoceptive Receptors. These have been less extensively studied. Free nerve endings, which are probably excited by such stimuli as distention, are found in the walls of many of the viscera. Rather complex terminals occur in the walls of some of the larger arteries, such as the arch of the aorta and the bifurcations of the common carotids, and also in such venous areas as the right atrium of the heart. These endings appear to be particularly sensitive to changes in blood pressure (p. 241). There are nerve fibers

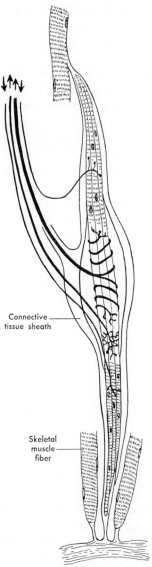

Connective tissue sheath

Skeletal muscle fiber

Figure 75. Schematic representation of a neuromuscular spindle. Parts of three skeletal muscle fibers are shown (cross-striated, nuclei at edge). Inside the connective tissue sheath of the spindle are three muscle fibers (thinner than regular skeletal muscle fibers, with central nuclei, and striations minimal or absent in region of sensory endings). Sensory nerve fibers form primary (annulospiral) and secondary (flower-spray) endings, the primary arising from the large fibers. (The

Nerve fiber   Muscle fiber of spindle

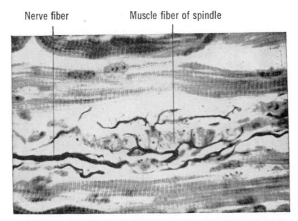

Figure 76. Photomicrograph of part of a neuromuscular spindle (mouse), showing a large nerve fiber forming the annulospiral ending. The muscle fibers within the spindle lack the cross striations so prominent in neighboring fibers. (Reproduced from Gardner: Anat. Rec., Vol. 83, courtesy of Wistar Institute of Anatomy and Biology.)

in the lungs which branch profusely and form endings sensitive to the stretching produced by the expansion of the lungs during inspiration (p. 273). Pacinian corpuscles are found in such connective tissue areas of the abdominal cavity as the mesenteries, and are associated with the branching points of small arteries. It may be that the effective stimulus to these endings is a deformation produced by changes in diameter of these vessels with each pulse. There are other types of interoceptive receptors, but their structure and function are less well known.

Receptors for the Special Senses. These include receptors sensitive to radiant energy (rods and cones of the retina), receptors activated by chemical changes (smell and taste), and special mechanoreceptors in the ear (activated by sound waves for hearing, and fluid pressure changes in response to changes in position of the head). These receptors are discussed in Chap. 12.

form of primary and secondary endings varies according to species. In some, such as rabbit and man, the primary endings of the large fiber may be flower-spray in type, not winding around the muscle fiber). Small nerve fibers (*gamma* efferents) form motor endings at each end of the spindle muscle fibers. Motor discharges over *gamma* efferents cause the spindle muscle fibers to contract at each end, thus stretching the intervening, non-contractile, sensory region and activating the sensory endings. Arrows indicate direction of conduction. (Based on Barker, D.. Quart. J. Micr. Sc., vol. 89, 1948.)

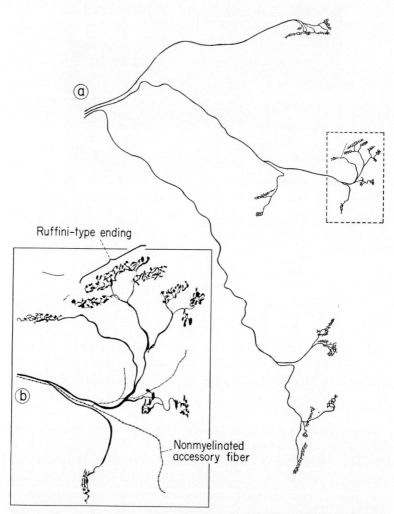

Figure 77. *a*, Drawing of three nerve fibers giving rise to proprioceptive receptors in the knee joint (cat), showing that many endings arise from a single fiber.
b, Drawing at higher magnification of endings in the region indicated in *a*. (Reproduced from Gardner: Nerve Supply of Diarthrodial Joints. Stanford M. Bull.,
Vol. 6.)

Physiology of Receptors

When a receptor such as a pacinian corpuscle is stimulated, there occurs a local depolarization of the nerve terminals in the ending. The mechanism whereby the energy of the stimulus activates the receptor and sets off a nerve impulse is obscure, but the initial process is evidenced by a negative *receptor potential.* This is a non-propagated potential, and it may be that spread of current from this potential depolarizes the nerve fibers at the nearest node of Ranvier and thereby initiates a nerve impulse, provided that the current flow is dense enough to reach the threshold of the nerve fiber.

Whatever the mechanism of receptor stimulation, for any receptor the impulses are always the same. That is to say, they are of the same magnitude and rate of conduction. But there is a variation in the number of impulses per unit time, depending upon the strength of the stimulus. A stimulus just above threshold initiates only one or at most a few impulses. A higher frequency of impulses results from stronger stimuli. If a stimulus is applied and maintained at a constant strength, a burst of impulses occurs initially; subsequently the frequency becomes lower and lower, until finally there are either no impulses, although the stimulus is still being maintained, or else there are impulses at a very low frequency. This phenomenon is known as *adaptation.* It is not a matter of fatigue of the receptors, for if the stimulus is even momentarily released and then re-applied, there is again an initial burst of activity and the process is repeated. This could not occur if the receptors were fatigued.

For example, an adaptation familiar to most people is experienced when one lies in bed with an arm or leg maintained in one position without moving; within a short time, one is no longer conscious of the position of that part of the body. Adaptation has occurred and the receptors are no longer active. A slight movement, however, interrupts the constant stimulus, and the consciousness of position returns.

The rate of adaptation differs for the various receptors (Fig. 78). Tactile receptors adapt in a few seconds. Neuromuscular spindles, on the other hand, adapt only after the stimulus has been maintained for a relatively long time, perhaps thirty minutes or more. Some receptors, such as those for pain, appear in some circumstances to have little or no adaptation.

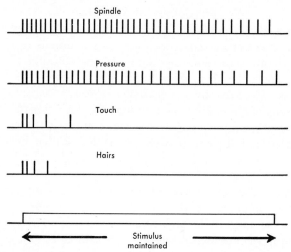

Figure 78. Schematic representation of adaptation in sensory endings. Each ending is stimulated for the same length of time, and nerve impulses are shown as if they were being recorded on moving film or paper. When a neuromuscular spindle is stimulated (by maintaining a stretch on its muscle), the spindle fires at a relatively high rate, a rate that decreases only slightly as the stimulus is maintained. A pressure receptor (pacinian corpuscle), on being touched or compressed, likewise continues to fire, but its rate of discharge decreases somewhat more. A touch receptor in skin, and receptors around hair follicles, adapt very rapidly, giving but a few impulses when the stimulus begins.

Of special interest in receptor physiology is the mechanism whereby the excitability of neuromuscular spindles can be altered. Nerve impulses over *gamma* efferents cause the spindle muscle fibers to contract. This shortening stimulates the sensory endings and the rate of firing to the spinal cord increases. Discharge over *gamma* efferents can be affected by reflex mechanisms or by discharges reaching the spinal cord from higher centers. Thus, there are two methods of producing sensory discharge from spindles—stretching the muscle and contraction of spindle fibers. Both are important in the reflex regulation of the movements of the muscle.

Effectors

Skeletal (Striated) Muscle. Muscles vary tremendously in size and shape, but the fundamental structural unit of any muscle is a multinucleated cell known as a muscle fiber. The variation occurs in the number and size of the constituent fibers. Skeletal muscle fibers are often many centimeters long, but only a few microns in

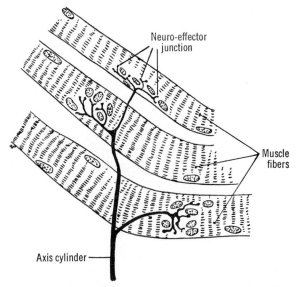

Figure 79. Schematic representation of three skeletal muscle fibers. An axis cylinder forms motor endings or neuro-effector junctions in the fibers. The myelin sheath is not shown.

diameter. Each fiber or cell has many nuclei, located along its sides. The cytoplasm is known as *sarcoplasm*, and running lengthwise in it are thin structures known as *myofibrils*. Each myofibril is made up of alternating light and dark segments. Because the segments of all the myofibrils occupy corresponding positions, the fibers appear to be cross-striated (Fig. 79). Between the skeletal muscle fibers are many blood vessels, particularly capillaries.

Muscle fibers contract rapidly, and their energy changes are accompanied by measurable electrical activity. This is followed by refractory periods, much the same as those observed in nerve fibers. Not all skeletal muscle fibers have the same contractile characteristics. Some contract more slowly and fatigue less easily; others contract faster and fatigue more easily. A muscle may contain both types of fibers or be predominantly of one type. For instance, muscles concerned in postural maintenance have large numbers of the more slowly contracting fibers.

Smooth (Nonstriated) Muscle. The unit of smooth muscle is a small, spindle-shaped cell which contains but a single nucleus (Fig. 80). Myofibrils are found in the cytoplasm, but do not ex-

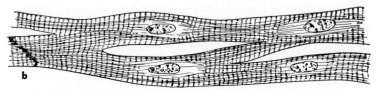

Figure 80. *a,* Smooth muscle cells. *b,* Cardiac muscle fibers.

hibit the alternations seen in skeletal muscle myofibrils and hence are not cross-striated, but smooth. The fibers are ordinarily arranged in sheets or bundles, within the walls of viscera, around glands, and in the walls of blood vessels. Contractions spread from one fiber to another through the sheet or bundle; hence smooth muscle is said to be characterized by contraction waves. These are slow in comparison with the contraction rates of skeletal muscle fibers and are usually not under voluntary control.

Cardiac (Cross-Striated) Muscle. As its name denotes, this type of muscle comprises the greater bulk of the heart. The fibers are multinucleated, and the myofibrils have alternating segments which give the fibers a cross-striated appearance. The fibers branch, however (Fig. 80), and fuse with each other, so that a continuous net or *syncytium* is formed. A contraction, then, can occur almost simultaneously throughout the heart.

Glands. Glands are composed of epithelial cells adapted for the formation of substances other than those directly concerned in their intrinsic metabolism. Glands secrete such substances as enzymes, hormones and mucus. They may be *unicellular,* and such single cells adapted for secretion are found in the mucous membrane of the respiratory and digestive systems. *Multicellular* glands are embryologically derived from the skin, as, for instance, a sweat gland, or from the epithelium of the respiratory and digestive systems and other hollow viscera. They frequently retain their connections with these surfaces by ducts, so that their secretions can be discharged onto these surfaces. Such glands are termed *exocrine,* or glands of external secretion. Certain glands, however, do not retain such connections, or else arise differently. The cells in such glands are arranged in groups or cords in such a relation to blood vessels that each cell can discharge its contents into the blood stream. These glands are termed *endocrine* glands, or glands of internal secretion.

Neuro-effector Junctions

Structure of Neuro-effector Junctions

Neuro-effector Junctions (Myoneural Junctions or Motor Nerve Endings) in Skeletal Muscle. Axons of motor neurons leave the spinal cord and brain stem via ventral roots or cranial nerves and eventually reach skeletal muscles. Each axon entering a muscle divides into a number of secondary branches. Each of these ends on the surface of a single muscle fiber forming a specialized ending known as a *motor end plate* or *myoneural junction* (Figs. 79, 81). The axon loses its myelin sheath just before reaching the end plate and then divides into filaments that arborize in the end plate. The sarcolemma and sarcoplasm subjacent to the nerve endings are also specialized. This junctional region between nerve and muscle represents a neuromuscular synapse, having properties similar to those of synaptic junctions in the central nervous system.

The axon of a single motor neuron supplies a number of skeletal muscle fibers (Fig. 81). The nerve cell, its axon, and the muscle fibers supplied by it, form a *motor unit.* A nerve impulse traversing the axon of a motor unit therefore excites the contraction of all the muscle fibers supplied by that axon. The number of motor units in any one muscle depends upon the number of muscle fibers in the muscle and upon their number in a motor unit. In man, some muscles have fewer than 100 muscle fibers per motor unit, while others may have between 1500 and 2000. Muscles with fewer muscle fibers per motor unit therefore have more motor units per given number of muscle fibers. It follows that a muscle with many motor units for a given number of muscle fibers is capable of more delicate and precise work than a muscle with fewer motor units for the same number of muscle fibers. Thus the muscles of the thumb have many small units, each with only a few muscle fibers, while the antigravity muscles are characterized by relatively fewer motor units, each of which has a large number of muscle fibers.

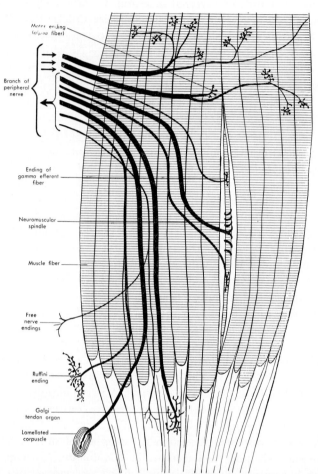

Figure 81.   Schematic representation of a muscle and its nerve supply. Arrows indicate direction of conduction. Each muscle fiber has a motor ending from a large myelinated (*alpha*) fiber. The muscle fibers within a spindle have motor endings from small myelinated (*gamma*) fibers. Muscle nerves have many sensory fibers. Some are large myelinated fibers coming from primary sensory (annulo-spiral) endings in spindles, from neurotendinous spindles (Golgi tendon organs), and from lamellated corpuscles (pacinian corpuscles) in the connective tissue between muscle fibers or external to the muscle as a whole. Smaller myelinated fibers arise from proprioceptive endings (such as Ruffini endings) in the connective tissue in and around muscle, or in joints. Finally there are small myelinated and non-myelinated fibers that form free endings (presumably for pain) in the connective tissue in and around muscle. (Modified after Denny-Brown.)

Neuro-effector Junctions in Smooth Muscle.   Smooth muscle cells are supplied by the autonomic system and usually by both the parasympathetic and sympathetic divisions. The impulses originate in the central nervous system, but are interrupted before they reach the effectors. For instance, an impulse from the thoracic cord reaches a sympathetic ganglion cell via a ventral root and a ramus communicans. The conducting fiber is thus a *preganglionic axon.* The *postganglionic axon* from the ganglion cell then goes to the smooth muscle fiber or fibers. This peripheral interruption is characteristic of the entire autonomic system (Chap. 13). Just how postganglionic fibers terminate in smooth muscle has not been satisfactorily determined. It is said that these nonmyelinated axons form free endings in the substance of the muscle fibers. Not every smooth muscle fiber, however, receives an ending as do all skeletal fibers, and it is uncertain how fibers without nerve endings are controlled.

Neuro-effector Junctions for Cardiac Muscle.   The heart is also supplied by the autonomic system. Both divisions contribute, the parasympathetic fibers being carried by the vagus nerves. In the heart, however, there is a peculiar circumstance. In the right atrium is a group of specialized muscle fibers forming the *sinoatrial node.* These are larger than other cardiac muscle fibers, are peculiar in being specialized for conduction rather than contraction, and are called *Purkinje fibers* (p. 289). They spread from the sino-atrial node throughout the atrial chambers of the heart. Apparently they conduct impulses which initiate contractions of the muscle fibers of these chambers. Between the atria and the ventricles of the heart is the *atrioventricular node,* from which Purkinje fibers spread throughout the ventricular chambers.

When the preganglionic fibers of the parasympathetic system reach the heart, they do not lead directly to the cardiac muscle fibers, but to ganglion cells in the vicinity of the two nodes. Postganglionic fibers are then distributed to Purkinje fibers; the exact manner of termination is uncertain. Postganglionic fibers of the sympathetic system are also distributed to the heart, and again the exact relationship to cardiac muscle fibers is uncertain.

Neuro-effector Junctions in Glands.   Gland cells may also be supplied by the autonomic system, and in such cases the postganglionic fibers form free nerve endings near or directly in the substance of the individual cells.

Physiology of Neuro-effector Junctions

Skeletal Muscle. If a muscle is given a brief electric shock, or its nerve so stimulated, the muscle responds by a brief contraction or *twitch*. If successive stimuli are rapidly applied, the contractions may summate, producing a prolonged *tetanic contraction* or *tetanus*. If the rate of stimulation is lessened, summation may be incomplete, and the tetanus is said to be incomplete. In a muscle as a whole, gradation of activity is further aided by motor units. If all motor units act at once (in phase, or synchronously) the muscle contracts once. But if nerve impulses reach motor units at different times (out of phase, asynchronously), a certain amount of tension is maintained in the muscle.

When a nerve impulse approaches a muscle fiber, it produces a localized negative *end plate* potential at the myoneural junction (Fig. 82). The end plate potential depolarizes the muscle fiber membrane. If the depolarization reaches threshold, a propagated muscle action potential results and the muscle contracts. It is held that the current flow of the nerve impulse spreads in to the myoneural junction, initiating the end plate potential, and that current

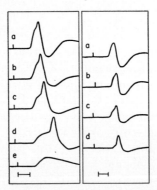

Figure 82. Records of end plate potentials of a single muscle fiber. In the left-hand column, the initial short deflections signal the stimulation of the motor nerve to the muscle fiber. In *a*, there is a compound deflection that, in *b–d*, breaks up into end plate potential and muscle action potential upon the application of curare at increasing strengths. In *e*, the preparation is deeply curarized, and only the end plate potential is left. In the right-hand column, the initial, short deflection signals the stimulation of the motor nerve to a single muscle fiber. In *a*, one electrode is on the end plate. In *b*, one electrode is on the nerve-muscle junction. In *c* and *d*, the electrode is placed at increasing distances from the end plate. Note that the end plate potential decreases in amplitude, indicating that it is not a conducted potential, but rather a local change. (Data from Kuffler, J. Neurophysiol., vol. 5, 1942.)

flow from the end plate potential in turn stimulates the muscle fiber. There is also evidence that a chemical transmitter (acetylcholine) is involved, this chemical being liberated by nerve impulses and stimulating the myoneural junction to produce the end plate potential. Whether electrical or chemical or both, a transmitter is involved, the sequence being nerve impulse, transmitter, end-plate potential, muscle action potential, contraction.

As in the case of central synapses, there is a delay of less than 1 millisecond between arrival of nerve impulse and beginning of end plate potential. The specialization of the myoneural junction is indicated by the fact that certain drugs, such as curare, may block transmission here without affecting conduction in the axon to it, or without preventing contraction of the muscle fiber in response to direct stimulation.

If acetylcholine is the transmitter, the chemical reactions must be sufficiently fast (experimental evidence indicates that they are) and there must be a means of removing acetylcholine once it has been liberated and acted. An enzyme, *cholinesterase,* destroys or at least inactivates acetylcholine, and is found in those regions where acetylcholine is formed. The action of cholinesterase in turn can be prevented or inhibited by *eserine,* which thereby indirectly accentuates the effect of acetylcholine.

Evidence relating to these effects is offered by the treatment of the disease *myasthenia gravis.* In this disease, when muscles are used they become weak and, to all intents, paralyzed. But after a variable period of rest, activity can be resumed, only to have the weakness set in again. In many cases, the use of eserine or of compounds with similar actions offers striking relief for a few hours or days. Since these compounds, by destroying cholinesterase, mimic the action of acetylcholine, it is presumed that in myasthenia gravis, acetylcholine is deficient or abnormally inactivated at neuromuscular junctions.

The action potential of the muscle fiber is similar to the action potential of a nerve fiber, and can be recorded by similar methods. When several fibers are active, the result is a complex type of potential change, complex because fibers may be oriented differently with respect to recording electrodes, at different distances, and active at different times. Nevertheless, the recording of muscle action potentials, *electromyography,* is a very valuable tool in studying muscle physiology.

Smooth and Cardiac Muscle and Glands. Certain chemicals are liberated at the terminals of postganglionic autonomic fibers, and act as transmitters. Acetylcholine is considered to be the transmitter or chemical mediator at postganglionic parasympathetic terminals. These fibers are, therefore, called *cholinergic* fibers. *Noradrenaline (norepinephrine)* is the mediator released at most postganglionic sympathetic terminals. These fibers are, therefore, termed *adrenergic*. Not all sympathetic fibers are adrenergic (p. 235). Adrenaline (epinephrine), formed by the medulla of the adrenal gland and by certain other cells, has actions similar to those of noradrenaline.

Many drugs have been used in investigations of the nervous system. *Nicotine,* for instance, has been a valuable tool in the analysis of autonomic functions. This drug acts on synaptic junctions in sympathetic ganglia. When locally applied, its initial effect is one of stimulation, but it soon blocks or inhibits transmission across synapses without preventing conduction in nerve fibers. It has, therefore, been effectively used to determine just where certain fibers synapse. *Strychnine* is another drug with striking effects. In poisonous doses it causes violent muscular contractions or convulsions, probably by blocking inhibitory mechanisms, and thus indirectly increasing the sensitivity of cells (p. 113). Therefore the slightest volley of afferent impulses from the periphery may be followed by almost continuous discharges from motor neurons. There is, therefore, a basis for the old "laying on of hands" in the treatment of strychnine poisoning. This attempt to quiet the patient unwittingly reduces the number of afferent impulses. In smaller doses, strychnine is a valuable analytical tool because it affords a relatively simple means of causing groups of cells to discharge. The electrical activity of these cells and any of their projections may then be recorded.

Dependence on Nerve Supply

Skeletal muscle is peculiar in that it cannot function without a motor nerve supply. Denervated fibers lose tone and eventually atrophy (p. 168). But other effectors are not so dependent. Cardiac muscle fibers contract rhythmically in the embryo before they receive their nerve supply. In the adult they do not lose their contractility when denervated. The autonomic nervous system appears rather to coordinate or time the contractions of various parts of the heart. Smooth muscle and glands are even more striking in their independence of nerve supply, being able to function in an almost normal manner when nerve connections are completely severed. This is particularly true of glands, since their secretory activity may be initiated by other means, as, for example, by hormones.

When afferent fibers are severed, the peripheral receptors ultimately degenerate, but the effect on associated non-nervous tissue is variable. Skeletal muscle, for instance, undergoes relatively little morphological change as long as its motor supply is intact. Denervated skin, on the other hand, is susceptible to infections and may become the site of persistent ulcers.

Strength-Duration Curves. If electrodes are applied to a normal muscle and electric shocks are given, the contractions which follow are the result of stimulation of the motor nerve of the muscle. Nerve impulses initiate the muscular contractions. If the times taken for varying strengths of current to stimulate are determined, a strength-duration curve is obtained which is characteristic for

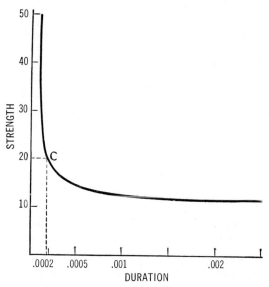

Figure 83. Strength-duration curve of a tibialis anterior muscle. The nerve supply is intact, so the curve is actually that of nerve. The chronaxie, *C*, is less than 0.2 of a millisecond. The final level of the rheobase is indicated by the dot on the right. The curve slopes to this at time intervals too great to be indicated on the graph. This, and Fig. 84, modified from Adrian, E. D., *The Electrical Reactions of Muscles Before and After Nerve Injury*, Brain, 39:1–33, 1916.

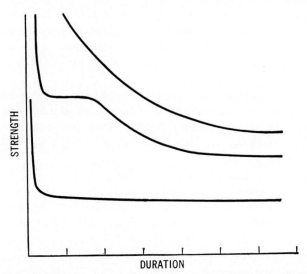

STRENGTH

DURATION

Figure 84. Composite graph which allows a comparison of the shapes of the various strength-duration curves. *Upper curve:* Denervated muscle, the curve being that for muscle. Although it cannot be shown in a composite graph, the chronaxie may be more than fifty times as great as that of normal muscle; *middle,* partially denervated, there being a mixture of two curves, one for normal muscle and nerve and another for denervated muscle; and *lower,* normal muscle and nerve, the curve being similar to that of Fig. 83.

nerve (Fig. 83). The chronaxie, which is one point of the curve, is less than 1 millisecond. But if electrodes are applied to a muscle deprived of its nerve supply, the contractions following electric shocks are the result of direct stimulation of muscle fibers. The time during which current must flow is considerably longer, so that the curve has a different shape and the chronaxie is much greater (Fig. 84). Therefore, in a muscle which is partially denervated, some muscle fibers will respond to direct stimulation and others to nerve impulses. As Fig. 84 shows, the curve is complex in shape, indicating that it is composed of the two simpler ones with different time relationships. These curves represent data that are more useful indices of denervation and recovery than single points, such as chronaxie.

Summary

Receptors are specialized terminations of afferent fibers. Ex-teroceptive receptors are concerned with the reception of touch, pain and temperature from the skin, as well as pain and pressure from deeper tissues; proprioceptive receptors are concerned with the reception of changes in tension of muscles and tendons and with changes in the position of limbs; interoceptive receptors are sensitive to various internal or visceral changes. Stimuli at or above threshold strength result in nerve impulses the frequency of which varies with the strength and duration of the stimuli.

Neuro-effector junctions are specialized terminations of efferent fibers in skeletal muscle fibers, smooth muscle fibers, cardiac muscle, and glands, these structures being the effectors. In skeletal muscles a single neuron supplies a number of muscle fibers (a motor unit), each branch terminating as a motor end plate. In smooth and cardiac muscle fibers and gland cells, the junctions are free endings. Certain chemical compounds, acetylcholine and noradrenaline, are probably released as mediators at neuro-effector junctions.

Skeletal muscle is the only effector fully dependent upon the nervous system for normal activity. Skeletal muscle exhibits a strength-duration curve of different time relationships from that of nerve, and this curve becomes apparent when the muscle is denervated.

Names in Neurology

Krause, Wilhelm (1833–1910)

Krause was a German anatomist who studied most of the peripheral receptors, including the end bulbs now named after him.

Meissner, George (1823–1893)

Meissner was a German histologist known primarily for the skin receptors he described.

Pacini, Filippo (1812–1883)

An Italian anatomist, Pacini is known for his studies of peripheral receptors.

Ruffini, Angelo (1864–1929)

An Italian anatomist, Ruffini was one of the most skilled investigators of peripheral receptors. He used a gold chloride stain, and his studies of such endings in deep tissues as neuromuscular spindles formed the morphologic basis for subsequent physiologic studies.

References

The histology, neuroanatomy, and physiology textbooks cited in previous chapters contain discussion of the structure and function of receptors, effectors, and so forth.

Bishop, G. H.: Neural mechanisms of cutaneous sense. Physiol. Rev., 26:77–102, 1946. An advanced review of this subject.

Clinical Examinations in Neurology. Members of the Sections of Neurology, Physiology, Mayo Clinic, Rochester. Philadelphia, W. B. Saunders Company, 1956. The chapter on electromyography is well organized and clearly written.

Granit, R.: Receptors and Sensory Perception. New Haven, Yale University Press, 1955. Difficult reading, but nevertheless a valuable and up-to-date discussion by one of the leading investigators in this field.

Sinclair, D. C.: Cutaneous sensations and the doctrine of specific energy. Brain, 78:584–614, 1956. Very well written account of the work that is now breaking down our firm, stereotyped ideas of sensory mechanisms.

CHAPTER 10

The Control of

Muscular Activity

THE PATTERN of muscular activity is controlled by the central nervous system, but this does not mean that one first thinks of movements to be performed in a particular activity and then initiates the nervous impulses causing them. On the contrary, most movements fit into complex, almost automatic patterns which Herrick (cited on p. 27) has termed "acquired automatisms." Walking exemplifies such a pattern. Once walking is learned (it has to be learned laboriously), it is carried out according to fairly definite patterns of nervous activity. Nearly all movements, including portions or the whole of automatisms, can be voluntarily controlled. This control resides mainly if not entirely in the cerebral cortex. It should be realized, however, that the term "voluntary control" is misleading. It generally refers only to a pattern of activity.

For example, suppose we reach out and pick something off a table. The use of the fingers is the component of which we are mainly conscious. But in order to get the fingers to the object, the forearm is extended, that is, straightened out, and in order to do this smoothly the muscles which flex or bend the arm at the elbow are relaxed. Yet this relaxation is not consciously carried out; we are not actually aware of this component of movement. Furthermore, in this reaching out and picking something up, other muscles stabilize the shoulder. At the same time the body leans forward, the center of gravity shifts, and compensatory, stabilizing

muscle actions in the trunk and lower extremities insure maintenance of posture.

The muscles that take part in any movement may be classified
as prime movers, synergists, antagonists, and fixation muscles (Fig.
85). The prime movers directly bring about the action desired, as
flexing the fingers in Fig. 85. When a prime mover crosses two or
more joints, synergists prevent undesired action at the intermediate
joints. Fixation muscles stabilize certain joints and also have postural functions, for example, maintaining the equilibrium of the
trunk. Muscles may also have a paradoxical action in the sense
that they can control movements in a direction opposite to that
in which they usually operate (Fig. 85). In this capacity, they do
negative work. Antagonists are those that act directly opposite to
the prime mover. Antagonists may either relax completely during
movement (when the movement is carried out against resistance),
or they may gradually relax while lengthening so as to control or
modify the action of the prime mover.

Thus an apparently simple act involves many muscles in a complex maneuver. We do not pay special attention to any of the
components except the prime movement. Walking, using a typewriter, playing a piano, fielding a baseball, talking, all are skilled
acts which we usually take for granted to the extent that we lose
sight of their enormous complexity and forget the months or years
of learning and practice.

Both in movement and in posture, muscles may act against the
influence of gravity, and the muscles most concerned are often
called antigravity muscles. It is held that reflexes involving neuromuscular spindles are most prominent in antigravity muscles. Most
experiments, however, have been made on lower animals, and it
is difficult and often inadvisable to conclude that findings from
such experimental studies are directly applicable to man. For example, the flexor muscles of the forearm in man, and not the
extensor muscles, are antigravity muscles. There is evidence that,
in an easy standing position, little if any muscular contraction or
tone can be detected in the so-called antigravity muscles of man.
Human joints are so constructed that in a standing position they
offer maximum stability and lessen the necessity for maintenance
of posture by muscles. Of course, when there are deviations from
this position, muscles come into action in increasing degree (Fig.
86). There is still not enough factual information on postural

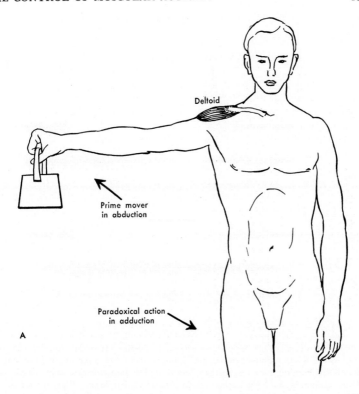

Deltoid

Prime mover
in abduction

Paradoxical action
in adduction

A

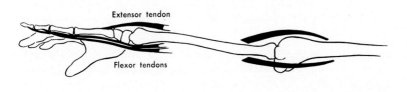

Extensor tendon

Flexor tendons

B

Figure 85. *A* shows that the deltoid muscle as an abductor is a prime mover in lifting a pail of water (other muscles stabilize elbow and hand), and that it also controls the action of lowering the pail (adduction). The latter is negative work—a paradoxical action because the deltoid is controlling adduction. The adductors are inactive unless resistance is offered to the movement. *B* shows flexor tendons inserting in the bones of a finger. If the flexor muscles contract so as to flex the fingers, the wrist would also flex were it not that the extensor muscle contracts and acts as a synergist, preventing undesired action at intermediate joints. The elbow joint can be fixed or stabilized in the desired position by simultaneous contraction of flexors and extensors.

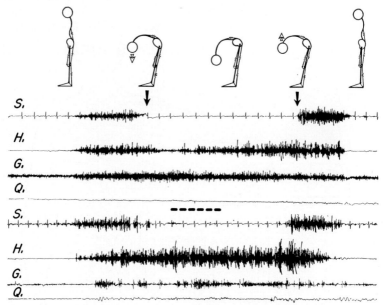

Figure 86. Electromyograms of two normal subjects during standing and bending down. In standing, no activity is recorded from sacrospinalis, S, hamstrings, H, or quadriceps femoris, Q. The short vertical deflections in S are the electrocardiogram. As the subject leans forward, activity appears in S (negative work; the muscles control the leaning forward as they lengthen), in hamstrings (same reason) and gastrocnemius, G. Activity stops in sacrospinalis at full flexion (ligaments now the support of the back), to reappear as the subject extends and returns to standing. These records show the lack of muscular activity in an easy standing position, and the complicated activity during movement. The upper four records are from one subject, the lower four from another subject. (Based on Figure 2, from Portnoy, H., and Morin, F., Am. J. Physiol., vol. 186, 1956. By permission of authors and publisher.)

mechanisms in general to allow an accurate assessment of the differences in neuromuscular mechanisms between man and lower animals.

Levels of Control

The normal contraction of a muscle is initiated only by impulses reaching it over axons of specific motor cells in brain stem or spinal cord. This is the *final common path;* it and the paths to viscera mediate all outward expression of behavior. Therefore, all motor tracts in the central nervous system, no matter what their origin, are directed toward motor cells in the brain stem and spinal cord.

It is convenient, particularly in an introductory work of this nature, to study motor paths and their part in the control of muscular activity as if the nervous system were made up of a series of levels, especially if the levels correspond to the major evolutionary changes discussed in Chap. 17. These levels are the spinal cord, the reticular formation of the brain stem, the cerebellum, the basal ganglia and the cerebral cortex.

The lowest level of organization is the gray matter of the spinal cord. Many cells in this gray matter, exclusive of motor cells, are capable of certain types of organized activity. The degree of organization or coordination depends upon the animal. For example, a frog with its head removed does not exhibit spontaneous activity, but does show coordinated responses to many types of stimulation. The functions of the spinal cord are discussed in more detail in Chap. 14.

The next level is the reticular formation of the brain stem. This mixture of gray and white matter contains countless numbers of cells and fibers concerned with many different functions. The axons of many of these cells descend to the spinal cord and are therefore called *reticulospinal fibers*. This brings up a matter of terminology. In naming paths, tracts or fibers of the central nervous system, direction is indicated by the order of naming. Reticulospinal, therefore, means from reticular formation to spinal cord. Other descriptive terms may be included. Thus a tract in the lateral part of the spinal cord originating in cerebral cortex is the *lateral corticospinal tract*. A *spinocerebellar tract* begins in the spinal cord and ends in the cerebellum.

Many cells in the reticular formation are important in the control of muscular activity. A useful concept, supported by experimental data, postulates that some of these cells inhibit motor neurons of brain stem and spinal cord and increase the threshold of reflex arcs. They are therefore responsible for any relaxation which may be necessary during movement. Others excite or activate motor cells and lower reflex thresholds, and can thereby initiate or maintain muscular contractions. Some of these excitatory cells are specifically associated with the vestibular portion of the eighth cranial nerve. In lower forms, such as fishes, the reticular formation, together with certain afferent systems and the spinal cord, initiates and controls all the behavior patterns of which the animal is capable. A comparable anatomical situation can be produced in

higher animals by cutting the brain stem at the level of the midbrain. In such situations the excitatory mechanisms appear to be
predominantly active, while the inhibitory mechanisms are relatively ineffective. As a result there are exaggerated reflex muscular
contractions, particularly in antigravity muscles. These reactions
are discussed in greater detail in Chap. 15.

The basal ganglia and certain portions of the cerebellum, which
appear to be necessary for coordinated movement, send fibers to
the brain stem reticular formation. These structures represent a
still higher level of control, one which has developed phylogenetically along with the limbs. An animal such as a cat, with cerebral
cortex removed but with basal ganglia intact, can walk almost like
a normal animal.

The highest level is the cerebral cortex, which is most highly
developed in man. The regions of the cortex from which motor
paths arise are called motor areas, most of which are located in
the frontal lobes. The cortex contains vast numbers of nerve cells,
the bodies of which tend to be arranged in six layers. In motor
areas the fifth layer is thick and contains many *pyramidal cells*
(Fig. 144, p. 313). The axons of these pyramidal cells leave the cortex and enter the white matter of the hemisphere, where they
descend in the internal capsule. Impulses may either reach motor
cells after traversing the various subcortical levels, or may use a
relatively new path, one which by-passes the phylogenetically older
systems and goes directly to spinal cord.

This has been a rapid survey of various levels of the nervous
system, an arrangement in which the lowest level is the most specific in function and the highest the least specific. That is, a motor
cell, the lowest level, supplies certain muscle fibers and no others.
Its activity cannot directly cause any other muscle to contract. The
cerebral cortex represents the greatest degree of lability. It controls activity through an almost infinite variety of combinations.

The present chapter will deal mainly with the longitudinal
motor pathways. In this and in other chapters the terms "integration," "coordination," and "correlation" are often used. These are
well-known terms, and many investigators attempt to use them in
connection with different functions. No really satisfactory distinction has ever been arrived at, however, and in this textbook they
will ordinarily be used synonymously.

Muscular Activity in the Trunk and Limbs

A few general rules can be cited which hold for normal activity. First, pathways concerned with movements of the lower limb arise from cortex near the midline and on the medial surface, while those dealing with movements of the head and neck come from cortex near the lateral fissure. Second, the control of limb musculature is largely contralateral. Third, movements of midline muscles, such as those concerned with breathing, are bilaterally controlled, that is, can be initiated by either hemisphere.

Nerve fibers to muscles in the trunk and limbs come mainly from motor cells in the spinal cord. Motor pathways in the central nervous system reach these cells in a variety of ways.

Pyramidal System. Present evidence indicates that the direct path from cerebral cortex to spinal cord is concerned especially with the extremities and particularly with the hands. In the movement complex cited previously, the reaching forward and picking something off a table, the movements involving the forearm and hand are particularly dependent upon this system. The fibers composing the direct system are axons of cells in several regions of the cerebral cortex, especially the cerebral cortex anterior to the central fissure, that is, the precentral gyrus. They descend by way of the internal capsule and cerebral peduncle and, when they reach the medulla oblongata, they collect into a prominent bundle of fibers, the pyramids, located on either side of the ventral midline (p. 260). The pyramids are named because of their shape, and not because their constituent fibers arise from pyramidal cells in the cerebral cortex. Just before the medulla oblongata joins the spinal cord, many of the fibers in each pyramid cross to the opposite side, interlacing as they cross. These crossing fibers descend in the lateral funiculi of the spinal cord as *lateral corticospinal tracts* (Fig. 87). Because these fibers descend in the medullary pyramids, the term *pyramidal tract* is synonymous with corticospinal tract. Of the fibers which do not cross, some descend in the anterior funiculi of the spinal cord as *anterior corticospinal tracts*. In some instances they may be traced to lumbar levels. Other uncrossed fibers descend in lateral funiculi and hence are also lateral corticospinal fibers. It has been estimated that 75 per cent of corticospinal fibers cross.

Corticospinal fibers do not go directly to motor cells, but instead synapse with internuncial cells in dorsal gray matter. These in turn relay to motor cells whose axons are distributed to skeletal

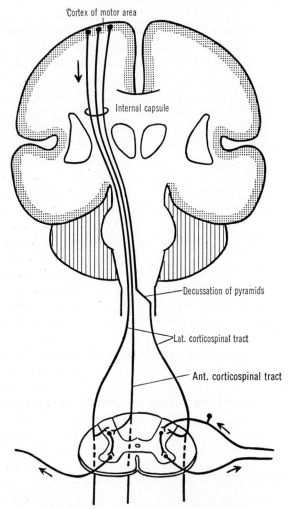

Figure 87.   Diagram of corticospinal tracts.

musculature. It is likely that the muscles especially controlled by
this system have motor units with relatively few muscle fibers.
Therefore, more nerve fibers per number of muscle fibers reach
these muscles; as a consequence, smaller portions of the muscles
can be independently controlled. This makes for greater delicacy
and precision of movement.

There is good evidence that the pyramidal system is primarily excitatory, and that the excitation can be manifested in a variety of ways. Impulses descending over pyramidal fibers may activate internuncial cells and motor cells. Impulses over pyramidal fibers may also facilitate cells, that is, lower their thresholds, without actually causing them to discharge. This is particularly true if impulses descend asynchronously and at a low frequency. Each sets up a local excitatory state, but, unless this occurs at approximately the same time another impulse sets up a similar change at the same region, summation does not result.

Some of these events can be indirectly demonstrated in man as follows: In many persons it is difficult to obtain a knee jerk. If, just before the patellar tendon is tapped, the subject clenches his fists, the knee jerk may then be marked. This enhancement or reinforcement results from the fact that impulses from the cerebral cortex reach not only the motor cells of the actively contracting muscles, but also other motor cells of the spinal cord and brain stem. The latter are facilitated, and, by summation with previously subthreshold afferent impulses from the quadriceps muscle, the motor cells fire off. Of course, facilitation and reinforcement are properties not peculiar to corticospinal fibers.

A widely held concept views the pyramidal system as primarily inhibitory. This is based mainly on interpretation of certain clinical findings in neurological disorders. According to such a concept, reinforcement would be explained as resulting from effectiveness of afferent stimuli in presence of inattention to (and therefore lack of inhibition of) the leg extensors while movement is carried out elsewhere. Although this particular concept of pyramidal functions has proved inadequate, the possibility that lack of inhibition is a factor in reinforcement cannot be discounted.

Extrapyramidal System. Other components of movement patterns, such as the relaxation or inhibition of opposing muscles and the stabilizing and postural acts of the previously cited movement complex, are beautifully and automatically coordinated by a variety of mechanisms. The paths concerned originate mainly from the precentral motor cortex (by this is meant the motor cortex anterior to the central fissure and is, of course, more than the precentral gyrus). The fibers descend in the internal capsule and through a variety of paths reach the excitatory and inhibitory mechanisms in the brain stem. The excitatory components then descend from brain stem to spinal cord as reticulospinal and ves-

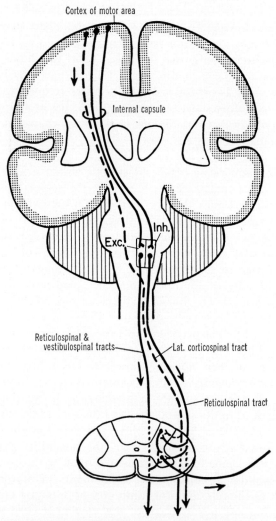

Figure 88.   Diagram of extrapyramidal pathways. The brain stem excitatory and inhibitory mechanisms are indicated schematically, and the lateral corticospinal tract is included so as to show its relationship to the reticulospinal tract.

tibulospinal tracts, the relative sizes and importance of which vary from one species to another. Both descend mainly in the anterior funiculus of the cord. The inhibitory component also descends as a reticulospinal tract, but mainly in the lateral funiculus of the cord. These descending tracts end in the gray matter of the cord, either by synapsing with motor neurons directly or with inter-nuncial neurons (Fig. 88).

The reticulospinal and vestibulospinal tracts do not enter the medullary pyramids. The system to which they belong is, there-fore, frequently termed the *extrapyramidal system*. In the spinal cord, however, the inhibitory reticulospinal tracts which descend in the lateral funiculi are intermingled with the fibers of the lat-eral corticospinal tracts.

Muscular Activity in the Head and Neck

The activity referred to here is that carried out by muscles sup-plied by cranial nerves. The pathways concerned are not sepa-rated anatomically into pyramidal and extrapyramidal, because most of the descending paths end before medullary pyramids are reached. Other distinctions are usually made, however. Frequently all fibers from cerebral cortex to brain stem are called cortico-bulbar. Less commonly, more specific terms are used, such as corticopontine (fibers from cortex to pons) or corticomesencephalic (cortex to midbrain). It seems likely that those fibers which do go directly from cerebral cortex to brain stem correspond functionally to the pyramidal system. In addition, there are many motor paths that reach the brain stem after a number of relays and then connect

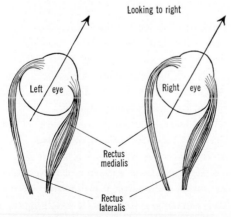

Figure 89. Conjugate activity in looking to the right. The right lateral rectus muscle and the left medial rectus contract, while the right medial rectus and left lateral rectus relax. This illustrates how a number of muscles coordinate in an apparently simple movement.

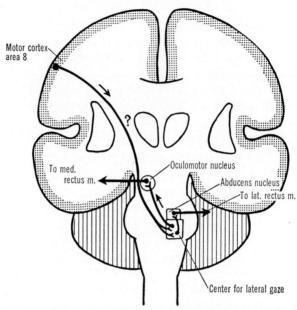

Figure 90. Pathway for horizontal (lateral) conjugate gaze. Descending fibers project to the center for lateral gaze in the pons, which in turn relays to eye muscle nuclei. The question mark indicates the possibility that the descending fibers relay in basal ganglia.

with reticular formation. Functionally these are extrapyramidal tracts.

From the standpoint of the various muscles concerned, a convenient organizational plan distinguishes among the paths concerned with eye muscles, the tongue and the branchiomeric muscles. The last are striated muscles that develop embryologically from branchial arch mesoderm. Many of them are closely associated with the alimentary and respiratory systems.

The motor paths for cranial nerves originate in cerebral cortex. They descend by way of internal capsule and brain stem and, either directly or indirectly, reach the *nuclei of origin* of many of the cranial nerves. Here again is a matter of terminology. The term "nucleus" means either a compact collection of many neurons within the central nervous system, or a nucleus of a single cell. "Ganglion," on the other hand, usually refers to a collection of neurons outside the central nervous system.

Eye Muscles and Tongue. Eye movements are nearly always conjugate; that is to say, the eyes move together. The simplest example of conjugate movement is horizontal (lateral) gaze. In looking to the right, the right lateral rectus muscle, supplied by the abducens nerve, and the left medial rectus muscle, supplied by the oculomotor nerve, act to turn the eyes to the right (Fig. 89). At the same time the opposing muscles relax. The motor path originates in the precentral motor cortex. The fibers descend in the internal capsule, and there is a possibility that they relay in basal ganglia. Sometime during their descent they cross the midline and then reach a group of nerve cells in the lower pons, the center for lateral gaze (Fig. 90). Some consider this center to be one of the vestibular nuclei. Connections are then established with the abducens nucleus, and thereby the lateral rectus muscle, and other fibers cross and ascend in the medial longitudinal fasciculus to the oculomotor nucleus (medial rectus muscle).

Several other pathways are concerned in eye movements. There is, for example, a type of horizontal gaze in which the eyes are kept fixed on an object as the head turns. The motor path concerned has never been determined anatomically in man, but it probably originates in the cortex of the occipital lobe. Conjugate gaze in vertical directions seems to be under the control of both frontal and occipital lobes, particularly the latter. The paths concerned descend to the midbrain, where they make connections with nuclei of oculomotor and trochlear nerves. Eye movements are rarely confined to strictly horizontal or strictly vertical axes. Consequently, both frontal and occipital lobes and their pathways are coordinated in eye movements.

There are probably pathways by which conjugate gaze in a particular direction can be controlled by the ipsilateral hemisphere. Whether these are normally in operation is uncertain. They undoubtedly account for the fact that after destruction of cerebral cortex or pathways on one side, conjugate gaze to the opposite side is lost for but a few days or weeks. Recovery is often complete.

Each hypoglossal nerve supplies one half of the tongue and each receives fibers from both cerebral hemispheres. The fibers enter the internal capsule, and on reaching the brain stem probably descend through the reticular formation to reach the hypoglossal nucleus in the medulla oblongata.

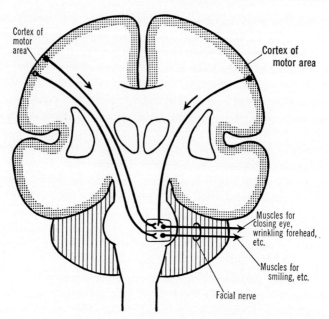

Figure 91. Motor pathway for facial muscles. The facial nucleus is subdivided. The upper part, which supplies one group of facial muscles, receives fibers from both cerebral hemispheres, whereas the lower part of the nucleus receives fibers only from the contralateral hemisphere.

Loss of one of the descending paths has little if any effect upon control of tongue movements, except for a few days or weeks. Section of the hypoglossal nerve itself is followed by paralysis of one half the tongue.

Branchiomeric Muscles. The nerves concerned receive fibers from both precentral motor areas. The fibers reach the motor nuclei by descending in the internal capsule and reticular formation of the brain stem. The muscles of mastication are supplied by axons arising from a motor nucleus on each side of the pons. The fibers from this nucleus reach the muscles by way of the trigeminal nerve. The muscles of expression, the facial muscles, are supplied by motor nuclei in the lower part of the pons. The axons reach the muscles by way of the facial nerve. Parts of these nuclei are exceptions to the rule about bilateral control of midline muscles. The cells in the upper portions of the nuclei supply the muscles around the eyes (closing the eyes and wrinkling the forehead). These cells receive fibers from both motor areas. But the cells in the lower part of the facial nucleus, which supply muscles of the lips, nose and cheek, receive fibers only from the contralateral motor cortex (Fig. 91). The muscles of swallowing (pharynx, palate and upper esophagus) and vocalizing (larynx) are supplied by nuclei in the medulla oblongata whose axons are distributed by way of the glossopharyngeal, vagus and accessory nerves. In addition, portions of two muscles, the sternocleidomastoid and trapezius, are partly of branchiomeric origin and are supplied by the portion of the accessory nerve arising from the upper part of the cervical spinal cord.

Clinical Importance of Motor Areas and Pathways

Upper Motor Neuron Lesions

The functions of the motor cortex have been studied in a variety of ways. Motor areas have been removed surgically, both in experimental animals and in necessary operations in man, and the functional losses observed directly. This method has been supplemented by cutting descending fibers in the internal capsule, cerebral peduncle, pyramid or spinal cord in experimental animals and studying the resulting degeneration and loss of function. Motor areas and paths have been stimulated and effects observed and recorded. Similar conditions or events in man are frequently the result of disease or injury, and valuable information has been derived from clinical and postmortem studies in such cases. Clinically speaking, any interruption of connections between the cortex and subcortical levels and the motor cells in the spinal cord is said to be an *upper motor neuron lesion*. Such a lesion may interrupt corticospinal fibers or extrapyramidal fibers, or both.

Upper Motor Neuron Lesions of Corticospinal Tracts. Not much is known about the effects of lesions limited to corticospinal fibers in man, because these fibers throughout most of their course are closely associated with fibers of other functional systems, and injury to one is almost automatically injury to the others. It has been deduced from the available clinical evidence, and from experimental work, that lesions of certain portions of the precentral gyrus, or of the medullary pyramids, destroy corticospinal fibers with a minimal involvement of other types. Lesions elsewhere, as in the remaining motor cortex or in the internal capsule or spinal cord, involve both corticospinal and extrapyramidal fibers. Destruction of corticospinal fibers in a medullary pyramid is followed by weakness or *paresis* on the opposite side of the body. The weakness is especially pronounced in muscles of the extremities, and there is great difficulty with movements of the hands. The affected muscles may become limp and almost flabby because of the loss of reflex arcs. This is not a paralysis, however, because, as has been emphasized before, the corticospinal fibers are not the only mediators of voluntary activity. Movements can still be initiated through extrapyramidal projections, particularly movements of the trunk and girdle regions. The voluntary control which remains can nevertheless effect a remarkable degree of compensation, and, after a few months, functional defects may be difficult to detect.

Upper Motor Neuron Lesions of Extrapyramidal and Corticospinal Tracts. In the internal capsule, cerebral peduncle, and lateral part of the spinal cord, extrapyramidal and corticospinal fibers are so closely intermingled anatomically that destruction of one system almost automatically affects the other. The most common upper motor neuron lesion is, therefore, a combined one. When this happens, the effects of extrapyramidal destruction predominate. Figure 92 illustrates some of the resulting degeneration.

There is weakness or paralysis to a varying degree, depending entirely upon the number of descending fibers destroyed. The closer the destruction to the spinal cord, the more chance there is of severing all the descending axons. Only those muscles near the midline remain relatively unaffected, provided the lesion is on but one side.

So far as cranial nerves are concerned, functional losses are difficult to predict because of the variable amount of bilateral cortical control. Unilateral lesions above the level of the pons partially affect the facial nerves. It was pointed out earlier in this chapter that only the upper part of each facial nucleus is bilaterally controlled. In these lesions, therefore, there is paralysis of the opposite lower facial muscles, but not of the upper ones around the eyes and forehead.

Paralysis is not the only symptom in upper motor neuron disorders. The extrapyramidal fibers mediate both excitatory and inhibitory functions, and the loss of inhibitory mechanisms leads to some pronounced effects. One of the fundamental characteristics of upper motor neuron lesions is that reflex arcs remain anatomically intact. Control or modification of these arcs, however, is hindered. The normal operation of gravity against the weight of the body may initiate stretch reflexes. Since there is no longer an

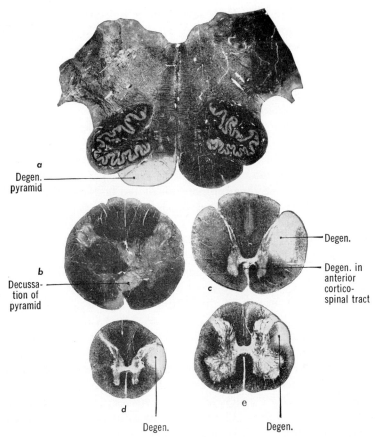

Figure 92.   Photomicrographs of sections of spinal cord and medulla oblongata from a case of thrombosis of the arterial supply of the left internal capsule. Weigert stain. The degenerating fibers lie in the unstained areas, and at the indicated levels are corticospinal fibers. In *a* the left pyramid is involved. In *b* the degenerating fibers are crossing to the right side. Some remain on the same side, as shown in *c*, cervical cord. In *d*, thoracic cord, and *e*, lumbar cord, the lateral corticospinal tract decreases in size as it descends in the lateral funiculus. (Courtesy of Department of Anatomy, University of Southern California, Los Angeles.)

inhibitory mechanism, the reflex contractions are exaggerated. The combination of this effect with contractions resulting from continuous discharge of brain stem excitatory mechanisms leads to a *spastic* or *hypertonic* state. Descending impulses to gamma efferents may activate spindle muscle fibers and thus enhance stretch reflexes. The examiner detects spasticity by bending a joint. The stretch thus put on the muscles leads reflexly to a resistance to flexion of the joint. Abnormal reflexes, such as the Babinski (p. 126), also appear, and these again are probably a result of loss of inhibitory mechanisms. The Babinski represents part of a general withdrawal or flexion of the lower limb (p. 252). The spasticity and loss of voluntary motion in this type of upper motor neuron lesions have led to the synonymous term *spastic paralysis*.

These lesions are common in the internal capsule, where all the descending fibers are closely gathered together and are thus particularly vulnerable to neurological disorders. Lesions here result in signs mainly in the opposite half of the body. Clinically speaking, weakness in one longitudinal half of the body is called *hemiparesis;* paralysis in one half of the body is a *hemiplegia.* If the fibers are destroyed after they have crossed and are descending in the lateral funiculus of the cervical cord, there is spastic paralysis on the same side of the body, involving both extremities. A lesion of the lateral funiculus of the thoracic cord is followed by paralysis in the lower extremity on the same side, a condition called *monoplegia.* The extent of the symptomatology is a clue to the location of the disorder.

In connection with the widely held concept of the pyramidal system as inhibitory, it is also widely held in clinical circles that upper motor neuron disorders are entirely the result of lesions to the pyramidal system. Consequently, the terms *pyramidal signs* or *pyramidal lesions* are synonymous with spastic paralysis or upper motor neuron disorders. The terminology is so deeply rooted that little attempt has ever been made to eradicate it.

Lower Motor Neuron Lesions

The pathway from the cortical motor areas is completed by motor neurons whose axons reach skeletal muscle fibers. Destruction of these neurons or their axons is followed by a characteristic clinical picture, whether the destruction is in the spinal cord, the ventral roots, or in spinal or peripheral nerves. In any case, impulses cannot reach the muscle fibers supplied by the destroyed nerve fibers, and voluntary control is completely lost. For the same reason, reflexes involving such muscles are impossible. Muscle fibers deprived of their nerve supply eventually shrink or atrophy, and during the course of this change the degenerating fibers show fibrillary twitchings. Strength-duration curves also change char-

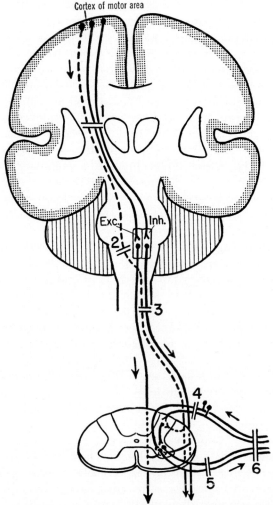

Figure 93.   Diagram illustrating lesions of motor and reflex paths. *1,* A lesion here (internal capsule) causes an upper motor neuron defect, the severity of which depends on the extent of the lesion. *2,* A lesion here (near decussation of pyramids) affects only corticospinal fibers. *3,* A lesion here (lateral funiculus of cord) causes an upper motor neuron defect more severe than that at *1* because more descending fibers are cut (this feature is not actually illustrated). *4,* Section of dorsal root or roots causes diminution or loss of reflexes, sensation, muscle tone and coordination, but no paralysis. *5,* Section of a ventral root or roots causes a lower motor neuron defect. *6,* Section of a spinal or peripheral nerve results in combined motor and sensory losses.

acteristics (p. 148). If there is no regeneration, the muscles eventually disappear and are replaced by connective tissue and fat. Because the nerve impulses necessary for muscle tone are lost, muscles become limp or *flaccid*. This lower motor neuron type paralysis is, therefore, frequently referred to as a *flaccid paralysis*.

Flaccid paralyses are not the only disorders in which reflexes are lost. For instance, if one or several dorsal roots are cut, no sensation can be perceived in the areas supplied by these roots. The afferent impulses cannot reach the spinal cord, and reflexes depending upon them are lost. Paralysis is not present, however, because ventral roots are still intact, and motor impulses for voluntary activity can still reach the muscles. A diagnosis of dorsal root involvement can be made because the areas in which sensory losses occur conform to the embryologic distribution of segments in which each spinal nerve supplies its own dermatome.

Lesions involving spinal nerves give both motor and sensory losses in segmental areas. Lesions of major peripheral nerves, such as the sciatic, cause flaccid paralyses of the muscles supplied by that nerve, accompanied by loss of cutaneous sensations. Differentiation can be made from spinal nerve lesions because the motor and sensory losses are in areas characteristic of peripheral nerve distributions rather than the embryological segmental distributions (p. 34).

Figure 93 is a composite diagram illustrating the paths involved in the various motor disabilities.

Summary

The control of muscular activity can be considered as if the nervous system were a series of levels. These are the spinal cord, brain stem reticular formation, the cerebellum, basal ganglia and cerebral cortex. All muscular activity is mediated by impulses leaving the brain stem and spinal cord.

Within the brain stem are excitatory and inhibitory mechanisms which project to the spinal cord and which in turn are influenced by higher centers, including the cerebral cortex. The paths from the latter originate mainly from the frontal lobe. All these levels and their connections constitute the extrapyramidal system.

The pyramidal system is phylogenetically newer. It consists of a direct path from cerebral cortex to spinal cord and is primarily excitatory in function.

Muscles in extremities are mainly controlled by the contralateral cerebral hemisphere, while muscles near the midline of the body are under bilateral cerebral control.

Interruption of connections between the cortex and motor neurons causes upper motor neuron lesions. Such lesions mostly involve both extrapyramidal and corticospinal fibers, and are characterized by a varying degree of paralysis, spasticity of antigravity muscles, exaggerated deep or tendon reflexes and abnormal reflexes.

Cutting the pathway from motor neurons to muscles causes a lower motor neuron lesion. This is followed by paralysis of voluntary motion with limpness or flaccidity of the involved muscles, muscular atrophy, loss of reflexes, and fibrillary twitching. When the lesion is in spinal or peripheral nerves, the flaccid paralysis is accompanied by sensory losses.

References

For discussions of motor functions, see physiology textbooks, also Grinker and Bucy, and Walshe (cited on p. 328).

Bucy, P. C., ed.: Precentral Motor Cortex. 2nd ed. Urbana, University of Illinois Press, 1949. The various chapters are written by outstanding investigators, cover the motor cortex from the standpoint of structure, function and disorders, and contain excellent bibliographies.

The following books deal with muscle function in man. The accounts by Duchenne and Beevor are classics, Duchenne having used mainly electrical stimulation, and Beevor and Wright, direct palpation of active muscles.

Beevor, C.: The Croonian Lectures on Muscular Movements, 1903, and Remarks on Paralysis of the Movements of the Trunk in Hemiplegia, 1909. Ed. and repr. London, Macmillan and Co., Limited.

Duchenne, G. B.: Physiology of Motion. Tr. and ed. by E. B. Kaplan. Philadelphia, J. B. Lippincott Company, 1949.

Wright, W. G.: Muscle Function. New York, Paul B. Hoeber, Inc., 1928.

CHAPTER 11

The General Senses and Their
Afferent Pathways

IN THE discussion of reflex arcs it was pointed out that a stimulus, such as a burn, may be painful. Although this perception is frequently more important to the subject than is the motor response, it is not part of the reflex, but rather is a result of activities of the cerebral hemispheres. This is true of all sensations. The perception or recognition of a sensation takes place only when impulses reach certain higher centers, which are usually in the cerebral cortex. Impulses from receptors reach the brain by entering the spinal cord and brain stem, then ascending in groups of fibers called tracts. These afferent tracts are interrupted at synaptic levels several times before reaching the cerebral cortex. These interruptions are more than simple relays. Their significance is discussed on p. 337.

According to the traditional conception, the different senses are vision, hearing, smell, taste and touch. An analysis of the primary sensory qualities, however, particularly those of the skin, reveals the inadequacy of such a classification. It has been pointed out previously that receptors may be classified according to the quality of sensations resulting from their stimulation. In the skin, for instance, there are not only exteroceptive receptors which are excited by touch, but also receptors sensitive to pain and to temperature changes. These last are sensations in the same measure as touch. Most classifications, then, are based not only upon the types of peripheral receptors concerned, but also upon the subjective interpretation occurring in the cerebral hemispheres. The various sensations may also be separated into general and special types. This is not a completely satisfactory arrangement, but for convenience in discussion will be used. Vision, hearing, smell, taste and balance are special senses. The general senses are those associated with the receptors discussed in Chap. 9.

Exteroceptive Sensations From the Skin

Light Touch. Nerve impulses resulting from touching the skin or hairs traverse myelinated fibers of various diameters, the range in conduction velocity being from 15 to 100 meters per second. The dorsal root fibers carrying these impulses enter the spinal cord and give off many branches. Some of these establish reflex connections, while others synapse in the gray matter with cells whose axons ascend to the cerebral hemispheres. These particular axons leave the gray matter, cross the midline and ascend in the opposite anterior funiculi. Their destination is the thalamus; hence they form the *anterior spinothalamic tracts*. One of these tracts is illustrated in Fig. 94. This, however, is not the only pathway for touch. Other branches of the entering dorsal root fibers ascend in the posterior funiculi on the side of entrance. Some terminate in gray matter at higher cord levels, and the axons of the cells with which they synapse cross the midline and join the anterior spinothalamic tracts. Still other ascending fibers reach the medulla oblongata, where they end in the nucleus gracilis or nucleus cuneatus.

There is a morphological feature of the spinal cord which is the result of lamination in the ascending tracts. As the fibers entering the cord from lower levels ascend in the posterior funiculi, they are displaced medially by those entering at higher levels. Beginning in the upper thoracic cord and continuing into the cervical cord, one sees a separation of each posterior funiculus into a *fasciculus gracilis* and a *fasciculus cuneatus* (Fig. 124, p. 247). The fasciculus gracilis contains fibers derived from the lower extremity and the lower trunk. It derives its name from its long, slender shape; it is the more medial of the two. The fasciculus cuneatus is shorter, and wedge-shaped. It contains fibers from the upper trunk and upper extremity. These fasciculi continue upwards and terminate in the *nucleus cuneatus* and the *nucleus gracilis*. These nuclei form the gracile and cuneate elevations on the surface of the medulla oblongata.

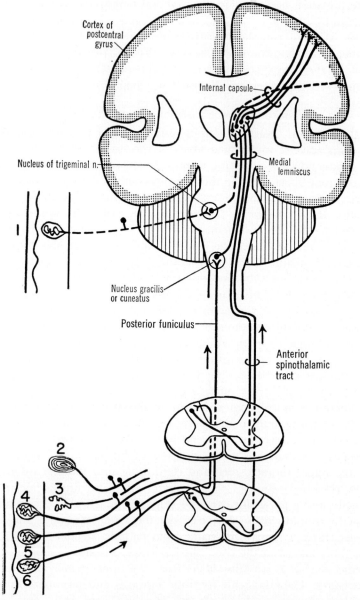

Figure 94. Composite diagram of several afferent paths to the cerebral cortex. *1, 4, 5* and *6* indicate Meissner's corpuscles. Note that tactile paths have several routes in the spinal cord and that *2* (pacinian corpuscle) and *3* (joint receptor) have paths which, in the spinal cord, are similar to the path taken by *5*, but, for purposes of simplification, are not drawn.

Axons arising from the cuneate and gracile nuclei cross the midline and ascend in a prominent tract, the *medial lemniscus.* Each medial lemniscus is joined by the anterior spinothalamic tract of the corresponding side shortly after the latter tract enters the medulla oblongata. In the spinal cord, tactile pathways are therefore both crossed and uncrossed, but in the medulla oblongata are largely crossed.

The medial lemnisci ascend to the thalami. They are joined by fibers carrying tactile impulses from the head and face. These enter the brain stem over branches of the trigeminal nerves, the unipolar cells being in the semilunar ganglia of these nerves. The central processes enter the pons and end in an area of gray matter on each side of the pons, the *main sensory nucleus.* Secondary axons then cross the midline and join the medial lemnisci.

Figure 94 illustrates the tactile pathways from their inception on one side of the body to their termination in the postcentral gyrus of the opposite parietal lobe. The projections from the thalamus to this gyrus are by way of the internal capsule. The postcentral gyrus is the *primary cortical receptive area* for general senses (except pain) from the opposite side of the body. Tactile impulses derived originally from the head and face terminate in the lower part of the gyrus, those from the lower extremity in the upper portion, while those from the upper extremity occupy an intermediate position.

The cells of the postcentral gyrus are arranged in layers, but the layers are arranged differently than in the motor areas. The fifth layer, that which in the motor areas contains large pyramidal cells, is present in the postcentral gyrus, but is thinner and overshadowed by a prominent fourth layer. This layer is pronounced because the nerve fibers which enter the sensory cortex extend vertically to it and there branch profusely. The branches extend horizontally throughout this layer, forming extensive intracortical connections. This arrangement is characteristic of all the cortical areas which receive many nerve fibers (Fig. 146, p. 321).

Pain. Impulses resulting from painful stimuli travel centrally over myelinated and nonmyelinated fibers at rates varying from 1 to 30 meters per second. Some impulses, therefore, reach the central nervous system before others. The time intervals may be so marked that a stimulus may be followed by a painful sensation, and then by a second or delayed pain. This phenomenon is familiar

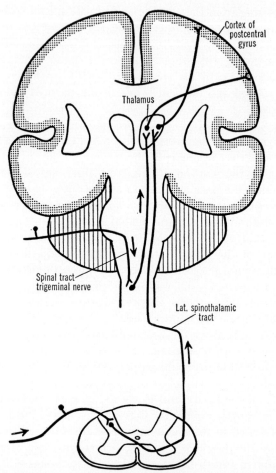

Figure 95. The pain and temperature path. Note that secondary fibers from the trigeminal nerve join the lateral spinothalamic tract. The uncrossed path for pain is not shown.

to anyone who has been kicked in the shin. The initial, sharp flash of pain is followed in a second or two by a more diffuse pain which tends to spread or radiate and which is extremely unpleasant. Differences in conduction rates are the most valid explanation, the probabilities being that the faster conducting or myelinated fibers come from the epidermis, and the slower, nonmyelinated fibers from the dermis and deeper tissues. It is not possible to elicit these two types of pain by stimuli which affect the epidermis alone.

Like all dorsal root fibers, the axons carrying these impulses enter the spinal cord and branch profusely, many of the branches establishing reflex connections. Others synapse in the dorsal gray matter with cells the axons of which cross the midline and ascend in the lateral funiculi as the *lateral spinothalamic tracts* (Fig. 95). On their way to the thalamus they are joined by fibers carrying impulses originating in the head and face. Painful stimuli in these areas initiate impulses that travel centrally over fibers of the trigeminal nerves. These fibers enter the brain stem and descend, some reaching the spinal cord before they end. They thus form the *spinal tracts* of the *trigeminal nerves* (Fig. 95, p. 176, and Fig. 126, p. 260). The axons of the succeeding cells cross the midline, join

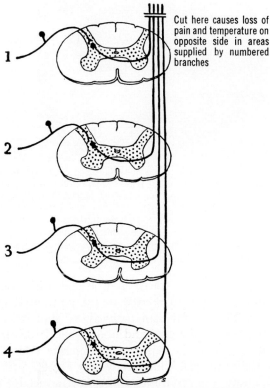

Cut here causes loss of pain and temperature on opposite side in areas supplied by numbered branches

Figure 96. Diagram indicating how sensory losses may result from a lesion of the pain and temperature path. The indicated lesion above segment 1 causes much more loss than one between segments 3 and 4, even though both affect the lateral spinothalamic tract.

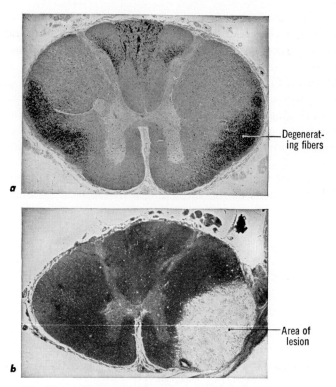

Figure 97. Photomicrographs of sections of spinal cord from a case in which both pain pathways had been cut to relieve intractable pain. *a,* Thoracic cord, above both incisions. Degenerating fibers in both lateral funiculi, Marchi method. Pain fibers located here, as well as spinocerebellar fibers unavoidably cut in this type of operation. Degeneration in the posterior funiculi is a result of the disorder which necessitated the operation. Compare this appearance of degeneration with that of Fig. 92 (p. 167). *b,* Section through one of the incisions in the midthoracic cord.

the lateral spinothalamic tracts, and ascend with them to the thalami. Impulses are then relayed to the postcentral gyri of the parietal lobes. The central pain pathway for skin is probably entirely crossed, both in the cord and brain stem. If this tract is cut, pain cannot be felt in the skin on the opposite side of the body below the level of the cut. This is shown by Fig. 96. Such a cut is a therapeutic measure in certain cases of severe intractable pain, such as might be present in the later stages of cancer, or after severe injuries. Since tactile paths in the cord are both crossed and uncrossed, the sense of touch is but slightly affected by such a procedure. Figure 97 illustrates the degeneration resulting from such a tractotomy.

Temperature. Changes in temperature above or below the normal body variations excite temperature receptors, from which impulses travel centrally over myelinated and nonmyelinated fibers. The central pathways, including those for the face and head, are almost identical to those for pain. Any lesion of the lateral spinothalamic tract, therefore, affects temperature as well as pain perception.

Exteroceptive Sensations From Subcutaneous and Deep Tissues

Pressure. There are somewhat comparable pathways for the various modalities of sensation referred to the deeper tissues. Pressure, for example, excites more deeply situated endings, such as pacinian corpuscles. The resulting impulses travel centrally over large myelinated fibers at rates of 100 to 120 meters per second. Upon entering the spinal cord, reflex connections are established; in addition, ascending branches convey the impulses up posterior funiculi on the side of entrance. When they reach the medulla, synaptic connections allow a relay to the opposite sides into the medial lemnisci and thence to the thalami. Finally they reach the postcentral gyri. The pathway is topographically identical to the light touch path which is uncrossed in the cord (Fig. 94). The pathway from the face and head is probably similar to that for touch from these areas.

Pain. The pathways for pain from the subcutaneous and deeper tissues are identical to those described for skin, save that the fibers are more likely to be nonmyelinated. There is also evidence that an uncrossed pathway exists. Two types of painful sensations cannot be elicited by stimuli that affect just the deeper tissues.

Proprioceptive Sensations

It is uncertain whether impulses from muscle spindles and tendon endings reach the cerebral cortex, but for the purposes of this discussion it is assumed that they may. Impulses from joints, periosteum, ligaments and fascia are known to reach the cerebral cortex.

Position Sense (Muscle-Joint-Tendon Sense or Conscious Proprioception). This is the quality which enables a subject to know just where his body and limbs are in space. It may be tested by having the subject close his eyes; the examiner then passively moves a finger or toe of the subject to a new position. The subject is then asked to state what the new position is, or to duplicate it with the opposite corresponding member. The passively induced movement stimulates receptors in deep tissues and the resulting impulses travel centrally over large myelinated fibers. These fibers enter the spinal cord, establish reflex connections, and then ascend in posterior funiculi to the nucleus gracilis or nucleus cuneatus (Fig. 94). Similar receptors are present in the head and face areas, but the central pathways are unique. The primary neurons, the unipolar cells, are not in the semilunar ganglia of the trigeminal nerves, but in the brain stem itself. The central processes of these cells presumably have connections which allow a relay to the opposite medial lemnisci. Impulses concerned with position sense anywhere in the body eventually reach the postcentral gyri of the opposite parietal lobes.

Interoceptive Sensations

Visceral Pain. This is one of those few modalities of visceral sensations with known central pathways. Visceral pain has a quality quite different from that of cutaneous pain, as anyone who has had intestinal disorders will testify. The pain is usually diffuse, it tends to radiate, and it is difficult to localize. In addition, it is often severe, even sickening, and may persist for minutes, hours or even days. In spite of those differences, visceral pain, no matter what the cause, apparently starts, as does cutaneous pain, with the stimulation of free nerve endings. The resulting impulses travel centrally over nonmyelinated fibers which end in the dorsal gray matter of the spinal cord. The axons of the secondary cells not only cross and ascend in the opposite lateral spinothalamic tract, but also ascend in the tract on the same side. The path to the thalamus and to the cerebral cortex is, therefore, a bilateral one. If operation is necessary for the relief of pain, both these tracts must be cut if visceral pain is present.

Referred Pain and Projected Sensations

Visceral disorders frequently cause pain that is felt in certain areas in the skin. The skin pain occurs in regions supplied by nerves originating from that segment of the cord in which the impulses from the involved viscera enter. For instance, if the diphragm, which is supplied by the fourth cervical segment

(phrenic nerve), is inflamed, pain may be felt in the skin areas supplied by the fourth cervical segment, namely, the tip of the shoulder. Referred pain is frequent enough to be clinically valuable as a
diagnostic sign. Heart disease may be accompanied by pain referred
down the left arm. In the early stages of appendicitis, pain may
be felt just below the sternum. The pain of a kidney stone passing
down the ureter may be referred to the back and groin. Physicians
are able to localize internal disorders more accurately when referred pain is present.

Current explanations of referred pain are inadequate. Undoubtedly the cerebral cortex is unable to distinguish accurately between
impulses from viscera and impulses supposedly arriving from skin.
Some of the causes of this inability are discussed on p. 336. Other
factors appear to be structural and functional characteristics of the
gray matter of the spinal cord. Figure 98 illustrates the closed circuit arrangements found in gray matter. Impulses started in such
circuits are factors in after-discharge, the phenomenon of continued
discharge of motor neurons after afferent impulses have ceased (p.
123). Furthermore, the afferent tracts of the cord evolve from such
interneuronal pools rather than from the simple relays which form

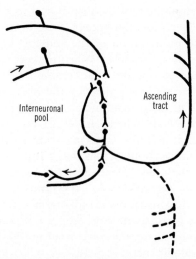

Interneuronal
pool

Ascending
tract

Figure 98.   Diagram of an interneuronal pool, a closed circuit of the type shown
in Figure 70 (p. 122). Connections are such that an ascending tract may convey
impulses derived from several afferent fibers, each of which impinges on the closed
circuit. Arrows indicate direction of conduction.

the conventional representation. It is probable that many of the impulses from viscera enter these circuits along with impulses from skin. If this be true, then the cerebral cortex would be unable to distinguish accurately between the two. This is possible because nerve impulses arriving at the cortex are the same no matter where initiated. A stimulus applied to a peripheral nerve causes impulses which are indistinguishable from those originating at receptors on the ends of the fibers of that nerve. The cortex actually interprets them as coming from the receptors. Striking the ulnar nerve at the elbow, that is, "hitting the funny bone," is such a phenomenon. The pain appears to radiate down the forearm and hand. This is known as projection of a sensation.

A classical example is found in *tabes dorsalis*, which is one of the manifestations of syphilitic infection of the nervous system. The inflammatory process involves dorsal roots. The irritation causes nerve impulses that reach the cerebrum, but, since they are the same as those caused by peripheral stimuli, are interpreted as coming from receptors. The patient, therefore, complains of severe pains in his extremities and viscera, the exact location depending upon the dorsal roots involved.

Even more striking are *phantom limb sensations*. Patients who have had a limb amputated, subsequently feel as if that limb were still present. The phantom limb may even become painful. Apparently some type of irritation of the ends of the nerve fibers in the stump initiates nerve impulses. When these reach the cerebrum, they are interpreted as coming from receptors in the absent limb, that is, the areas normally supplied by the fibers. In other words, during the lifetime of the person, previous to the amputation, there has been built up a body scheme in which the brain has become used to the fact that impulses arriving from certain nerves were coming from certain portions of the body. Impulses initiated anywhere along the path are identical with those starting at the peripheral receptors. Sensations due to stimuli at portions of afferent paths other than receptors may be termed referred, projected or spontaneous. It is apparent that when a person complains of pain somewhere in his body, the cause need not be there at all, but may be anywhere along the pain pathway.

Occasionally, the predominating sensation in a phantom limb is pain. It is interesting that in medical history and in folklore, there are references to the practice of digging up amputated parts which had been buried, in order to straighten out the fingers or toes in the belief that this would relieve painful spasms of the absent limb. These spasms were attributed to the devil.

Clinical Importance of the Afferent Pathways

Because of the anatomical differences in the afferent pathways, symptoms resulting from lesions of these paths will differ according to the location of the lesion (Fig. 99).

Suppose that the posterior, lateral and anterior funiculi (one half of the cord) are destroyed on the left side of the thoracic cord. Pain and temperature perception are lost over the right lower extremity because of destruction of the left lateral spinothalamic tract. Pressure and position sense are lost in the left lower extremity—destruction of left posterior funiculus. Touch is but slightly affected, because the fibers ascending in the left posterior funiculus are destroyed, but those which crossed below the lesion and ascended in the right anterior spinothalamic tract are intact; impulses, therefore, reach the cerebral cortex. Such a lesion, of course, causes a spastic paralysis of the left lower extremity because of destruction of corticospinal and extrapyramidal fibers. If this lesion were in the upper cervical cord, there would be similar signs in the upper extremities as well. The symptoms resulting from hemisection of the spinal cord constitute the *Brown-Séquard syndrome* (p. 186).

Suppose, however, that the lesion is in the brain stem above the level of entrance of fibers from the head and face, and that it destroys one of the medial lemnisci. Since touch is by now entirely crossed, it, as well as pressure and position sense, is lost over the opposite extremities and opposite side of the trunk and head. If the lesion is large enough to include the lateral spinothalamic tract, then pain and temperature perception are lost over the same areas. If the lesion is extended to include the descending motor fibers, spastic paralysis of the opposite extremities occurs. Of course, any brain stem lesion often involves one of the cranial nerves, in which case there are signs and symptoms relating to its destruction.

It should be emphasized that our knowledge of sensory pathways in man is far from complete, as indicated by the fact that it is rare for any sensation to be lost completely following a lesion that destroys pathways on one side of the brain stem or spinal cord.

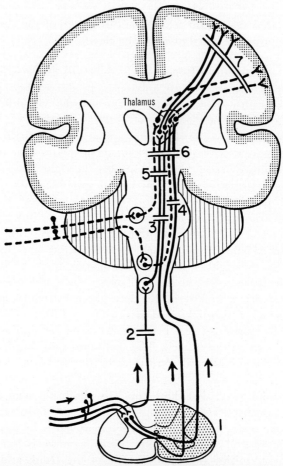

Figure 99. Diagram illustrating lesions of sensory paths. *1,* The shaded area represents a hemisection of the cord (Brown-Séquard syndrome; described in text). *2,* Section of fibers ascending in the posterior funiculus, causing loss of position sense, pressure and vibratory sense, but not touch, because the latter has additional routes in the spinal cord. *3,* Section of the medial lemniscus here causes loss of general senses (except pain and temperature) in opposite side of the body. *4,* Section of the lateral spinothalamic tract causes loss of pain and temperature in opposite side of the body and face. *5,* Section of the medial lemniscus similar to *3,* except that the loss included the opposite face as well. *6,* Lesion of all sensory fibers with loss of all general senses in opposite side of the body and face. *7,* This represents a lesion in the internal capsule or cortex. The signs are quite variable, but the characteristic feature is that some perception of pain and temperature often remains.

Primary Receptive Areas

When impulses from peripheral receptors arrive at the cerebral hemispheres, they terminate in *primary receptive areas.* Here the impulses are perceived as sensations. Only perception and recognition are functions of these areas, which are not responsible for the localization of stimuli, that is, the determination that stimuli are affecting a particular portion of the body, such as the hand. The recall or memory of a sensation does not occur in the primary areas, nor is the accurate differentiation of intensity one of their functions. These are all functions of higher or *association areas,* to which impulses are relayed by the primary areas.

The primary areas for the general sensations include both the thalamus and the postcentral gyrus. The functions of the postcentral gyrus are not known with any certainty. If the gyrus on one side is destroyed, the patient may subsequently be able to detect pain and temperature on the opposite side of the body, although the capacity to localize and to discriminate intensities of stimulation is impaired or lost. It may be postulated, then, that the thalamus is the primary receptive area for pain and temperature, and the postcentral gyrus a primary area for other general senses. These are only partial explanations, however, and other phenomena are difficult to clarify. Our knowledge is so inadequate that the only generalization possible is that both the thalamus and the postcentral gyrus are concerned in the initial recognition of pain, temperature, touch, pressure and position sense.

Summary

The various general sensations, exteroceptive, proprioceptive and interoceptive, are the result of interpretations of impulses by primary receptive areas in the thalamus and postcentral gyrus. The pathways for these impulses differ in their course through the spinal cord and brain stem. Tactile impulses reach the cord and ascend via both crossed and uncrossed paths, but once in the brain stem they are entirely crossed, ascending in the medial lemniscus to the thalamus. Position sense and pressure follow the same path as does uncrossed touch. Pain and temperature ascend in the lateral spinothalamic tract, the pathway being crossed for skin and deeper tissues and both crossed and uncrossed for viscera. This tract ascends to the thalamus, and, like the medial lemniscus, the impulses it carries are relayed to the postcentral gyrus.

Referred and projected sensations are related to the fact that impulses originating in any part of an afferent path are indistinguishable from those originating in receptors.

Names in Neurology

Brown-Séquard, Charles-Edouard (1817–1894)

This physician, though associated mainly with France, led a roving existence, teaching at Harvard as well as in various French colleges. He produced experimental lesions of the nervous system, studied their effects, and also carried out considerable work on the sympathetic system.

References

For the anatomy of the afferent pathways, refer to the neuroanatomy textbooks. The physiology textbooks, and Grinker and Bucy, and Walshe (cited on p. 328), contain sections on the functions and disorders of these tracts.

White, J. C., and Sweet, W. H.: Pain, Its Mechanisms and Neurosurgical Control. Springfield, Ill., Charles C Thomas, 1955. An outstanding volume, of advanced nature, by distinguished neurosurgeons.

CHAPTER 12

The Special Senses and Their Afferent Pathways

THE SEPARATION of senses into general and special types is partially based on the causative stimuli. General senses are those aroused by stimuli acting on and within the body. These energy changes are usually mechanical in nature, though differing in frequency. We usually think of special senses as those which are aroused by stimuli originating at a variable distance from the body, as, for example, light, sound waves, and the like. The term "special sense" when used in this manner is, however, inadequate, because, even if the source of a stimulus is some distance away, the effective energy must still impinge upon receptors; that is to say, sound waves must reach the ear. Taste cannot be considered the result of stimuli originating at a distance. Balance or equilibrium, as a function of the labyrinth, is associated with movements of the head. The classification is nevertheless valuable if by special senses we refer broadly to sensory qualities dependent upon receptors in the cranial region, whose afferent paths are over cranial nerves and which may allow perception of distant objects.

In man these senses are rather uniformly developed to a high degree. This does not mean that taste is as subjectively important as vision. It means that taste is associated with a system of pathways and cortical areas which allow for functional elaboration if necessary. Man, therefore, differs from other animals in which one or more of these senses may be highly developed. Hearing in a bat is certainly more acute than in man. A dog has a remarkable olfactory sense. Birds may have extraordinarily keen vision. But in these animals many of the other senses are functionally inferior. Relative uniformity is characteristic of man.

Vision

The peripheral stimuli necessary for this sensory quality are radiations in the visible spectrum varying in wave length from 400 to 700 millimicrons. The receptors are in the sensory layer of the retina. The retina is the innermost layer of the eye, that complex and efficient optical instrument which is designed to gather and focus light upon it.

If one compares the eye to a camera, the retina would represent the light-sensitive plate or film. There is a focusing system composed of the *cornea* and the *crystalline lens*. These are shown in Fig. 100. The cornea is composed of connective tissue and is covered on both surfaces by epithelial cells. It is transparent and is devoid of any

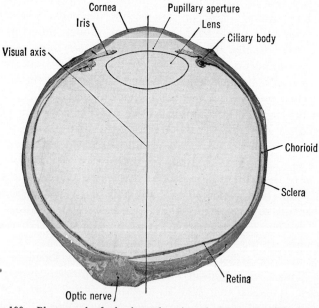

Figure 100.   Photograph of a horizontal section of a human eye. The lens, which was removed to facilitate making the section, has been drawn in its correct position, but the suspensory strands around it have been omitted. Note that the retina has partially separated from the other coats of the eyeball. The dark line in the posterior part of the iris is the result of pigment.

blood vessels that might interfere with this property. The cornea is curved, with the convexity forward or outward, and, when viewed from the front, is the clear portion of the globe, surrounded on all sides by the "white" of the eye, the *sclera*.

Much of the refraction of entering light occurs during its passage through the corneal surfaces. Light undergoes further refraction as it passes through the lens. The total refraction is such that when light from any object reaches the retina, it forms on it a real and inverted image. Just behind the cornea is the *iris*. This has an opening in its center, the *pupil*. There are smooth muscle fibers in the iris, some of which are arranged circularly so that the pupillary aperture narrows when they contract. Others are arranged radially, spreading out like a fan, and their contraction widens the pupillary opening (Fig. 101). Thus, like the variable aperture of a camera, there is a mechanism for regulating the amount of light admitted to the eye.

The color of the eyes is caused by pigment, most of which is concentrated in cells on the posterior surface of the iris. Pigment is also present in the outer or nonsensory portion of the retina, and in the middle coat of the eye, the *chorioid*. This probably serves to prevent blurring or multiplication of images by internal reflection; in the camera this is prevented by painting the interior a dead black.

Sharp pictures at different distances can be taken with a camera by changing lenses or by varying the distance between lens and film. In the eye this is done by changing the curvature of the lens.

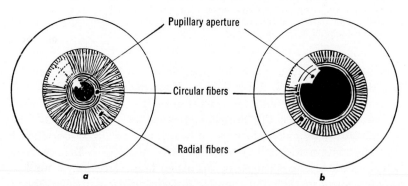

Figure 101.   Circular and radial fibers in the iris. *a*, Pupillary constriction with contraction of the circular fibers. *b*, Pupillary dilatation with contraction of radial fibers and relaxation of circular ones.

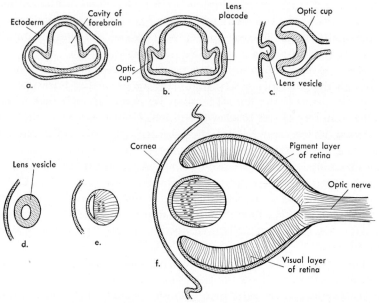

Figure 102. Various stages in the development of the eye. *a*, Cross section of forebrain showing outpocketings in the region of the future diencephalon. *b*, Outpocketings are definite optic cups, and the thickened ectoderm on each side is the beginning of the lens (lens placode). *c*, Just the region of the eye is shown. The lens placode has invaginated further. The optic cup shows how the retina begins as two layers. *d* and *e*, The lens vesicle detaches and its cavity begins to disappear. *f*, The lens is well formed. The cavity in the retina has disappeared. The posterior or outer layer of the optic cup becomes the pigment layer of the retina, and the anterior or inner layer contains the rods and cones, bipolar cells and ganglion cells. When, for any reason, the retina separates in the adult, it generally separates between pigment layer and sensory layer, and not between pigment layer and chorioid. The above is a very schematic representation, the actual development being considerably more complicated.

The structures which make this possible are as follows: Surrounding the outer margin of the lens and attached to it by fine suspensory strands are bundles of smooth muscle fibers which form the *ciliary muscle*. When this muscle contracts, the area to which the strands attach is pulled forward. The strands are thus shortened, and the tension which they maintained on the lens is thereby lessened, allowing the elastic lens capsule to bulge forward.

Some fibers in the ciliary muscle are arranged circularly. When they contract, the entire ciliary area moves inward, thereby providing another means of shortening suspensory strands. The resulting increased thickness of the lens refracts the light to a greater degree, thus allowing near objects to be brought into sharper focus. This process is known as *accommodation*. It is accompanied by a narrowing of the pupillary aperture, that is to say, by pupillary constriction, and by a medial movement or convergence of each eye.

Between the iris and the cornea is the anterior chamber (Fig. 100); between the iris and the lens is the posterior chamber. Both are filled with a thin watery fluid, the *aqueous fluid* or *humor*. It is similar in composition to cerebrospinal fluid, since it is a blood plasma filtrate. It circulates through the chambers and after absorption into tissue spaces in the coats of the eye is eventually returned to the venous circulation. Behind the lens is the *vitreous humor,* a gelatinous, clear substance that is permanent; that is, it is not undergoing a constant formation, circulation and absorption.

This complicated structure of the eye may be made somewhat clearer by reference to the formation and development in the embryo and fetus. This is illustrated in Fig. 102. It can be seen that the retina is an extension of brain substance and that, because of its manner of formation, it is a double layer. The posterior or outer layer becomes the pigmented epithelium, and the anterior or inner layer the receptive portion of the retina.

The Retina

The retina is a part of the brain, having layers of specialized nerve cells, and being connected to the rest of the brain by a fiber tract called the optic nerve. The retina is the only portion of the nervous system which can be seen directly in the intact living subject. With an *ophthalmoscope* all portions of the retina may be seen. This instrument is so designed that light from it, when flashed into the eye of the subject, is reflected from the retina back to the eye of the observer.

Light entering the eye along the visual axis (Fig. 100) falls upon a portion of the retina known as the *macula lutea,* so called because it is a yellow spot. In the middle of the macula is a depression, the *fovea.* Just medial to the macula lutea is a whitish area from which small arteries and veins spread throughout the retina. This is the *optic disk,* the point of exit of the optic nerve. The vessels are the retinal arteries and veins, which reach the disk by running in the substance of the optic nerve. The optic disk and

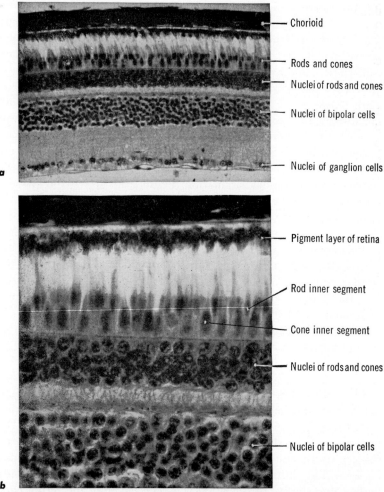

Figure 103. Photomicrographs of retina of copperhead snake (similar in many respects to human retinae). *a*, Includes all the layers. *b*, At a higher magnification, showing particularly the rods and cones. The staining method does not demonstrate neuronal processes. (These sections, made by Dr. Gordon Walls, were obtained through the courtesy of Dr. Parker Heath.)

the vessels accurately reflect many pathological changes. Increased intracranial pressure, for instance, may so compress the retinal veins that circulation in the retina is seriously impaired. Fluid is forced out of capillaries because the venous pressure rises; this escaping fluid permeates the retina, and especially the optic disk. This becomes swollen and in such conditions is usually called a *choked disk.* The amount of choking is a good index of the amount of increase in the intracranial pressure. Vascular changes, such as atherosclerosis, usually affect the retinal vessels in the early stages of the disorder. Since these pathological processes can be seen directly, the disorder may often be detected before there is evidence of its presence elsewhere in the body. Ophthalmoscopic examination, therefore, is an important diagnostic tool for the general practitioner as well as for the ophthalmologist and the neurologist.

As shown in Fig. 103, the retina is composed of cells arranged in layers. It is not necessary to name all the layers, it being sufficient to state that outermost in the retina proper is the layer of *rods* and *cones;* next the layer of *bipolar cells,* and innermost the layer of *ganglion cells.* In general, these cells are arranged somewhat perpendicularly. At the region of the optic disk, however, the cells are arranged so obliquely that they are absent just in front of the disk. Light striking this region does not impinge on receptor cells, and no visual function is possible. This is the *blind spot* of the eye.

Rods and Cones and Their Connections

The receptive cells, that is, those sensitive to radiations in the visible spectrum, are the rods and cones. In order to reach these specialized cells, light must traverse the other layers of the retina, except in the fovea, where the cells are arranged obliquely so that cones are directly exposed. The schematic representation of Fig. 104 illustrates that the rods and cones are so named because of the shape of their outer segments. The outer segments of the rods contain a pigment, *rhodopsin* or *visual purple.* The nature of any photosensitive pigment in mammalian cones has not yet been determined.

In considering the retina as a whole, there are about four times as many rods as cones. In the macula, however, cones predominate, and the fovea is occupied exclusively by them. As one progresses toward the periphery of the retina, the rods become predominant.

The general arrangement of retinal cells is such that rods and cones connect with bipolar cells, which in turn synapse with ganglion cells. The axons of the ganglion cells course toward the back of the eye; at the optic disk they collect to form the optic nerve. There are 115 to 130 million rods and cones, but, at the most, only one million optic nerve fibers. This necessitates a gen-

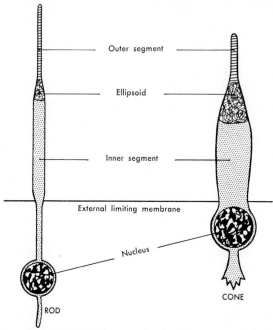

Figure 104. Diagram of a human rod and cone. The neuroglial cells in the retina have long processes that, in the inner and outer parts of the retina, fuse to form internal and external limiting membranes. The external limiting membrane is shown here, perforated by the rod and cone. Cone nuclei are placed nearer the membrane. (Based on Walls, The Vertebrate Eye, Bloomfield Hills, Mich., Cranbrook Institute of Science.)

eral convergence within the retina. In other words, one or a few ganglion cells receive impulses from a number of bipolar cells, and these in turn from many rods and cones.

These connections are of two general types, the one-to-one and the multiple (Fig. 105). Figure 105, however, does not represent a specific region of the retina, but merely shows the types of connections. Nor are all the possible connections indicated, since this would make the diagram entirely too complicated. The one-to-one connection is a path from cone to bipolar to ganglion cell which is found almost exclusively in the fovea. The mixed systems and the rod systems are examples of the multiple types of connections, and these are in the majority.

Also omitted from Fig. 105 are neurons that connect or associate various parts of the retina, because little is known of the manner in which they function. It is possible that they form multiple and closed circuits of a type similar to those in gray matter elsewhere.

All the retinal connections are synapses. The cells are neurons, though in the rods and cones considerably modified ones. The retina is comparable to the cerebral cortex in its complexity. Between the cells, and forming a supporting framework for them, are neuroglial cells such as are found in the rest of the central nervous system. The optic nerve, being a fiber tract and not a true peripheral nerve, also contains neuroglial tissue. Its fibers lack neurilemma and are, therefore, incapable of regeneration when once destroyed.

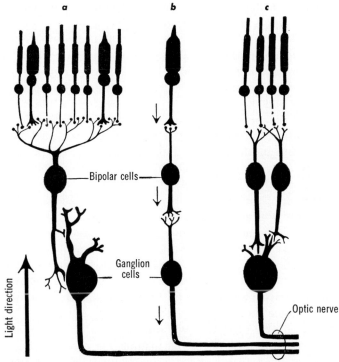

Figure 105. Three types of retinal connections. Association neurons have been omitted. *a,* Mixed rod and cone system, both types synapsing with one bipolar cell and this in turn with a ganglion cell. *b,* Single cone system, found only in the fovea. *c,* Multiple rod system, several rods converging upon bipolars and these upon a ganglion cell. The optic nerve is formed by axons of the ganglion cells. (Modified after Polyak.)

Retinal Functions

Light striking a rod or a cone initiates a series of processes that result in nerve impulses leaving the eye by way of an optic nerve fiber. There is a pigment in rods and cones that is sensitive to light. What this pigment is in mammalian cones is not known. That in rods is rhodopsin or visual purple. This is the common pigment in marine fishes and land vertebrates, the various rhodopsins having a characteristic absorption maximum at about $500m\mu$. Human rhodopsin has an absorption maximum at $497m\mu$. Many fresh water fishes have porphyropsins rather than rhodopsins, the porphyropsins having absorption maxima at about $522m\mu$. Both types of pigments are related to the vitamin A complex, vitamin A_1 (retinene$_1$) being a chromophore for rhodopsin, and vitamin A_2 (retinene$_2$) being a chromophore for porphyropsin.

Light that reaches rods is absorbed by rhodopsin. A photochemical change results, with rhodopsin being bleached in the process. The process is reversible, rhodopsin being resynthesized. In some way, the photochemical reaction is followed by excitation of bipolar cells and then ganglion cells. The reaction is also signalled by electrical changes of such magnitude that they can be recorded by electrodes placed on the surface of the eye. The recorded electrical changes constitute the electroretinogram (ERG), with characteristic deflections (Fig. 106). The velocity at which the photochemical reaction proceeds is proportional to the intensity of light and the concentration of rhodopsin. Only a small part of the total amount of rhodopsin is bleached when exposed to light.

Rhodopsin is found in the outer segments of rods and light must therefore traverse the layers of the retina to reach it. The mechanism of excitation is extraordinarily sensitive. Recent evidence indicates that one to three quanta of light reaching rods are sufficient for excitation and it may be, therefore, that one quantum can activate a single rod.

A photosensitive pigment, *iodopsin,* has been isolated from cones of birds, but little is known about mammalian cone pigment, there being no evidence that it is iodopsin. The eyes of most mammals have both rods and cones. This situation has led to what is termed the duplicity theory of vision, which holds that rods are concerned with one set of functions and cones with another. It has been observed, for example, that in nocturnal animals, which have great

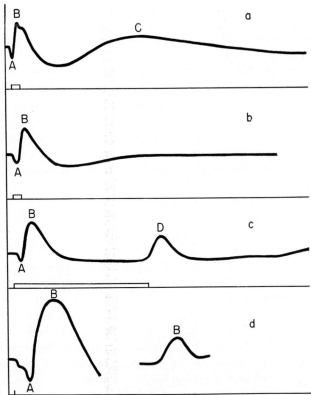

Figure 106. Examples of electroretinograms, recorded so that an upward deflection indicates positivity at an electrode in front of the retina, in contrast to an electrode behind or at the side of the retina. *a* is an ERG of a guinea pig (with a pure rod retina, or nearly so), in response to a flash of light, the onset and duration of which is signalled on the base line. There is an initial, negative *A* wave, a larger positive *B* wave, and a long lasting, positive *C* wave. *b* is an ERG of a ground squirrel (with pure cone retina) in response to a short flash of light, showing *A* and *B* waves. With a long flash of light (*c*), there is a *D* wave or off-effect when the light is turned off. *d* shows human ERG's. That on the left is in response to a flash of high intensity light, showing *A* and *B* waves. That on the right shows just a *B* wave when the stimulus is of low intensity. The nature of the ERG is still obscure. It is a general reaction, and the various waves or components cannot be assigned specifically to either rods or cones. All ERG's are in dark-adapted state, and human ERG's are based on Armington, Johnson and Riggs, J. Physiol., vol. 118, 1952.

visual sensitivity, the receptors are mainly rods. In diurnal animals, they are mainly cones.

Dark and Light Adaptation.   If the eyes have been in complete darkness for forty minutes or more, so as to allow as complete a resynthesis of rhodopsin as possible, it will be found that the sensitivity of the eye has greatly increased. The energy of light necessary to stimulate is much less, by about a thousand-fold, than that required in daylight. If the dark-adapted eye is exposed to light of varying wave lengths, of equal energy, it is found that sensitivity is greatest to a wave length of 510 millimicrons, the green region of the spectrum. The light seen is not green, however, but some intensity of gray. The dark-adapted eye cannot distinguish colors. The maximum sensitivity is at a different wave length than is the maximum absorption of rhodopsin. Shorter wave lengths are absorbed by the media of the eye before they reach the retina. When the dark-adapted eye is stimulated with other wave lengths, it is found that sensitivity decreases according to the manner illustrated in Fig. 107 (*scotopic curve*). Part of the decrease in sensitivity toward the violet or shorter wave length portion of the spectrum is more apparent than real, because some of the shorter wave lengths, as mentioned above, are absorbed by the refracting media, such as the lens. Patients who have had lenses removed because of cataracts (*aphakia*) may, by ultraviolet radiation, be able to see objects that are invisible or less visible to others. The dark-adapted eye is quite insensitive at the longer wave lengths, or red end of the spectrum. Hence, one can dark-adapt by wearing red goggles with the proper transmission characteristics. The red light that gets through stimulates cones, thus enabling one to see. Rods are not stimulated, hence can adapt just as if one were in darkness.

If an eye is exposed to strong light or daylight, it becomes light-adapted, and the greatest sensitivity is found in the region of 557 millimicrons (*photopic curve,* Fig. 107). This shift to the red-green portion of the spectrum is the *Purkinje shift,* and represents functional differences between rods and cones. The threshold is at least a thousand times greater than in the dark-adapted retina.

It has been shown that in animals with pure rod and pure cone retinae, there is no Purkinje shift, nor is there one in man when the stimulating light is so arranged that it falls only on the fovea, where only cones are present. On the basis of the evidence cited, and of other evidence, there is reason to believe that rods are primarily concerned with visual sensitivity, being active in the dark-adapted eye, and that cones are primarily concerned with visual acuity, being active in the light-adapted eye. This, however, is not a clear-cut functional separation. Rods are active in day vision. Nocturnal animals, for example, can see in the daytime. Color vision is supposed to be primarily a cone function, but rods may be concerned to some extent.

Visual Sensitivity. This is the ability to see in dim light and is primarily a function of the rods. There are several reasons for this. As mentioned above, rhodopsin is extremely sensitive to light. Hence, in the dark-adapted eye, little energy is necessary for rod stimulation. Furthermore, as shown in Fig. 105, the rods in multiple rod systems converge upon one bipolar cell, or at least upon one ganglion cell. Therefore, if light of low intensity falls upon each of many rods, the resulting excitation may summate at the succeeding bipolar cells and thereby reach the threshold of that neuron. Visual sensitivity is aided by reflex widening of the pupil in dim light. This illuminates rods previously unaffected and thereby increases the chances for summation.

Several mechanisms seem to be responsible for the increase in sensitivity during dark adaptation. Only a small part of the total amount of rhodopsin is bleached, even in strong light, and the amount resynthesized in the dark accounts only in part for the increase in sensitivity. It is held that in dim light, or in darkness, there are conditions that are favorable for a horizontal spread of excitation. Perhaps, in the absence of cone activity, certain inhibitory mechanisms are lost, so that an increasing number of neurons have a lower threshold. Thus, one can speak of both photochemical and neurological components in dark adaptation.

Since vitamin A is involved in the metabolism of rhodopsin, vitamin A deficiency may result in night blindness. This vitamin, however, has the general property of being necessary for the maintenance of epithelium, and its role in night blindness may therefore be related to the latter property. Cone functions may also be affected in so-called night blindness.

Rods are more numerous in the periphery of the retina. Therefore, in dim light, such as at twilight, objects are best seen from an oblique angle rather than viewed directly ahead, since in the latter case light falls on the macular region where cones predominate.

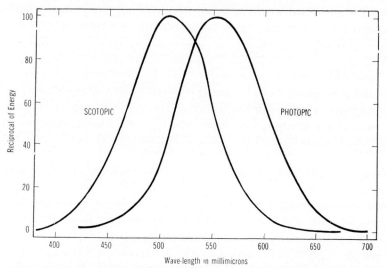

Figure 107. Graph illustrating the Purkinje shift. The scotopic curve is the visibility curve of the dark-adapted eye (achromatic vision), with maximum sensitivity at 510 millimicrons. The photopic curve is the visibility curve of the light-adapted eye (chromatic vision), with maximum sensitivity at 557 millimicrons. The two curves, for convenience, are plotted in the same units of sensitivity, although the scotopic eye is many times more sensitive. (Modified from Hecht and Williams: J. Gen. Physiol., Vol. 5.)

Visual Acuity. With the light-adapted eye, color sensation becomes possible, as well as an increased sharpness of object contour and detail. One is therefore able to distinguish small objects as separate entities and to observe them in sharp outline.

Everyone is familiar with the fact that if one moves away from two closely approximated objects, they eventually fuse and appear as one. If the objects are lines, visual acuity may be tested by measuring the least separation by which two lines may be discerned. The smallest visual angle, the angle subserved by the distance separating the two lines, is 1 minute or less. There are many factors, more than can be discussed here, involved in visual acuity. One is probably the *grain* of the retina or the denseness of receptors within it. That is, if receptors were relatively far apart, light from one or the other of the lines or from the area between might fall on nonsensitive portions of the retina, and this would certainly diminish resolving power. Another factor is undoubtedly the one-to-one type of cone projection of the foveal region. This allows separate paths for impulses due to light from different, small sources, such as two lines. The fact that visual acuity is more pronounced in the fovea corroborates the functions of the cones in this matter.

The theoretical conditions for the smallest visual angle may be shown as follows: Suppose two thin black lines on a white background are separated by such a small or narrow distance that the light from the intervening white would illuminate but a single row of cones. It follows that the row of cones on each side would not be illuminated (corresponding to the black lines), but those still farther laterally would be. The brain is thus furnished a means of distinguishing the two separable lines, since there are no nerve impulses from the retinal region corresponding to the lines, in contrast to the impulses arriving from the intervening and neighboring retina. These conditions, however, are not actually found. The focusing and fixation of the eyes are not accurate enough to meet these theoretical demands. Slight movements of the eyeballs result in illumination of the row of cones corresponding to the intervening white background, and in illumination of the row on each side (corresponding to the black lines) as well. Hence impulses from all these cells eventually reach the brain.

There is this difference, however. It was pointed out on p. 137 that receptors respond to increasing intensities of stimulation by higher frequencies of discharges. Accordingly, the row of cones corresponding to the white background is more intensely stimulated, and discharges at higher frequencies than the less intensely illuminated row on each side. As discussed on p. 337, differences in frequency are interpreted by the cerebral cortex as differences in intensity. Visual acuity thus becomes a matter of intensity discrimination, in which the cerebral cortex is most important.

Visual acuity may also be tested by determining the smallest object which can be seen when viewed against a homogeneous field. The apparent size of a star, for instance, is minute. The angle subtended by it may be much smaller than the minimum visual angle necessary to deal with separable objects. The angle subtended by the minimum visible object has been shown to be a few seconds or less, even one-half second. The extremely fine dark line which may be seen in such tests probably lessens the illumination of a row of cones, the surrounding ones being uniformly illuminated by the homogeneous background.

Critical Fusion Frequency for Flicker. A flash of light on the eye generally elicits a burst of impulses over the optic nerve. With successive flashes of light, successive bursts of impulses reach the brain, and successive electrical changes can be recorded from the eye. But as the frequency of flashes increases, the ability to distinguish separate flashes decreases. If a sectored disc is rotated in front of a light source, it is found that as the rate of rotation increases, there is a frequency at which the flashes fuse, and give a sensation of continuous brightness. The critical frequency at which such fusion takes place is dependent upon the intensity of the light (a higher frequency for higher intensities), and upon a number of other factors, including attention, the condition of the retina, and the condition of the brain. A familiar example of fusion is that of motion pictures. The number of frames per second is high enough so that individual frames are not seen.

Color Vision. The problem of color vision cannot be given more than a limited discussion here.

The sensation of color is influenced by a number of factors, including:

1. *Hue* or *tone,* which is a function of the wave length. Thus red and green, each of different wave lengths, are different hues.

2. *Brightness,* which depends upon the intensity of the light. Thus, a single hue, such as green, can have many degrees of brightness. Brightness may be compared to mixtures of black and white to produce gray, in the sense that as one adds black, brightness is lessened. This is because black absorbs all wave lengths and lessens the amount of reflected light. Brilliance is the subjective sensation due to brightness.

3. *Saturation* or *purity,* which depends upon the mixture with white light. The more white light and, therefore, the more of other colors, the less saturated or pure is a given hue. Colors exhibiting saturation are commonly referred to as pale or pastel.

It has long been known that there are certain primary colors, such that any color of the spectrum can be matched by mixing two primary colors in correct proportions. The primary colors (when dealing with light) are red, green, and blue (or violet). The matching is not quite precise, however, unless a third color is used. For example, if one wished to match a spectral yellow with a mixture of red and green, a precise match is obtained only if some blue is added to the yellow. Methods of color matching are useful in studying defects in color vision, since color blindness can be classified on the basis of defects in primary colors.

There have been, and are, a number of theories of color vision. The one most widely accepted is the three-color theory (Young-Helmholtz Theory, p. 223). This theory postulates that there are three types of receptors (presumably cones), each sensitive to one of the primary colors. However, three different types of cones cannot be distinguished histologically, nor has the mammalian cone pigment (or pigments) been isolated and determined to have three absorption maxima. Furthermore, perception may be affected by a number of factors. For example, if a small object of a specific color is placed in the field of vision so that light from it falls on a specific part of the retina, the color perceived may vary according to the part of the retina stimulated. This is due in part to the incidence of the light. Light entering the eye through the center of the pupil is more or less parallel to receptors, but light entering at the edge of the pupil strikes receptors at an angle (because the eyeball is curved). The color perceived is different in the two instances.

Other theories have received considerable support, among them a four-color theory with red and green and yellow and blue pairs of receptors, and a polychromatic theory (with seven receptors). But it must be emphasized that although many facts regarding color vision have accumulated, theories are still tenuous, including the one most widely accepted, the three-color theory. Color vision may not be entirely a retinal function. If green light is flashed in one eye, and red in the other, the color seen is yellow, indicating that the fusion occurs centrally, in the brain.

Color Blindness. Color blindness is a common defect, being found in some degree in about four per cent of all men. It may be acquired, but is otherwise a strongly sex-linked characteristic. Color blindness may be classified according to primary color defect.

Trichromats (three-color vision) include 1) those with normal vision, 2) those with anomalous (weak) red vision (protanomaly), and 3) those with anomalous green vision (deuteranomaly).*

Dichromats (two-color vision) include those who cannot perceive red (protanopia); those who have green blindness (deuteranopia),

* The words indicating the type of color defect are of Greek origin. *Protos* means first, hence protanomaly (weakness of) and protanopia (loss of or without) are defects in the first of the three primary colors. *Deuteros* means second, hence deuteranomaly and deuteranopia are defects in the second of the primary colors. *Tritos* means third, and tritanopia is a defect in the third primary color.

but who can match spectral colors with red and blue, and to whom the luminosity of colors appears normal; and, finally, and quite rarely, those who are blue (violet) blind (tritanopia). The fovea of man appears to be tritanopic, the blue end of the spectrum being absorbed by media and by the yellow pigment of the macula. Diurnal mammals with pure cone retinae have yellow lenses, thus limiting the amount of blue reaching the retina.

Monochromats (total color blindness) are quite rare. There appear to be two kinds, with and without photophobia (pain on exposure to strong light). The ones with photophobia seem to react as if they had no cones in their retinae.

It should be emphasized that the above is a classification based on subjective defects in perception, and not on any proven defect in or absence of a specific kind of color receptor.

Central Connections of the Retina

The optic nerves converge at the base of the brain to form the optic chiasma. A partial decussation occurs here in a manner indicated in Fig. 108. Behind the chiasma, the axons continue into the optic tracts, which curve around the outside of the cerebral peduncles and disappear from the surface.

Some of the axons terminate in or near the region of the superior colliculi. Because of these connections, reflex pupillary reactions or body movements in response to light can occur. Most of the optic fibers, however, end in the lateral geniculate body of the thalamus and are relayed by way of the internal capsule to the occipital lobes. Here they end around the calcarine fissure in a cortical area numbered 17, the primary receptive area (Fig. 148, p. 324). As in the postcentral gyrus, the entering fibers dispose themselves throughout the fourth cell layer (Fig. 146, p. 321). They are so concentrated here that they form a white band, the band or stripe of Gennari, visible to the naked eye. Because of this, the visual cortex is sometimes called the *striate cortex*.

As indicated in Fig. 108, the fibers from the medial or nasal half of each retina cross, while those from the lateral or temporal half do not. This means that objects on the right are visualized by left Area 17, and vice versa. This perception is therefore contralateral, as it is in other sensations.

Binocular Vision. When one looks at an object, an image is formed in each eye, and impulses go from each eye to both cerebral hemispheres. But only one object is seen. To obtain this result, the points of the image must fall on corresponding parts of the retinae. Thus the temporal half of the left eye and the nasal half of the right eye are corresponding halves. If there is a disturbance of binocular vision, such as may follow paralyses of extrinsic eye muscles, then double vision or *diplopia* may result. This is because image points do not fall upon corresponding parts of the retinae, and two images are seen. Diplopia can be demonstrated by lightly pressing upon the lateral side of one of the eyes while gazing steadily at an object some distance away. The pressure shifts the eye so that images are formed on noncorresponding portions of

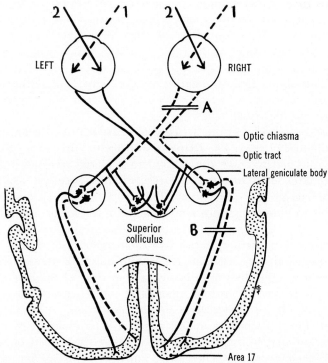

Figure 108. The visual pathways. Arrows numbered *1* indicate that light from objects in the right visual fields (when looking straight ahead) reaches the left halves of the retinae. The reverse is true for the opposite visual fields. The collaterals from the visual path (to the superior colliculi for reflexes) are really separate fibers and not branches of true visual fibers. Cutting the optic nerve at *A* causes complete blindness in that eye. A lesion at *B*, however, causes blindness in the left half of each field of vision (arrows numbered *2*).

the retina, and diplopia results. If diplopia is due to a persistent disorder, one lasting for weeks or months or longer, false images usually become suppressed and the eye functionally blind.

The anatomy of the visual system is such that damage in various portions of the optic pathways causes visual defects with differences which enable one to locate such lesions rather accurately. Destruction of one optic nerve, for instance, will cause complete blindness in that eye. Destruction of the pathway on one side behind the chiasma (Fig. 108) will cause, not total blindness, but blindness in half of the visual field of each eye, a *hemianopia*. If such a lesion is on the left side, the patient will be unable to see objects on his right side when he is looking straight ahead.

This further corroborates contralateral vision perception, which one can demonstrate by a simple experiment. Close the eyes and turn the right eye toward the nose, then press lightly on the temporal side (right side) of the right eyeball. A bright ring or a blue ring with a bright halo is seen in the nasal or left field of the right eye. This shows that stimulation of the right half of the retina produces an effect which appears to come from the opposite or left part of the visual field.

That retinal images are actually reversed may be demonstrated in a number of ways. The retina is sensitive to any x-rays that may happen to penetrate the eye. Metal letters placed in front of closed eyes and exposed to x-rays are recognized as shadows against a bright background. (The x-rays that reach the retina apparently cause it to fluoresce.) Since x-rays are not refracted or bent during their passage through the eyes, the shadows are not inverted upon the retina. The brain performs its customary reversal during interpretation, and the letters appear upside down. If the letters are to appear upright, they must be inverted in front of the eyes. There is not, however, a conscious analysis of retinal inversion. Perception is of objects in visual fields and not of impulses from the retinae. From infancy on, object position determination by vision is substantiated by impressions produced by the objects on other senses, such as touch. Thereafter, impulses from specific retinal areas become visual perceptions for objects in certain portions of the visual fields.

The interpretation of these cues from retinal stimulation probably depends to a great extent upon learning. If subjects wear lenses which invert the retinal fields, the images on the retina become upright and the perceived field is inverted. In spite of the resulting confusion, the subjects can, by wearing the lenses for considerable periods of time, adjust themselves fairly well to the situation and perform coordinated movements.

Hearing

Hearing follows the stimulation of certain specialized epithelial cells by sound waves. These cells are part of a receptor system situated in the *labyrinth,* or inner ear (Fig. 109). The labyrinth is a group of small, fluid-filled chambers and canals, one of which, the *cochlea,* is especially concerned with auditory mechanisms. There is an intricate, delicate mechanism by which sound waves enter the external ear and are then funneled into the middle ear,

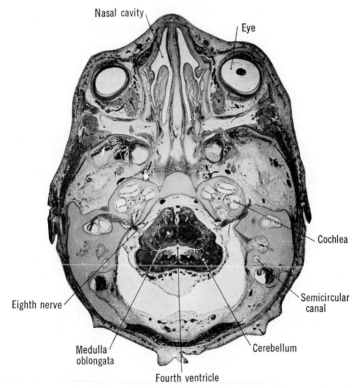

Nasal cavity

Eye

Cochlea

Semicircular canal

Eighth nerve

Medulla oblongata

Cerebellum

Fourth ventricle

Figure 109. Photomicrograph of a horizontal section of a four-month human fetal head. Note the left acoustic nerve dividing into cochlear and vestibular portions, the latter going to the macula utriculi.

from which three tiny bones transmit the vibrations to the fluid-filled cochlea.

The External and Middle Ears

As shown in Fig. 110, the external ear includes the auricle, which is attached to the side of the head, and the external auditory meatus or ear canal. Whether the auricle is of any great importance in man is doubtful. The external ear canal transmits the air vibrations to the middle ear. Separating this canal from the middle ear cavity is a thin *tympanic membrane.* To it is attached one of the three ossicles which form a chain across the middle ear cavity. When vibrations of air strike the tympanic membrane, they cause it to move at the same frequency as the impinging waves. These vibrations are transmitted through the ear ossicles in such a manner that the innermost ossicle, the *stapes,* moves inward when the tympanic membrane moves inward. It can be seen from Figs 110 and 111 that the foot of the stapes impinges upon one of the fluid-filled

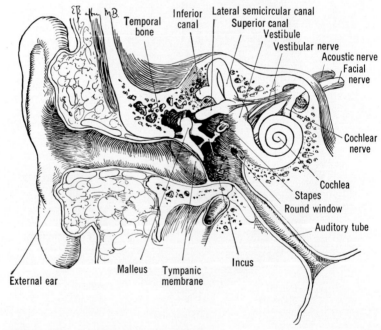

Figure 110. Semischematic drawing of the ear. Note the ossicles extending across the middle ear cavity. The greater part of the course of the facial nerve through the ear has been omitted. (Modified from Max Brödel.)

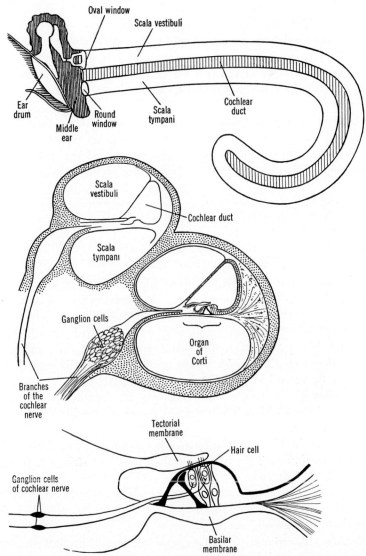

Figure 111. Various schema of the inner ear. The upper drawing represents the cochlea as if it were uncoiled. Note how the stapes fits into the oval window. The scala vestibuli communicates with the scala tympani which terminates at the round window. Compare with Fig. 110. The middle drawing represents the cochlea cut at a right angle to or across the first plane, indicating the shape and relationships of the cochlear duct. The peripheral processes of the bipolar ganglion cells extend to the organ of Corti (in brackets). The lower drawing is of the receptive area, the organ of Corti. Most of the cells have been omitted, since all are either hair cells or supporting cells.

canals of the cochlea, and its vibrations are, therefore, transmitted to the fluid. It can also be seen from these figures that at the other end of the fluid system is an aperture, the *round window,* which is closed off by a thin membrane. Since fluid is incompressible, an increase in pressure at the end where the stapes is located is compensated for by a bulging outward of this membrane in the round window.

Marked changes in external air pressure might seriously affect the tympanic membrane were it not for the fact that the middle ear cavity communicates with the pharynx by means of the auditory tube (Fig. 110). Pressure on both sides of the membrane may be equalized through this passageway. All are familiar with the "popping" of the ears when ascending or descending considerable distances. This is due to periodic openings of the auditory tube at the point where it reaches the pharynx.

The Inner Ear and Cochlea

The cochlea is a fluid-filled cavity in the temporal bone, being arranged in coils resembling those of a snail shell. Within the cavity is a small fluid-filled duct, the *cochlear duct,* in which are found specialized epithelial cells (Fig. 111). Some of the cells have fine, hairlike processes at their free ends. Other cells surround and support the hair cells. Fibers of the cochlear division of the acoustic nerve end around the bases of the hair cells. The bipolar cell bodies giving origin to these fibers are located in the bony portion of the cochlea. Their central processes are directed toward the brain stem.

As shown in Fig. 111, the hair cells rest upon a membrane, the *basilar membrane.* This is composed of *auditory strings* that vary in length in different portions of the cochlea. Above the hair cells is a mass of gelatinous material, the *tectorial membrane,* into which the hairs project. Nearly all these structures can be related to the functions of the cochlea.

Cochlear Functions. Broadly speaking, nerve impulses are produced as follows: The vibrations of air strike the tympanic membrane and are transmitted by the ear ossicles to the cochlea, where pressure waves are set up in the fluid, causing the hair cells to move up or down, toward or away from the less movable tectorial membrane. This produces a deformation of the hair cells. In some manner this stimulates the nerve fibers ending around them. It is possible that the cells are like piezoelectric crystals which, upon being deformed, develop a voltage. If this were true of the hair cells, the voltage could act as a stimulus for the nerve fibers. Whatever the explanation, deformation of hair cells is accompanied by a rapidly developing potential change which can be recorded. This is the *microphonic potential*. The system is extraordinarily sensitive, more than could be expected of a passive system, and behaving much as if the cells were amplifiers.

There is also a resting potential in the cochlea, the organ of Corti being negative to the fluid in scala tympani and scala vestibuli. It is not known whether this potential, or the microphonic potential, or both, are directly involved in depolarizing cochlear nerve fibers.

Certain properties and qualities of sound must be mentioned before proceeding with the discussion of cochlear functions.

1. *Pitch.* This refers to the level in the musical scale in which a sound may be placed. It is mainly dependent upon the frequency of the sound waves, that is to say, the number of waves per second.

2. *Intensity.* In ordinary usage this is synonymous with loudness, but this is not strictly accurate. Intensity is a physical value which refers to the energy or power of the sound waves and is proportional to the amplitude of these waves. Loudness is a subjective sensation. That the two are not the same is shown by the fact that while tones of high pitch are inaudible to man, no matter what their intensity, they may be audible to other animals, such as the dog.

There is in common usage a unit for expressing differences in intensity of two sounds which is based on a logarithmic scale. If one sound has a power ten times greater than another, it is said to be 1 bel greater (log of $10 = 1$). But the bel (named after Alexander Graham Bell, the inventor of the telephone) is too large a unit, and one-tenth of this or 1 decibel (db) is used. Within the auditory range 1 decibel is a change just detectible subjectively. Bels and decibels used without a reference level are meaningless. To say that a sound wave is 1 decibel more than another means nothing, since both may still be inaudible. Accordingly, a standard reference may be used. This is 0.0002 dyne/cm.^{2}, and the threshold of hearing at 1000 cycles is of this order of power. From this point the audible range extends 120 decibels, that is, 12 bels or 10^{12} times. The upper limit represents the loudest sound tolerable to the human ear.

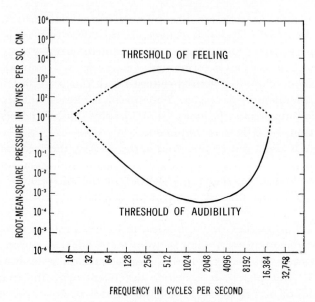

Figure 112. An audiogram of the human ear. The curves are plotted from data obtained from a large number of subjects. The audibility threshold curve represents the pressure variations necessary to produce sound of minimum audibility between 20 and 20,000 cycles per second. The feeling threshold curve represents pressure variations beyond which pain is felt. The broken lines indicate regions where data are inexact or lacking. Note that hearing is most sensitive in the region of 2048 cycles per second. (Slightly modified after Fletcher: Speech and Hearing. New York, D. Van Nostrand Co., Inc.)

3. *Timbre or Quality.* This is determined by the wave form, and is the property by which two sounds of the same pitch and intensity can be distinguished. It probably depends upon the overtones or harmonics of a particular sound.

Just how all these properties are detected is uncertain. The range of vibrations or frequencies audible to the human ear is from 16 to 20,000 per second, with considerable individual variation. Furthermore, there is a striking difference in sensitivity at different frequencies. When the relation between sensitivity and frequency is plotted, the resulting curve (audiogram) is that shown in Fig. 112. This shows that the human ear is most sensitive to vibrations in the neighborhood of 2048 cycles per second. At this frequency the cochlea is comparable in sensitivity to the retina. By this is meant that under optimum conditions one can detect sounds of such low intensities that the amplitude of vibration at threshold is no more than the longer wave lengths in the visible spectrum (see Intensity).

It was mentioned previously that the basilar membrane on which the hair cells rest is composed of auditory strings of varying lengths. The concept most widely held is the place theory. According to this theory, a pure tone will throw a stretch of the basilar membrane into vibration, with a maximum amplitude of vibration at some point. One version of this, the Helmholtz resonance theory, is that the auditory strings are of such lengths that for any audible frequency, there is a string or group of strings that will be thrown into vibration, that is, will resonate. Another theory holds that a pure tone produces a standing wave in the basilar membrane, the position of the wave changing according to the frequency of the tone. There is, however, considerable evidence that sound waves produce traveling waves along the membrane. These waves have a flat maximum that shifts in location along the membrane as

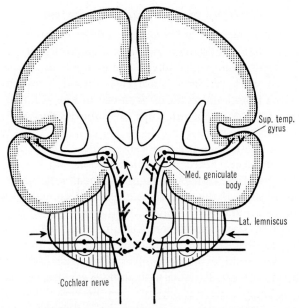

Figure 113.   Simplified version of the auditory pathways. The cochlear nerves carry impulses from the receptors, the primary neurons being bipolar cells. The brain stem path (lateral lemniscus) is probably a multineuron path, but the relays have been omitted. The branches indicated are those which form reflex connections. The medial geniculate body is a portion of the thalamus.

frequency changes. The theories are not radically different. Whatever the type of vibration, there is a maximum at some point, and
nerve fibers from this point will discharge at a higher rate than
other nerve fibers from the area of the wave vibration. The basilar
membrane in the apical part of the cochlea is wider than elsewhere,
and this region responds mainly to low tones.

Central Auditory Connections. When the central fibers of the
cochlear division of the eighth nerve reach the brain stem, they
end in masses of gray matter, the *cochlear nuclei*. These project to
cranial nerve nuclei that provide for reflexes in response to sound,
and also give axons that ascend in a myelinated tract on each side,
the *lateral lemniscus* (Fig. 113). There are several synaptic interruptions along this pathway, but eventually the fibers reach the
medial geniculate body of the thalamus and are then relayed to
the temporal lobe, specifically to that portion of the superior temporal gyrus forming Area 41 (Figs. 113 and 147, p. 323). This is the
primary receptive area for hearing.

Lesions of the Auditory System

If a cochlear duct or nerve on one side is destroyed, complete
deafness on that side results. But a unilateral lesion within the
central nervous system which affects one of the auditory paths does
not cause complete deafness, since each lateral lemniscus carries
fibers derived from both cochleae, as shown in Fig. 113. A unilateral
lesion, therefore, does not interrupt all impulses derived from the
cochlea of the same side.

Diseases of the middle ear may cause middle ear or transmission
deafness. Sounds are heard incompletely, if at all, because pathological changes of the ossicles or tympanic membrane interfere with
their transmission. If the vibrations are strong enough to set bone
in motion, or are started in bone, then they may reach the cochlea,
and perception is ultimately possible. This can be demonstrated
by placing the base of a vibrating tuning fork on the skull. The
vibrations are audible, but disappear when the fork is held in
the air beside the ear. Patients with middle ear deafness have difficulty in ordinary conversation, but may hear well over the telephone because the sounds are conducted through the bones of the
skull. Hearing aids are, therefore, useful in such cases, but not
when deafness is due to destruction of a cochlea or cochlear nerve
(nerve deafness).

Balance or Equilibrium

What is ordinarily called the sense of balance or equilibrium is functionally integrated with muscle-joint-tendon sense. An important component of the sense of balance arises from the stimulation of certain receptors in the labyrinth. One of the labyrinthine canals, the cochlea, was discussed in the preceding section of this chapter. The rest of the labyrinth consists of a small chamber, the *vestibule,* which communicates with three small canals known as *semicircular canals,* each of which is in the form of a half-circle (Fig. 114). There are two small membranous sacs in the vestibule, the *utricle* and *saccule.* In each of these is a specialized epithelial layer or *macula,* around the cells of which fibers of the vestibular portion of the acoustic nerve terminate. At one end of each semicircular canal there is also a specialized epithelial layer, a *crista,* around the cells of which other fibers of the vestibular nerve terminate. All these nerve fibers are peripheral processes of bipolar cells in the nearby vestibular ganglia. The central processes enter the brain stem near the junction of the pons and medulla oblongata.

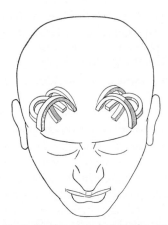

Figure 114. A drawing indicating the semicircular canals in relation to each other and to the rest of the head. Compare with Figure 110 (p. 208), in which they are shown with the rest of the ear. Note that the two lateral canals are in the same plane, and therefore form a functional unit. Likewise the anterior or superior canal of one side forms a functional unit with the posterior or inferior canal of the opposite side. The canals are much smaller than indicated here.

The Semicircular Canals

The semicircular canals are small membranous tubes filled with a slightly viscous fluid. The structure of each crista is similar to that of the organ of Corti. That is, there are hair cells held together or supported by sustentacular cells, while the processes of the hair cells are embedded in an overlying gelatinous substance. Vestibular nerve fibers terminate at the bases of the hair cells. Pressure changes in the fluid of the canals constitute effective stimuli. The mechanisms are probably similar to those of the hair cells of the cochlea.

Each of the three canals on either side of the head occupies a different plane in space (Fig. 114), so that when the head is moved or rotated in any direction, the cells in one or more cristae are stimulated because of pressure changes which come about in the following manner. When the head is turned, say to the right (clockwise), the fluid in the horizontal canals tends to remain stationary because of its inertia. The actual result is that a hydrostatic pressure develops. In clockwise rotation the pressure is exerted against the anterior end of the right horizontal canal, the end which contains the crista.

Similar phenomena are seen when a glass of water is rotated. At first the water remains stationary. Then, as inertia is overcome, the water rotates with the glass. Translated into familiar, everyday experience, similar phenomena are experienced when a car accelerates rapidly. Anyone in the seat tends to remain where he was, so to speak, and the result is the development of pressure against the car seat. But within a short time, particularly if the car reaches a uniform rate of speed, the sensation of pressure stops because inertia has been overcome and the car and person are in effect traveling at the same rate. If, now, the car slows or stops suddenly, anyone in the car tends to keep on going on the same direction, just as one tends to keep going in the same direction when the car goes around a curve. Likewise, when the rotation of the glass of water is suddenly stopped, the water keeps on rotating for a time.

In the case of the canals, continued clockwise rotation can be carried out if, instead of just turning the head, the whole body is rotated. This is most easily done by sitting in a special chair which can be turned (children commonly do this by sitting in a swing which is wound up and then allowed to unwind). When rotation reaches a uniform rate, there is no pressure in the canals. When rotation stops, the fluid tends to keep on going in the direction of rotation; as a result pressure develops against the crista in the anterior end of the left horizontal canal.

It is often necessary in experimental and clinical work to test a canal separately. This can be done by irrigating the external ear canals with hot or cold water. The temperature changes are sufficient to reach the internal ear and set up convection currents in the fluid in the semicircular canal. These currents create pressures, with an end result just as if the subject were being rotated. With hot water the currents tend to rise, and with cold water to fall. Consequently it is only necessary to have the subject so tilt his head that the canal under study is vertical in order to create pressure changes at whatever end of the canal the experimenter wishes.

The Utricle and Saccule

The maculae of the utricle and saccule resemble the cristae in structure. Each consists of sustentacular cells and hair cells. The hairs project into an overlying gelatinous mass which is peculiar in containing small masses of calcium carbonate called *otoliths*. Vestibular nerve fibers end around the bases of the hair cells, and the mechanism of stimulation is probably basically similar to that in the cochlea.

The functions of the saccules in man are not known with any certainty. The maculae of the utricles are sensitive to any position the head occupies in space, whether it is moving or not. It is maximally sensitive (or stimulated) in the upside-down position, as standing on one's head. Apparently, pulling or tension on hairs is most effective, since in this position the gelatinous mass is below the cells. The otoliths probably increase effectiveness of gravity.

Central Vestibular Connections

Impulses over nerve fibers from the maculae and cristae travel centrally to the brain stem and cerebellum. In the brain stem they end in masses of gray matter, the vestibular nuclei, which are specialized portions of the reticular formation. These relay impulses to the spinal cord by way of vestibulospinal tracts and medial longitudinal fasciculi (Fig. 115). They also relay impulses to various nuclei of cranial nerves, particularly those supplying extrinsic eye muscles, by way of the medial longitudinal fasciculi and also diffuse

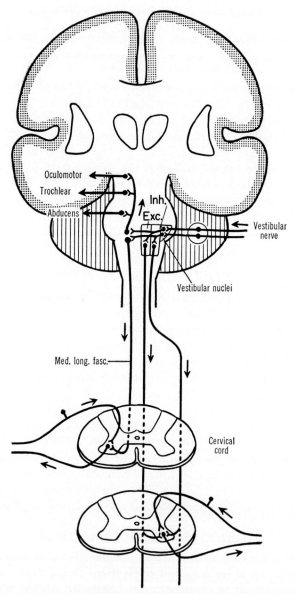

Figure 115. Simplified version of vestibular pathways. The primary neurons are bipolar cells. Direct connections with the cerebellum have been omitted. The vestibular nuclei are represented as projecting to excitatory and inhibitory mechanisms of the brain stem and to various motor nuclei by way of the medial longitudinal fasciculus (both fasciculi are actually used). The vestibulospinal tract (from lateral vestibular nucleus) was omitted because it follows much the same course as does the tract from the excitatory center. The ascending path to cerebral cortex has also been omitted. It is probably similar to that for auditory fibers.

projections through reticular formation. Connections are also made with visceral centers of the brain stem. Impulses are known to reach the cerebral cortex, but the central pathways are not known with any certainty. There is some evidence that they are topographically the same as the auditory paths and that the primary receptive area is probably the superior temporal gyrus, either in or near Area 41.

Functions of the Vestibular System

This system is important in the control of muscular activity, for reasons mentioned in Chap. 10 and discussed in more detail in Chap. 15. In spite of the importance of this system in balance or equilibrium and position sense, reflex functions often overshadow sensory functions. The cristae in semicircular canals are stimulated mainly by changes in rate of movement, during acceleration or deceleration and especially in rotational movement. The canals thus function in kinetic or phasic activity. The maculae utriculi are stimulated mainly when the head is being held in one position, during movement uniform in rate and during linear acceleration or deceleration. Macular functions are, therefore, mainly static in nature. These distinctions are extremely general. There is actually considerable overlap in functions. The central connections and nuclei of the vestibular system are an important part of the extrapyramidal motor system.

Lesions of the Vestibular System

Rapid or prolonged rotation or other type of movement may produce severe side effects, such as vertigo, nausea and vomiting. These symptoms are the familiar ones of seasickness. Some persons are so sensitive that these symptoms may follow relatively mild rotations.

Although a number of disorders affect the vestibular system, the symptoms may be difficult to interpret. For example, an inflammatory process in the vestibular system of one side may produce symptoms such as dizziness or nausea because it irritates or stimulates on that side. But a lesion which destroys the opposite side, by leaving an unopposed or unbalanced normal side, may produce apparently identical symptoms. Consequently, it is necessary to have confirmatory signs referable to other nerves. For example, a destructive lesion of the right vestibular nerve will almost surely destroy the right cochlear nerve. The patient will have, therefore, complete nerve deafness on that side, a symptom which in itself so localizes the lesion that there may be little point in analyzing the vestibular symptoms in detail.

Taste

The peripheral receptors for this special sense are located in the mucous membrane of the tongue, pharynx and larynx. Taste, as ordinarily perceived, is a complex sensation, compounded of both taste and smell. The interference with taste during a cold is really the result of a temporary loss of smell. The receptors for taste are found in *taste buds*. These are small cellular areas located in the mucous membrane. They contain specialized cells which are closely related to nerve fibers (Fig. 116). Food substances dissolved in saliva are able in some way to stimulate these cells, and this in turn initiates impulses in the adjacent nerve fibers. Single receptors may be sensitive to one of a number of primary qualities, such as sweet, salt, bitter, and sour, and perhaps others as well. These are usually compounded to give rise to more complex sensations of taste.

Nerve impulses are transmitted centrally over the facial nerves from the anterior two-thirds of the tongue, by way of the glosso-pharyngeal nerves from the posterior third of the tongue and part of the pharynx and over the vagus nerves from the pharynx and larynx. The primary neurons are unipolar cells located in ganglia

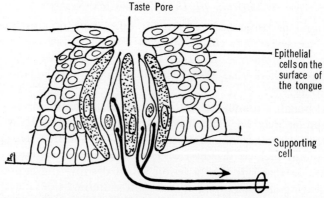

Taste Pore

Epithelial cells on the surface of the tongue

Supporting cell

Figure 116. Schematic representation of taste-sensitive cells in mucous membrane of the tongue. These and the supporting cells comprise a taste bud. Nerve fibers ending around the receptive cells are peripheral processes of unipolar neurons.

along the course of these nerves. The central processes of these cells enter the medulla oblongata. Some secondary fibers establish reflex connections, and others ascend in the opposite medial lemnisci to the thalami and thence to the postcentral gyri, the primary receptive areas.

Smell

The olfactory receptors are located in the upper part of the nasal mucous membrane on each side of the nasal cavity. This membrane consists of bipolar nerve cells surrounded and supported by nonnervous cells (Fig. 117). The surface of the membrane is covered with a watery fluid. Small particles of gases go into solution in this fluid and are then able, by a means as yet unknown, to stimulate the bipolar cells. This is an exceedingly sensitive mechanism by which incredibly small amounts of gaseous substances can be detected. The fact that wood has an odor, for instance, means that oils in the wood are given off in the air and reach the olfactory membrane. The olfactory sense is much more sensitive than that of taste and distinguishes a greater variety of modalities.

The central processes of the bipolar cells form the filaments of the olfactory nerves. These ascend through tiny openings in the base of the skull (Fig. 118) and end in masses of gray matter, the olfactory bulbs. Axons from cells in the bulbs travel posteriorly as the olfactory tracts to the rhinencephalic area (p. 29). The subsequent pathways are so complex and widespread and yet so uncertain as regards function that they will not be discussed here. Even the location of the primary receptive area is not definitely

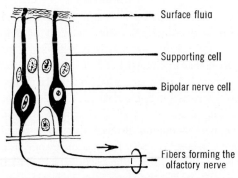

Figure 117. Drawing of olfactory epithelium. The nerve fibers project to the olfactory bulb. See Fig. 118.

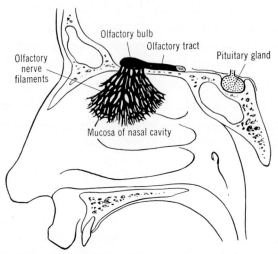

Figure 118. Drawing of olfactory structures in the nasal cavity (a sagittal section, exposing the interior of the nose). Numbers of axons interlace as they ascend through the floor of the skull. The olfactory tract is cut anterior to its termination (see Figure 8, p. 15).

known. Olfaction is nevertheless an important and sensitive quality. The reflexes which it may initiate are often rapid and forceful, as, for example, violent nausea from a putrid odor. Yet because of many factors in civilized life, such as smoking, contamination of city air, and the like, interferences with and even losses of smell are so common that unless such a loss is restricted to one side of the nose, it cannot be regarded as a definitely important clinical sign.

Summary

The special senses include vision, hearing, balance, taste and smell. Vision is the cortical interpretation of impulses which are the result of excitation of specialized receptors, the rods and cones in the retinal layers of the eyes. These cells are connected to bipolar cells, and these in turn to ganglion cells. The axons of these ganglion cells form the optic nerves. The optic nerves intermingle at the chiasma in such a way that impulses resulting from light entering the eye from one side of the body finally reach the opposite primary area (Area 17), located on either side of the calcarine fissure of the occipital lobe. The retina itself probably has a double function related to its structure, the rods serving for visual sensitivity, the cones for visual acuity and color vision. In normal binocular vision all image points fall upon corresponding retinal points.

Hearing is the cortical interpretation of impulses resulting from sound waves striking specialized cells in the cochlea of the inner ear. These cells are sensitive to vibrations ranging from 16 to 20,000 cycles per second, and presumably the auditory strings of the cochlea are sensitive to different pitches according to their lengths. The nerve impulses are transmitted centrally over the cochlear nerves and eventually reach both primary areas, numbered 41, in the superior temporal gyri of the temporal lobes.

Impulses resulting from stimulation of the maculae utriculi and the cristae of the semicircular canals eventually reach the temporal lobes, as well as reflex pathways in the brain stem. The superior temporal gyri are probably the primary receptive areas.

Solutions of food substances stimulate receptors in taste buds of the tongue, pharynx and larynx. The nerve impulses are transmitted centrally over the facial, glossopharyngeal and vagus nerves to the brain stem. From here they eventually reach the primary receptive areas, the postcentral gyri, by way of the medial lemnisci, thalami and internal capsules.

Smell depends upon the stimulation of bipolar cells in the olfactory mucous membrane by substances dissolved in the overlying watery fluid. The central processes of these bipolar cells form the olfactory nerves, which end in the olfactory bulbs. From here the impulses follow a complex path to a primary receptive area whose location is still uncertain.

Names in Neurology

Helmholtz, Herman von (1821–1894)

Helmholtz was a German physician, physiologist and physicist and one of the giants in scientific attainment. He was a man of widespread interests who, at various times, occupied chairs of physiology, anatomy, pathology and physics. He applied the law of conservation of energy to all living material. He showed that muscles were the main source of animal heat. During the years 1850–1852, he measured the velocity of the nerve impulse. In 1851 he invented the ophthalmoscope and, with the aid of other instruments of his own devising, measured ocular constants and explained the mechanism of accommodation. During the years 1856–1867, he wrote his *Handbook of Physiological Optics,* which is a permanent scientific classic. Incredibly, in spite of all this work, he found time to publish on acoustic mechanisms, including the functions of the tympanic membrane and the ear ossicles. From him we have our most widely accepted theory of cochlear functions. From 1887 on he made outstanding contributions in the fields of dynamics, hydrodynamics, thermodynamics and electrodynamics. It is difficult to see how one man could have done so much work fundamental to present day knowledge.

Young, Thomas (1773–1829)

Young, a Quaker physician in England, was one of the great men of science. He was called the father of physiological optics. He studied accommodation, gave the first description of astigmatism, and stated that color vision was possible because of retinal structures sensitive to red, green and violet. He studied blood flow and stated the laws governing it. He announced the wave theory of light. He introduced concepts of energy and work done and defined the modulus of elasticity, "Young's modulus." He was interested and accomplished in many other activities, including Egyptology. Altogether, he ranks with Helmholtz as a scientific great.

References

Again, for further details, the student should turn to the textbooks of physiology, anatomy, and neuroanatomy. The following are recommended as even more advanced references:

Polyak, S. L.: The Retina. Chicago, University of Chicago Press, 1941. This is an outstanding volume on the structure and neurological connections of the human retina. It contains a section on operative and microscopic techniques, and considerable space is devoted to the history of visual investigation.

Stevens, S. S., and Davis, H.: Hearing. New York, John Wiley & Sons, Inc., 1938. This is a well-written discussion of the psychophysiology of hearing.

Walls, G. L.: The Vertebrate Eye. Bloomfield Hills, Mich., Cranbrook Institute of Science, 1942. This is another outstanding work dealing with the comparative anatomy and functions of the eye. In both this and Polyak's volume the illustrations are superb.

The following are papers, reviews, and monographs on specific subjects.

Békésy, G. v.: Current status of theories of hearing. Science, 123:779–783, 1956.

Crescitelli, F., and Dartnall, H. J. A.: Human visual purple. Nature, 172:195–200, 1953.

Davis, H.: Biophysics and physiology of the inner ear. Physiol. Rev., 37:1–49, 1957. Especially valuable for the bibliography.

Granit, R.: Sensory Mechanisms of the Retina. London, Geoffrey Cumberledge, Oxford University Press, 1947. As is true of his book on receptors (cited on p. 150), this is difficult reading but nevertheless valuable.

Hartridge, H.: Recent Advances in the Physiology of Vision. Philadelphia, The Blakiston Company, 1950.

CHAPTER 13

Control of Visceral Activity

THE FUNCTIONS of the various viscera are as necessary to body economy as those activities about which a person is more or less aware. But these visceral functions are either carried out without conscious recognition or are perceived in an ill-defined manner. An excellent illustration of a complex pattern of visceral activity is afforded by the process of regulation of body temperature.

Cold-blooded vertebrates, such as fishes, amphibians, and reptiles, have body temperatures which vary with the ambient temperature, but warm-blooded animals, such as birds and mammals, keep their body temperatures constant within certain limits and are to a large extent independent of their thermal environment. Heat production and heat loss are relatively balanced. The heat produced during metabolic activities is lost through radiation from the blood vessels which lie near the surface of the body. If these vessels dilate, that is to say, increase in diameter, a greater volume of blood flows through them per unit time, and more heat is then lost by radiation. A certain amount of heat is also lost with the evaporation of sweat and through the air and water vapor expired from the lungs. The nervous system can regulate the caliber of the cutaneous arterioles, capillaries and venules, thus controlling the volume of blood flowing through them and, thereby, the amount of heat loss.

This nervous control may be initiated in a number of ways. For example, skin exposed to the cold air becomes blanched or pale. This results from a reflex narrowing or constriction of the cutaneous vessels. The cold air stimulates receptors sensitive to a temperature lower than that of the skin surface; the central path is through

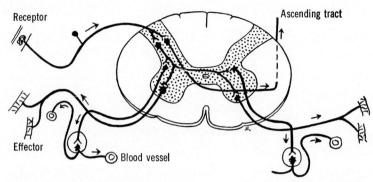

Figure 119. Diagram illustrating how exteroceptive impulses can cause both somatic and visceral responses. Impulses from a receptor (in this case a temperature receptor) reach motor neurons supplying skeletal muscles and also neurons in the intermediate gray. By way of the latter connections the impulses reach smooth muscle in blood vessels of the body cavity and peripheral regions. The impulses may also traverse an ascending tract and reach the cerebral hemisphere.

the spinal cord and the efferent through the sympathetic system (Fig. 119). The reflex reduction in heat radiation enables the internal temperature to be maintained even though the skin may be cold, both subjectively and objectively.

There are many physiological processes of which we are usually unaware. The contraction of the heart and other vascular functions, digestive processes and glandular secretion are but a few of these. Many visceral functions together with certain somatic mechanisms maintain the internal environment of the body in the face of factors which tend to change it. This maintenance is a general process known as *homeostasis.*

The term "viscera" is a general one. In the past it has referred to structures supposedly not under voluntary control, in contrast to structures such as skeletal muscle. For example, older terminology lists smooth muscle as involuntary muscle and striated skeletal muscle as voluntary muscle. The distinction is, however, more apparent than real. Many skeletal muscles, such as the diaphragm, are not subject to complete voluntary control. Organs containing smooth muscle are often as much under voluntary direction or control as many so-called voluntary muscles. "Visceral" also has embryological significance from the standpoint of development of cranial nerves, many of which supply viscera. Yet some of these nerves supply striated muscles that are closely associated with or a part of some of these viscera.

There has evolved a concept of the term "viscera" as referring to those organs which contain cardiac muscle or smooth muscle or glands and which receive their motor supply from the nervous system according to a specific type of distribution. This motor supply forms what is ordinarily called the *autonomic* or *visceral nervous system*. This classification, however, has led to confusion, since it no more tells the whole story than the term "motor fiber" or "final common path" tells the whole story about control of skeletal activity. Afferent fibers, for example, are just as important as efferent fibers, as in the situation cited previously in which blood vessels reflexly changed in diameter subsequent to stimulation of temperature receptors.

General Plan of Organization

In order to simplify the method of presentation, the portions of the nervous system concerned with visceral activities will be considered as if they were a series of levels. These are cerebral cortex, hypothalamus, brain stem, spinal cord and ganglionic. Each differs in function in that the higher the level, the more general, widespread and nonspecific the function; the lower the level, the more restricted and specific the function. For example, one of the functions of the hypothalamus is the maintenance of body temperature. This obviously involves many structures and organs throughout the body and is a general function. A single sympathetic ganglion, on the other hand, such as the third thoracic, is concerned only with specific structures in specific regions—in this instance, blood vessels, sweat glands and smooth muscle in part of the upper extremity. This ganglion, along with many others, may be activated by the hypothalamus during the process of temperature control or during other visceral activities.

Levels of Organization

Cerebral Cortex. Little is known of the specific regions of cerebral cortex concerned in visceral mechanisms, except that portions of the frontal lobes, especially basal and medial parts, send fibers to the hypothalamus and brain stem.

Hypothalamus. The hypothalamus is a portion of the diencephalon. Its location and relation to other nervous structures may be determined by reference to Chap. 2 and Figs. 13 and 14 (pp. 20 and 21). Study of microscopic sections reveals rather dense

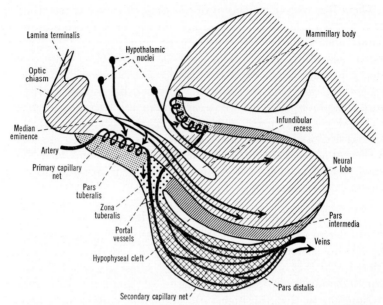

Figure 120. Drawing of a generalized mammalian pituitary gland to illustrate certain basic features. The *adenohypophysis* is that part derived embryologically from oral epithelium and includes the *pars tuberalis,* which lies in contact with the median eminence; the *pars intermedia,* in contact with the neural lobe; and the *pars distalis,* the remainder of the adenohypophysis. The *zona tuberalis* is a specialized portion of the pars distalis which contains the portal vessels. The *neurohypophysis* is derived embryologically from the diencephalon and includes the *median eminence,* which receives its blood supply from the hypophysioportal circulation or which has a common vascularization with the adenohypophysis; and the *neural lobe,* which has an independent blood supply. Some vessels may reach the adenohypophysis directly, but they have not been indicated in this drawing. The projections from hypothalamic nuclei represent nerve fibers which descend to the neural lobe, giving branches to the portal vessels as they descend. (These definitions are according to J. D. Green: Comparative Anatomy of the Hypophysis, with Special Reference to Its Blood Supply and Innervation. Am. J. Anat., Vol. 88.)

collections of nerve cells and fibers. The fibers are for the most part nonmyelinated, so that with Weigert stains the hypothalamus appears as an area of gray matter. Various investigators have succeeded in defining the cells of the hypothalamus into nuclear groups, but as yet the functions of these nuclei have not been elucidated except in the most general way.

The hypothalamus is further characterized by a rich blood supply and by a specific relationship with the pituitary gland or hypophysis. This endocrine gland has a double embryological origin, partly from the pharyngeal region and partly from the diencephalon. The various divisions of the hypophysis are illustrated in Fig. 120. In addition to nervous connections, there are vascular relationships between the hypothalamus and the pituitary. The blood supply of the pars distalis is derived in part from vessels reaching it directly, but mainly from vessels which have already broken up into a capillary network elsewhere. Specifically, blood vessels enter the median eminence and form what is termed the *primary capillary net*. These capillaries then collect into a number of vessels, the portal vessels, which enter the substance of the pars distalis and break up into a network of sinusoids, the *second capillary net*. These then drain into nearby veins. The pituitary has therefore a true portal circulation (Fig. 120). The significance of this system is that most of the blood destined for the pars distalis first passes through the median eminence. The neurohypophysis is independently vascularized.

The hypothalamus receives fibers from many afferent paths. For example, many fibers in the olfactory tracts are destined for the hypothalamus. Afferent fibers relaying in the thalamus also send branches to it. In addition, there are fibers from the cerebral cortex, particularly the frontal lobes. All the afferent connections are complex, and little is known of their ultimate connections and effects except that they synapse with most, if not all, of the hypothalamic nuclei. Efferent fibers from the hypothalamus are widely distributed. Many descend in the neural stalk to the posterior part of the pituitary gland and in addition appear to supply the vessels of the median eminence. It is doubtful that any significant number reach the cells of the anterior part. The majority of fibers from the hypothalamus project posteriorly and caudally to the brain stem, some as far as the medulla oblongata, and connect with the motor and visceral areas throughout the brain stem.

Brain Stem. The brain stem contains regions or centers that are found in the reticular formation and are not well defined anatomically. They are composed of cells scattered diffusely throughout areas the limits of which can be determined only by physiological methods.

These visceral centers receive fibers from the cerebral cortex and hypothalamus and collaterals from ascending sensory systems and reflex paths. In turn they project to the nuclei of certain cranial nerves and also to neurons of the spinal cord, particularly those in the thoracic region, the first three segments of the lumbar cord, and the second and third sacral levels. The descending axons are scattered throughout the lateral and ventral funiculi.

Brain Stem and Spinal Cord. Within the brain stem itself, and also in the spinal cord, there are still lower levels of organization. These are groups of cells associated with cranial and spinal nerves. The axons of these cells are known as *preganglionic fibers* because they leave the central nervous system by way of a cranial nerve or ventral root and synapse with cells in peripheral ganglia. The cells in the brain stem are associated with the oculomotor, facial, glossopharyngeal, vagus and accessory nerves. Those in the spinal cord form a long column in the intermediolateral part of the gray matter of the thoracic cord, upper lumbar cord and middle sacral cord.

All these groups of cells receive descending fibers from the brain stem, and collaterals from sensory and reflex paths.

Ganglia. This level is formed by the various autonomic ganglia, such as those in the paravertebral sympathetic trunk. The ganglia are composed of cells which receive preganglionic fibers from the brain stem and spinal cord. The axons of the ganglion cells are called *postganglionic fibers*. They project to various viscera in specific parts of the body and form effector junctions with cardiac muscle, smooth muscle or gland cells.

Levels of Outflow and Anatomical Organization

The foregoing account illustrates how impulses from higher centers such as the hypothalamus may reach a viscus by traversing various structural levels. The levels from which axons leave the central nervous system and are distributed form the bases for present day terminology and the classification or separation into *sympathetic* and *parasympathetic* systems. These two systems comprise the autonomic nervous system. It is obvious, therefore, that the latter term (or any available term) is inadequate, since it does not take into account higher levels of organization or afferent fibers from viscera.

Sympathetic System (Orthosympathetic, Thoracolumbar). Those cells in the thoracic and upper lumbar spinal cord send their axons over ventral roots to the ganglia of the paravertebral sympathetic trunks or else through these ganglia to other cells in more peripherally located ganglia, such as the celiac (Fig. 121). Each preganglionic fiber is myelinated and synapses with a number of ganglion

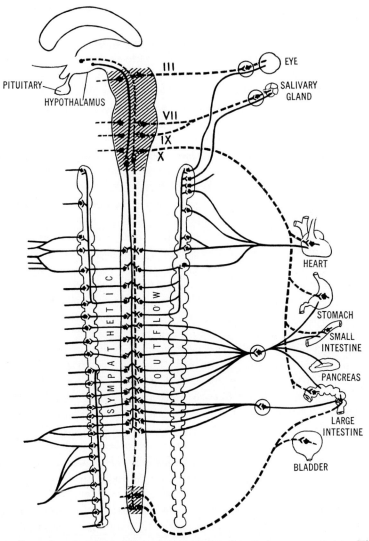

Figure 121. The general arrangement of the autonomic nervous system. The projections from the hypothalamus to the pituitary gland have been omitted, while those to lower centers are shown in solid lines (sympathetic) and broken lines (parasympathetic). The portions of the brain stem and sacral cord from which the parasympathetic preganglionic fibers leave are indicated by oblique lines, while the sympathetic outflow from the thoracic and upper lumbar cord is labeled. Autonomic fibers to organs of the head and trunk are shown on the right side, while those on the left side represent the sympathetic outflow to blood vessels, sweat glands, and smooth muscle fibers attached to hairs.

cells. The preganglionic fibers reach the ganglia by leaving the spinal nerve as rami communicantes. The postganglionic fibers, that is, the axons of the ganglion cells, are nonmyelinated and are distributed in several different ways. Some return to spinal nerves (as rami communicantes) and thus reach blood vessels and sweat glands and smooth muscle fibers in skin. Others go directly to blood vessels and organs in the head, neck, thorax, abdomen and pelvis. All those from the celiac ganglia are distributed to the abdominal and pelvic viscera.

Parasympathetic System (Craniosacral). This system comprises those fibers which leave by way of the cranial nerves mentioned earlier and also by way of the second and third sacral ventral roots (Fig. 121). The preganglionic fibers are myelinated. Unlike the sympathetic system, the peripheral ganglia are not found in well-defined trunks, but instead the various cells form small ganglia or scattered groups in or near the organs to be innervated. The nonmyelinated postganglionic fibers are thus short. Furthermore, each preganglionic fiber synapses with relatively few cells or just one cell, and the postganglionic fibers supply fewer structures than do postganglionic sympathetic fibers.

Those parasympathetic cells in the oculomotor nucleus send axons to a small ganglion in each orbit. The postganglionic fibers supply smooth muscle in the eye. The parasympathetic fibers in the facial nerve synapse in several peripherally located ganglia, and the postganglionic fibers supply the lacrimal gland, some of the salivary glands, and glands in the mucous membrane of the nasal cavity, oral cavity, and pharynx. The axons leaving by way of the glossopharyngeal nerve undergo peripheral synapses and are distributed to a salivary gland. Axons leaving by way of the vagus and accessory nerves are distributed to the heart, lungs, esophagus, stomach, pancreas, liver, small intestine and part of the large intestine. The terminal ganglia are located in the walls of these organs.

With regard to the sacral portion, the axons arise from cells in the second and third sacral segments and leave by way of the ventral roots of these segments. They are distributed to those viscera not supplied by the vagus, that is, part of the large intestine, and to the pelvic viscera, such as the bladder, rectum and genital organs. The terminal ganglia are in the walls of these organs.

Aside from certain blood vessels in the thorax, abdomen, pelvic and external genitalia, there are no parasympathetic fibers to blood vessels or to sweat glands or smooth muscle of skin.

Physiological Organization

In certain respects the anatomical classification is unsatisfactory. It implies a rigid or sharp distinction between the subdivisions that functionally may not exist. Also, some organs are supplied by sympathetic fibers that functionally appear to be parasympathetic. It is more satisfactory if the anatomical classification is supplemented by a physiological one (Fig. 122) based on distinctions between cholinergic and adrenergic fibers, and by a pharmacological one based on reactions to certain drugs. These distinctions were first mentioned in Chap. 9, in which the terminations of nerve fibers in smooth muscle, cardiac muscle and glands were described. Cholinergic fibers are postganglionic fibers at the terminals of which acetylcholine is released. These are parasympathetic fibers and those sympathetic fibers which supply sweat glands and smooth muscle of skin. Acetylcholine is also released at all preganglionic terminals, whether sympathetic or parasympathetic, at motor end plates and perhaps at all synaptic junctions, but it is the substance released at postganglionic terminals on which classifications are based. Adrenergic fibers are postganglionic sympathetic fibers at the terminals of which noradrenaline is released.

Mediation of Visceral Impulses. The following is a more detailed account of the events involved in transmission in autonomic fibers. For both types of fibers the following basic processes are involved.

Impulses traveling over preganglionic fibers arrive at ganglion cells and initiate the formation or release of acetylcholine. As has been mentioned, this is true for both sympathetic and parasympathetic ganglia. In studying the events involved in transmission, pharmacological methods have been of great value, particularly the use of various drugs. For example, the drug *nicotine,* when applied to ganglia in low concentrations, stimulates the cells, whereas in high concentrations it depresses and blocks synaptic transmission. Acetylcholine has a similar effect on ganglion cells, and this is called its *nicotinic effect.* Under physiological conditions, the concentration of acetylcholine is ordinarily low and therefore excitatory. Its release, therefore, initiates impulses in

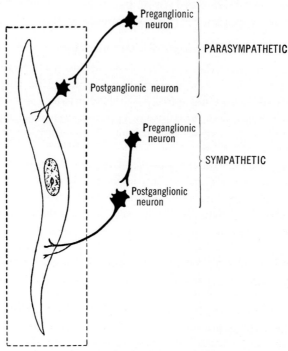

Figure 122. Diagram of the differences in sympathetic and parasympathetic distribution. The dotted line represents an organ containing effectors such as a smooth muscle cell. As indicated for this organ, nearly all parasympathetic postganglionic neurons lie within the organ they supply. The postganglionic axons travel at the most a few millimeters. Sympathetic synapses, however, occur in paravertebral ganglia, and the postganglionic axons travel considerable distances.

ganglion cells and postganglionic fibers. Acetylcholine is likewise released at motor endings in skeletal muscle. This region is comparable to a synapse, and the action of acetylcholine here is also a nicotinic one.

Postganglionic impulses arrive at effector junctions and in some way initiate the release of the chemical mediator, acetylcholine for cholinergic fibers and noradrenaline for adrenergic fibers. The origin of the mediators is unknown. It is possible that they are formed in non-nervous tissue and are released in some way by nerve impulses, after which they combine with some part of the effector organ which is then activated, or that they are formed directly in nerve terminals.

In pharmacological studies a number of drugs can be classified according to their actions on the autonomic nervous system. For example, a parasympathetic drug is one which, when administered, acts in a manner similar to the parasympathetic system. One such drug is *muscarine*. The action of acetylcholine at postganglionic terminals is called its *muscarine* action. It is blocked by another drug, atropine, which, however, has no effect on the nicotinic action of acetylcholine. As mentioned in Chap. 9, acetylcholine is rapidly hydrolyzed by *cholinesterase,* an enzyme normally present in tissues, and this in turn may be blocked by *eserine.* Several compounds act in a manner similar to the sympathetic system, and are classified as sympathetic drugs. Likewise, there are drugs such as *ergotoxin* and *ergotamine* which can block the action of epinephrine or sympathin.

That chemical mediators actually exist has been shown by a variety of experiments. If the sympathetic fibers to a frog heart are stimulated, and the blood leaving that heart is perfused through the heart of another frog, then the second heart responds as does the first in that its rate of contraction increases. The only explanation is that the stimulation resulted in the formation of some substance which entered the blood and was thus able to reach the second heart. Likewise, if the vagus (parasympathetic) nerves are stimulated and a similar experiment is carried out, the second heart responds as does the first in that its rate of contraction decreases.

Neither of the mediators is specific in its effects on the different effectors. In the intestine, for instance, acetylcholine ordinarily stimulates contraction of those smooth muscle coats which push forward the intestinal contents, but it usually inhibits the smooth muscle of the various intestinal sphincters, thereby allowing the material to pass through. Acetylcholine inhibits cardiac muscle, whereas noradrenaline has the opposite effect. The effects of either of these substances may, therefore, be inhibitory or excitatory, depending on the specific structure involved. Table 2 lists the effects of these two mediators on different viscera.

Most organs are supplied by both systems. When this is so, the systems tend to have opposite effects on the effectors, as in the case of the heart. Nearly all the peripheral blood vessels, however, are supplied by the sympathetic system alone. Yet opposite effects are possible, as constriction or dilatation. Either some of the fibers supplying these vessels are cholinergic and others are adrenergic; or the adrenergic fibers are able to mediate excitation or inhibition

Table 2.   Functions of the Autonomic Nervous System

Organ	Parasympathetic	Sympathetic
Eye..................	Stimulates constrictor muscle of iris	Stimulates dilator muscle of iris
Lacrimal, nasal, palatine, and salivary glands....	Stimulates secretory cells and vasodilatation	Mediates constriction of vessel supplying glands
Heart.................	Inhibits cardiac muscle	Stimulates cardiac muscle
Lungs................	Stimulates smooth muscle constricting bronchioles	Inhibits smooth muscle of bronchioles
Esophagus and gastro-intestinal tract.......	Stimulates smooth muscle of walls and inhibits that of sphincters	Inhibits smooth muscle of walls and stimulates sphincters
Glands associated with gastro-intestinal tract..	Stimulates secretory cells	Inhibits secretory cells
Adrenal medullae......		Stimulates secretory cells
Urinary bladder........	Stimulates smooth muscle of bladder wall	
Genitalia..............	Stimulates smooth muscle and glands; mediates vasodilatation	Mediates vasoconstriction
Peripheral blood vessels..		Mediates constriction and dilatation
Sweat glands and smooth muscle of skin........		Stimulates secretory cells and smooth muscle (cholinergic)

of the smooth muscle in the vessels, depending upon the concentration of the mediator.

Functions of the Various Levels

Cerebral Cortex.   Little is known of the functions of the cerebral cortex with regard to visceral activities. Electrical stimulation of various parts of the frontal lobes, especially the basal and medial surfaces, may have profound effects upon visceral activity. These are not specific effects, however, because stimulation of a certain area may give different results, depending on the frequency of stimulation. Extensive cortical destruction in the frontal lobes of human patients may be accompanied by severe visceral disorders such as incontinence.

The cerebral cortex is probably involved in visceral responses to emotional situations, particularly when they are in the form of conditioned responses. There is no visceral activity that cannot be modified, or even completely disorganized, by emotional upsets.

Blushing, for instance, is a sudden dilatation of facial blood vessels in response to an emotional situation or to the memory of one. Fright, anger, fear or apprehension may completely upset digestive processes and, at the same time, cause blood pressure to rise and heart rate to increase. Students are well acquainted with such phenomena before examinations; speakers may encounter them in the form of stage fright.

Hypothalamus. The hypothalamus is concerned in many physiological activities. Its exact role is by no means known with certainty, but it appears to effect a general regulation of water balance, body temperature, and the development of secondary sex characteristics, to mention but a few. The functions necessitating parasympathetic activity appear to be mediated by the anterior portion of the hypothalamus, and sympathetic activity by the posterior hypothalamus.

Many hypothalamic functions are ultimately mediated by way of the hypophysis. For example, the elimination of water by the kidneys appears to be directly regulated by a hormone of the posterior lobe of the pituitary gland. The liberation of this hormone is in turn controlled by the hypothalamus, undoubtedly by means of nervous connections which descend in the pituitary stalk. There is evidence that a precursor of the hormone is formed in hypothalamic nuclei, travels down nerve fibers and is released in the neural lobe, to reach the blood stream. Severance of this stalk, or destruction of the nuclei of origin of the fibers within the hypothalamus, leads to a deficiency in the hormone. The result is a disorder known as *diabetes insipidus*. The kidneys excrete tremendous quantities of fluid, as much as several liters a day; consequently, correspondingly large amounts of water must be drunk. The functions of the pars distalis also appear to be under the control of the hypothalamus. These include many endocrine and metabolic activities.

The question arises as to how such control is mediated. It does not seem to be nervous, since few if any nerve fibers can be traced to glandular cells of the pars distalis. The portal circulation is probably concerned. It has been suggested, and there is good supporting evidence, that nerve fibers from the hypothalamus act upon vessels of the capillary net in the median eminence in such a way as to cause the formation and release of some chemical mediator. This travels by way of the blood stream to the pars distalis and there activates the glandular cells. It is still uncertain just what this substance is. It is also possible that chemical mediators may be released elsewhere in the body and reach the pituitary through the general circulation.

Other functions are mediated by connections to lower centers, such as the brain stem. In the regulation of body temperature, for example, changes in external temperature stimulate skin receptors, and central connections allow impulses to reach the hypothalamus. In addition, certain cells in the hypothalamus are themselves directly sensitive to changes in temperature of the blood flowing through the area in which they are situated. If the external temperature drops, the posterior hypothalamus initiates the sympathetic activities necessary to prevent heat loss and, under more extreme conditions, initiates the metabolic processes which increase the production of heat. Included with the latter would be contractions of skeletal muscle evidenced as shivering. If the external temperature rises, the anterior hypothalamus initiates the parasympathetic activities necessary to increase the loss of heat. Under normal conditions, these various mechanisms maintain body temperature within a degree or so of 98.6° F.

There are many circumstances in which this hypothalamic balance is altered. For instance, a common sign of a bacterial infection is a fever. Bacterial toxins alter the sensitivity of the hypothalamic cells so that the balance point at which they operate is raised or set, as it were, at a higher level, like a thermostat. For the body temperature to conform to this new level, the processes of heat retention are started. Cutaneous vessels constrict, thus reducing the loss of heat by radiation. This is accompanied by a subjective sensation of cold. Shivering appears, thus increasing heat production. The chills which frequently signify the onset of a fever are shivering plus the sensation of cold. Body temperature rises because more heat is produced than can be lost. When the temperature reaches the new operating level of the hypothalamus, a compensatory process occurs. This is an increase in the loss of heat resulting from a dilatation of cutaneous vessels evidenced by the flushing of the skin. The loss is not great enough, however, to cause the temperature to drop to normal. That these phenomena are the result of an altered hypothalamic sensitivity is shown by the fact that surgical operations in or near the hypothalamus may be followed by marked changes in body temperature. The trauma incident to the operation probably interferes with the control of either heat loss or heat production. Postoperative rises or falls of temperature may be so extreme that the patient may die.

Other hypothalamic functions may be affected by lesions in this area. Marked adiposity, abnormalities of secondary sex characteristics, and states of marked sleepiness are a few of the conditions which may follow hypothalamic lesions, and these are probably a reflection of injury to areas which control the pars distalis of the pituitary.

Brain Stem. The specific functions with which the brain stem is concerned are numerous. In the pons and medulla oblongata, for instance, are *respiratory, vasomotor* and *cardiac centers.* Still others are concerned with intestinal movements, salivation and many other visceral functions. These centers are functionally restricted in the sense that the respiratory centers do not control the vasomotor centers, although they may affect them. But the hypothalamus, projecting to both, may control or activate them simultaneously, as when respiration and blood pressure increase during emotional states. These centers also function on a reflex level, as in the control of blood pressure. They are, furthermore, frequently integrated with somatic activities. Respiration, for instance, involves skeletal muscles. Because of the multiplicity of their functions, some of these centers will be discussed in more detail in Chap. 15.

An idea of how brain stem levels function may be gained by studying decerebrate animals, that is, animals in which all the nervous system above the midbrain has been removed. Descending fibers from the cerebral cortex and hypothalamus are thereby interrupted. A decerebrate cat can breathe by itself. Its blood pressure is maintained reflexly at a fairly normal level. It cannot eat or maintain body temperature or adjust to any severe environmental changes. How some of these functions are carried out can be illustrated by a brief discussion of the processes involved in the control of blood pressure, processes which take place in a similar manner in a normal animal.

Control of Blood Pressure. There must be a pressure gradient in order for blood to circulate. This can be measured in terms of the ability of the blood to raise a column of mercury above atmospheric pressure. A device used to measure blood pressure is a *sphygmomanometer.* A hollow cloth cuff is wrapped around the

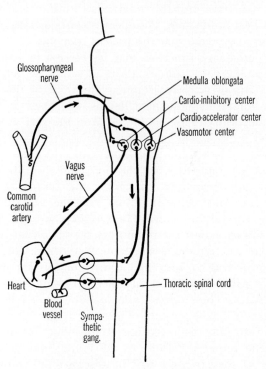

Figure 123.   Diagram indicating some of the pathways involved in reflex control
of blood pressure. See text for description.

arm and pumped full of air until the flow of arterial blood is
stopped. This cuff is connected to a tube filled with mercury, and
air pressure in it is thereby exerted against the mercury column.
The latter, therefore, rises as the air pressure increases. The height
which the mercury column reaches when the blood is shut off
averages about 120 mm. This, then, is the highest pressure in the
blood stream. Since it is related to the contraction of the heart, or
systole, it is termed systolic pressure. Between contractions, that is,
during *diastole,* the pressure drops to a base line or minimum
pressure which averages about 80 mm. of mercury. In referring to
blood pressure one should always include the two figures, systolic
and diastolic; in the example cited the values would be written as
120/80. The 40 mm. difference is the pulse pressure and represents
the efficiency of the heart in raising pressure above the base line
and pumping the blood around the body.

Reflex mechanisms help to maintain blood pressure at these average levels. In the bifurcation of the common carotid arteries in the neck and also in the arch of the aorta are interoceptive receptors which are sensitive to changes in pressure. For instance, if the blood pressure increases, the nerve impulses initiated ascend by way of the vagus and glossopharyngeal nerves to the medulla oblongata, and reach the cardiac and vasomotor centers (Fig. 123). Efferent impulses over the vagus nerves inhibit the heart, thereby slowing its rate of contraction. Other impulses descend to the spinal cord and are distributed by the sympathetic system to peripheral blood vessels, there initiating dilatation. The resistance of these vessels to flow of blood decreases and the pressure drops, much as widening the nozzle of a garden hose decreases the force of the stream of water going through it. With the decrease in pressure, stimulation of the carotid and aortic receptors lessens. Fewer impulses thus reach the medulla oblongata, and the process reverses. The pressure then rises as the peripheral vessels constrict and the heart rate increases. Under resting conditions, then, there is a slight fall, rise, then fall, and so on, continually occurring; the net result is a blood pressure reflexly maintained at an average level. This illustrates how finely balanced and integrated the two systems are in equilibrating a given activity.

Other Reflex Phenomena. Still other reflex activities may be cited. Reflex salivation may occur after taste of a food, even in decerebrate animals.

Pupillary reactions likewise can occur. If a light is flashed in an eye, the pupils of both eyes narrow and restrict the amount of light which can enter. This reaction is known as the *light reflex.* The impulses initiated by the light traverse those fibers of the optic nerve which go to the region between the superior colliculi and the thalami. After several synaptic connections, impulses leave by way of the oculomotor nerves and eventually reach the constrictor muscle of each iris. A widening of the pupils, on the other hand, may be the result either of sympathetic stimulation of the dilator muscle of the iris or of inhibition of the parasympathetic fibers supplying the constrictor muscles. The constrictor is much the stronger of the two opposing muscles, and the parasympathetic system is, therefore, the more important in pupillary reactions.

The various processes mentioned in the foregoing discussion illustrate how afferent impulses are necessary for the integrated control of visceral activities, and how meaningless it is to restrict a concept of such control to the motor side.

Brain Stem, Spinal Cord and Ganglia. These levels, which constitute the origin of preganglionic fibers, are still more restricted in functions. In a spinal animal, that is, an animal in which the spinal cord has been severed, the blood pressure and temperature in the part of the body supplied by the isolated spinal cord fall markedly and respond but poorly to reflex stimuli. Other functions, such as the control of the urinary bladder, may occur reflexly, but without integration with other visceral activities. Furthermore, visceral activities may be initiated by stimuli which in normal animals would be ineffective. In spinal man, for example, scratching the skin may lead to sweating, vasodilatation, and even emptying of the bladder.

The ganglia are still more restricted in outflow and function and differ functionally in at least one major respect from preganglionic cells in the spinal cord in that no reflex connections are established within them.

General Functions of the Autonomic Nervous System

Parasympathetic System. The parasympathetic system is concerned with the initiation and maintenance of a number of specific functions, such as digestion, intermediate metabolism of foods, and excretion. These are usually initiated in response to specific stimuli; hence the necessity for rather specific anatomical arrangements. Widespread connections such as are found in the sympathetic system would interfere with parasympathetic functions. This does not mean that widespread parasympathetic discharge cannot take place. It can, but usually not as a normal process, since it would be rather undesirable if, for example, the stimuli which initiated glandular secretion in the stomach or duodenum at the same time automatically initiated evacuation of the bladder and rectum.

Sympathetic System. The sympathetic system tends to respond as a whole, particularly during emergencies or sudden environmental changes, and is therefore an important part of the mechanisms by which a person reacts to stress. There are many stressing situations which particularly implicate the sympathetic system. Among these are pain, rage, fright, exercise, cold, drugs, asphyxia and anesthesia. Any of these may evoke a similar pattern of response. Certain phases of the response are acute and are mediated mainly by the nervous system. For example, there may occur a rise in blood pressure, increased cardiac output, increased blood sugar, increased oxygen consumption and sweating, to mention but a few. These changes come as a result of sympathetic discharge following cortical and hypothalamic activity after the stressing situation. These sympathetic effects are enhanced or maintained because the adrenaline released into the blood stream as a result of sympathetic stimulation of the adrenal medullae has about the same effect on viscera as do the sympathetic nerve fibers.

In addition, in response to stress, there are more slowly developing changes involving both the nervous system and the endocrine system. For instance, there is increased secretion of adrenocorticotrophic hormone (ACTH) of the pituitary, and this in turn is followed by increased activity of the adrenal cortex, evidenced in part by a fall in blood lymphocytes. Since adrenal cortical hormones are concerned with a wide variety of metabolic activities, there is therefore a mechanism by which stress can affect such activities. The question arises how the increased secretion of ACTH is brought about. It is possible that its formation is initiated and regulated by the amount of adrenaline circulating in the blood stream, and reaching the pituitary by the portal system, or else entering the portal system as a direct result of hypothalamic impulses to the blood vessels.

Summary

Visceral activities are controlled, directly or indirectly, by the nervous system. The levels of nervous control are the cerebral cortex, hypothalamus, brain stem, spinal cord and ganglia. The higher the level, the more general, widespread and nonspecific are connections and functions. The term "autonomic system" refers to fibers leaving the central nervous system as preganglionic fibers, synapsing with peripherally located ganglion cells and reaching viscera as postganglionic fibers. Axons leaving by way of the oculomotor, facial, glossopharyngeal, vagus and spinal accessory nerves and by way of ventral roots of the second and third sacral nerves form the cranial sacral or parasympathetic division of the autonomic system. The ganglia are in or near the organs innervated. The axons leaving by way of the ventral roots of the thoracic and first three lumbar roots form the thoracolumbar or sympathetic system. The peripheral synapses occur in the paravertebral and prevertebral ganglia.

The autonomic system supplies smooth muscle, cardiac muscle and gland cells. Most organs made up of these tissues are supplied by both divisions of the autonomic system. Acetylcholine is released at parasympathetic postganglionic terminals, and epinephrine at most sympathetic postganglionic terminals. These postganglionic fibers are known respectively as cholinergic and adrenergic fibers. Fibers supplying sweat glands and smooth muscle of skin anatomically are sympathetic, but functionally are cholinergic. Neither acetylcholine nor epinephrine is specific in its effects. Either may be excitatory or inhibitory, depending upon the viscus concerned.

Little is known of the functions of the cerebral cortex with regard to visceral activities. The hypothalamus is involved in a number of visceral and metabolic functions, and carries out its functions by means of projections to the brain stem and to the hypophysis. Thus it acts both upon the endocrine system and upon other nervous levels. The brain stem is concerned with a number of visceral activities, each rather specific, such as the reflex control of respiration and blood pressure. The brain stem and spinal cord contain still lower and functionally more specific levels which project to peripheral autonomic ganglia. The latter constitute the lowest and most specific autonomic level.

The parasympathetic system as a whole is concerned with fairly specific functions, such as digestion and excretion, each of which is initiated by fairly definite stimuli. The sympathetic system is particularly concerned in responses to stress, and its pattern of activity may be initiated by a wide variety of situations and agents.

Names in Neurology

Bernard, Claude (1813–1878)

Bernard was a French scientist and one of the greatest of experimental physiologists. He was the founder of experimental medicine. To him we owe much of our knowledge of the digestive and vasomotor systems. In 1843, he discovered that cane sugar appeared in the urine after being injected into the veins, but not if it had been first treated with gastric juice. This observation was the beginning of a long series of investigations of digestive processes. In 1849 he discovered that a puncture of the floor of the fourth ventricle produced a temporary diabetes. Shortly after this he investigated the factors controlling blood vessels and demonstrated the mechanisms of constriction and dilatation. Later he used curare in an investigation of muscle and showed that the paralysis it produced was the result of an effect on the myoneural junction, thus showing the independent excitability of muscle and nerve. Later he studied carbon monoxide poisoning. One of the most fundamental concepts in physiology results from his statement that all the vital processes maintain the constancy of the *milieu intérieur* or internal environment. Although Bernard was not primarily a neurophysiologist, if his work on the nervous system were all that he had done, his name would still go down in scientific history.

References

Refer to anatomy and physiology textbooks for extensive treatment of the autonomic system.

Cannon, W. B.: The Wisdom of the Body. New York, W. W. Norton and Company, 1939. Dr. Cannon was one of the outstanding investigators of the autonomic system. In this volume he emphasizes homeostatic mechanisms.

Cannon, W. B., and Rosenblueth, A.: Autonomic Neuro-Effector Systems. New York, Macmillan Company, 1937. An excellent treatise of the autonomic system.

Goodman, L., and Gilman, A.: Pharmacological Basis of Therapeutics. 2nd ed. New York, Macmillan Company, 1955. Drugs are discussed by showing how and where they act and by correlating their effects with physiological processes. It contains excellent sections on the pharmacology of the autonomic system.

Harris, G. W.: Neural Control of the Pituitary Gland. London, Edward Arnold (Publisher) Ltd., 1955. Clear, concise, well-written, instructive.

von Euler, U. S.: Noradrenaline. Springfield, Ill., Charles C Thomas, 1956. A discussion and summary of work showing that noradrenaline is the sympathetic mediator.

White, J. C., Smithwick, R. H., and Simeone, F. A.: Autonomic Nervous System. 3rd ed. New York, Macmillan Company, 1952. This is a book of an advanced nature, especially valuable from a clinical standpoint. It discusses the anatomy and physiology of the system briefly but clearly.

CHAPTER 14

The Spinal Cord, Spinal
Nerves and Peripheral Nerves

THE PRESENTATION of neurological structure and function
has been, up to this point, from what might be termed a longitudinal point of view. That is, after the introduction to general
form and arrangement, the long tracts of the nervous system were
discussed according to their relations with motor and sensory functions. This is logically followed by a consideration of the local or
horizontal levels or functions.

The Spinal Cord

The spinal cord is the least modified portion of the original
neural tube. To a large extent, its segmental differentiation is retained. The spinal cord has essentially the same structure throughout. Its gray matter has a fundamental arrangement which is
modified locally, as indicated in Fig. 124. This is the result of
differences in numbers and types of its contained neurons. Thus
the gray matter of the cervical and lumbosacral regions is more
abundant because these regions supply the extremities. That of
the thoracic cord and upper lumbar segments is relatively scanty
because it supplies only the trunk. It is characterized, however,
by a lateral projection of its intermediate portion which contains
those autonomic neurons whose axons ultimately enter sympathetic ganglia.

The white matter similarly differs but little in its fundamental
arrangement throughout the spinal cord. It is contained within
246

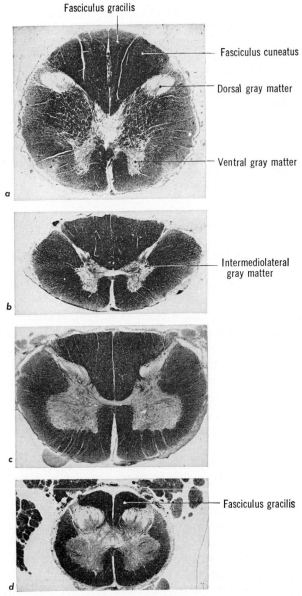

Figure 124. Photomicrographs of cross section of human spinal cords. *a*, Upper cervical; *b*, thoracic; *c*, lumbar; *d*, sacral. Note how the gray matter varies in shape and volume. The structures around the sacral cord are spinal roots of the cauda equina. Tracts cannot be distinguished in this normal material. Compare with Fig. 92 (p. 167) and Fig. 97 (p. 178). For diagram of tracts, see Fig. 125. Weigert stain.

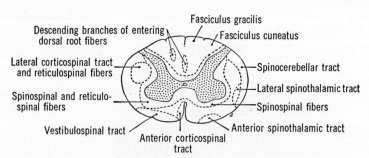

Figure 125. The main tracts of the spinal cord. Afferent, ascending tracts on the right side; efferent, descending tracts on the left. It must be remembered, however, that both ascending and descending fibers are actually present on each side.

three funiculi on each side, as indicated in Fig. 18 (p. 24). These funiculi, of course, vary in shape and size at different levels, because of variations in the shape of the gray matter and because of additions of ascending and terminations of descending fibers. These funiculi are simply morphological divisions which have no striking functional characteristics. The functional units of the white matter are tracts (Fig. 125). These, however, cannot be distinguished from each other in normal material. The lateral corticospinal tracts, for instance, can be morphologically demonstrated only by their absence, as shown in Fig. 92 (p. 167). The fibers of the lateral spinothalamic tract are intermingled with spinocerebellar fibers (Fig. 97, p. 178). Thus the lateral and anterior funiculi contain ascending and descending tracts which are anatomically congruent. In man, motor tracts are not found in the dorsal funiculi.

A large part of the white matter is composed of spinospinal or propriospinal fibers, that is, fibers arising and terminating within the spinal cord, thereby linking various levels and providing for coordinated activity (Fig. 68, p. 120). These spinospinal fibers are of short and long types. The short ones interconnect levels within a given region, such as from one cervical segment to another. The long ones pass from one region to another, as cervical to lumbar.

Functions of the Spinal Cord

The functions of the spinal cord are difficult to analyze in an intact animal, so that recourse is often had to spinal animals (animals with their spinal cord either transected or severed from the brain stem). An approximate idea of certain functions can be gained by a study of such animals. For example, certain reflex patterns may be elicited in a relatively unmodified form. How closely these patterns resemble those of the normal animals depends upon the species under study. If, for example, the spinal cord of a frog is severed, immediately after the section spinal cord functions are depressed, but within a few minutes it is possible to demonstrate reflex withdrawal to painful stimuli, reflex squatting and swimming movements and a variety of reactions similar to those seen in normal frogs. The spinal cord of the frog is therefore capable of much autonomous activity. Little of this activity, however, is spontaneous; that is, it does not take place without adequate external stimuli.

In higher animals, such as the cat or dog, the period of depression or *spinal shock* may last for several hours or days. Subsequently, certain patterns of reflex behavior can be demonstrated. Although spinal cats and dogs either cannot stand or can stand for but short periods of time, if they are properly supported and adequate stimulation supplied, alternating flexion and extension movements which resemble running patterns may be elicited. The reflexes forming these patterns are combinations of the fundamental types discussed in Chap. 8. There, it was pointed out that the two-neuron or stretch reflex is a highly restricted or *local reflex* of both phasic and static types. The phasic type, that is, the knee jerk, can be elicited in spinal cats and dogs, but the degree to which the static type is present is variable. Those animals which exhibit some degree of reflex extensor activity also show periods of reflex standing, whereas in others the knee jerk may be the only type of extensor response which can be demonstrated.

Another type of extensor activity is the *crossed extensor reflex*. This is most easily elicited by painful stimuli. The afferent impulses, after entering the spinal cord, are relayed by interneurons to various levels so as to provide for the reflex withdrawal (flexion) of the stimulated or ipsilateral extremity and the simultaneous inhibition of the antagonistic extensors. At the same time, interneurons project to various levels of the opposite side of the spinal cord and provide for enhancement of the postural contractions of the contralateral extremity. This total reaction is a mechanism for providing support when an extremity is lifted from the ground.

The crossed extensor reflex is a *segmental static reflex* and is not always easy to elicit in spinal cats.

From a study of spinal animals it is known that a simple reflex is an abstraction, an anatomical situation which cannot be demonstrated physiologically. Certain general principles regarding more complicated patterns can, however, be pointed out.

Reflexes exhibit *local sign* or *specificity*. For example, scratching movements may follow light scratching of the skin of the flank, but not of the foot. A painful stimulus to the skin of the flank is followed, not by scratching, but by withdrawal.

Reflexes exhibit *rhythm*, which appears to be an intrinsic property of the spinal cord. For example, one may scratch the skin of the flank of a spinal dog at a certain frequency, say several times a second. Yet the scratching movements which the animal carries out reflexly are not necessarily the same number of times per second. They may be much slower, and independent of stimulus frequency to the extent that the rate of scratching remains the same even when the stimulus frequency is varied. Likewise, for a particular animal it is likely that a basic rhythmic discharge from gray matter is responsible for the locomotor pattern of activity. Afferent stimuli, then, although extremely important in locomotion, modify the basic rhythm rather than determine it.

There are a variety of other principles, having mainly to do with allied and antagonistic reflexes. Some type of *coordination* is necessary because there are more afferent fibers entering the spinal cord than there are efferent fibers leaving it. As a general rule, if stimuli which normally result in different reflexes are applied simultaneously, and if one of the stimuli is painful, the response to pain is dominant.

Reflexes may be *allied*. For example, the scratch response is several simpler types of reflexes which are coordinated into a fairly complicated pattern.

Not infrequently, the cutaneous stimulation is subthreshold, that is, ineffective. In such cases a similar subthreshold stimulus applied nearby at the same time (simultaneous combination) or applied to the same region immediately after the first (successive combination) will summate with the first and produce a response. *Summation of subthreshold stimuli* is commonly seen in connection with many reflexes.

Some reflexes are *antagonistic,* as in the case of extensor and flexor components of locomotion, in the sense that they initiate movement in opposing directions. When they are coordinated into locomotor patterns involving forelimbs and hindlimbs, they form what are called *intersegmental reflexes*. Intersegmental relationships are further illustrated by the changes subsequent to spinal transection in a decerebrate animal (p. 268). If the transection is made in the thoracic region, stretch reflexes in the forelimbs become exaggerated, indicating that the caudal portion of the spinal cord had been carrying out an inhibitory function.

It is apparent that the spinal cord in cats and dogs does not function as well as that of the frog when separated from the rest of the nervous system. The higher the animal in the vertebrate scale, the more dependent on higher centers and the less autonomy there is of the spinal cord. This can be shown by reference to spinal man.

Spinal Man

When the spinal cord is completely severed above the fourth cervical segment, death rapidly follows because of the interference with respiration (p. 275).

Severance at lower levels is compatible with life. The initial effect is a complete cessation of spinal cord functions below the lesion. This *spinal shock* is much more pronounced in man than in lower vertebrates and is characterized by complete flaccid paralysis and absence of reflexes and sensation below the level of the lesion, and marked disturbances of bladder and rectal functions. The reasons for its appearance are not fully understood. One of the main factors is sudden section of descending tracts, because, if a transection develops slowly over days or weeks, shock may not appear. If, after transection, the isolated cord happens to be severed again, the cord distal to the second transection does not develop signs of shock. Evidently, then, fibers descending from higher levels are implicated. These would not be involved in the second transection.

There are certain fundamental reactions to any pathological changes in the nervous system, their specificity depending on whether there is a destruction of nervous tissue or an irritation. (1) If part of the nervous system has been destroyed, two fundamental reactions occur: (*a*) functions performed by the affected area are lost, and (*b*) abnormal phenomena appear because of the hyperactivity of areas normally held in check or inhibited by or opposing the affected part. In an upper motor neuron lesion, for instance, the paralysis represents loss of function; the spasticity and hyperactive reflexes represent hyperactive functions. (2) If a disorder irritates part of the nervous system by a stimulating action, the fundamental reaction is an exaggeration of the normal functions of the affected area. In infantile paralysis, for instance, there may be irritation of motor neurons, and muscle spasm results. Any or all of the fundamental reactions may occur in a neurological disorder. Furthermore, some lesions are initially irritative and later destructive; in such cases the type of fundamental reaction may change during the course of the disorder. Spinal man exhibits the first two reactions.

Following cord transection, there are generally the following stages: spinal shock, minimal reflex activity, flexor spasms, and alternating flexor and extensor spasms. In most instances of uncomplicated long-surviving cases of complete cord transection, extensor activity below the level of transection becomes dominant.

Flaccid paralysis, with complete loss of all reflexes, persists during spinal shock. The paralyzed bladder contains stagnant urine, a potential source of infection, and care has to be taken to prevent infections from involving the urinary system.

As spinal shock subsides, the isolated part of the spinal cord becomes more or less automatic in function. Muscles are not severed from motor neurons except at the level of the transection itself, and reflex arcs are, therefore, intact. But all descending motor tracts are severed and reflex arcs are, therefore, modifiable by local influences (cutaneous stimulation, muscle stretch, gamma efferents, etc.). All ascending tracts are cut, and sensation is completely lost below the level of the lesion.

The first signs of reflex activity appear in the distal parts of the limbs, one to six weeks after transection. These consist of mild reflex contractions of flexor muscles following cutaneous stimulation.

Flexor activity becomes more marked until flexor spasm or *mass flexion* is seen. In its best developed form this consists of withdrawal of the limbs, with flexion at hip, knee and ankle, and strong Babinski responses, these occurring in response to cutaneous stimulation. Tendon reflexes become very active, and at a variable time after transection can be elicited in extensor muscles, as, for example, a phasic type of knee jerk.

Commonly, extensor spasm (straightening of lower limbs) begins to appear and eventually becomes predominant (*mass extension*). Extensor activity is best elicited by stretch of muscles. In a few instances, extension may be so pronounced that patients, on being placed in a standing position, may continue to stand reflexly, even though no voluntary control exists.

Autonomic functions are lost during the period of spinal shock. With recovery, evidences of sympathetic activity reappear. The cutaneous vessels constrict, and sweating may be reflexly induced. Thus a mass flexion is accompanied by sweating in the affected areas. The upper limit of the area of sweating indicates the approximate level of the cord lesion. This illustrates the localized distribution of the autonomic outflow.

With recovery from spinal shock, the bladder may function almost automatically and become a "cord bladder," tending to fill and empty spontaneously. The bladder normally functions as follows: Urine formed by the kidneys flows down the ureters into the urinary bladder. The walls of the bladder are composed of smooth muscle. At its base is an opening into the urethra, and around this opening is a sphincter of smooth muscle which by contraction prevents the escape of urine to the exterior. Under normal conditions the smooth muscle of the bladder wall is contracted to a certain degree. These contractions are mediated by the parasympathetic system. When the amount of urine in the bladder increases enough to raise the intravesical pressure, several things may happen. Afferent impulses due to the increase in pressure are interpreted as a vague sensation of bladder fullness. If voiding is initiated, the smooth muscle of the bladder contracts. The external abdominal muscles likewise contract, thereby increasing intra-abdominal pressure and aiding in the evacuation of the bladder. At the same time, the smooth muscle sphincter is inhibited. Here, then, is a situation in which smooth muscle supplied by the parasympathetic system is partially under voluntary control and is coordinated in its activity with skeletal muscles.

If the bladder is not emptied, the afferent impulses inhibit the parasympathetic cells in the sacral cord. The smooth muscle relaxes and the pressure drops until afferent impulses cease and the muscle resumes its tonicity. As more urine enters, the same processes may be repeated. But there is a limit to the relaxation of the bladder. When a certain pressure is reached, the sensation of fullness becomes acutely and increasingly uncomfortable.

In spinal man the bladder is paralyzed during the period of spinal shock. It fills with urine which cannot be voided except by artificial means. But as spinal shock disappears, the reflex arc begins to function. Eventually, the parasympathetic cells in the sacral cord begin to function and may be excited by afferent impulses resulting from a rise in intravesical pressure. When the bladder begins to contract reflexly, an automatic or "cord bladder" is established.

Other types of visceral activities are affected by cord transections. In spinal man, during the period of shock, the nervous mechanism controlling evacuation of the rectum is almost completely depressed. With gradual recovery from the shock, local reflexes reappear whose stimulus seems to be distention of the rectum and whose response consists in rectal contraction and relaxation of the sphincters at the anal orifice.

Likewise, sexual functions are interfered with. Psychic stimuli are generally unable to influence sexual activity. But there appears to be an area in the lumbosacral cord capable of initiating integrated sexual activity, not only after direct stimulation of the sex organs, but frequently after any type of cutaneous stimulation.

Spinal Nerves

All the expressions of behavior are mediated through effectors, and no matter what they are, the final or ultimate path from the central nervous system is the motor neuron of the brain stem and spinal cord, the final common path.

The ventral roots thus contain efferent fibers. These fibers supply skeletal muscles which developed in the embryo segment corresponding to the cord segment of the ventral root.

The afferent fibers of the dorsal roots are derived from areas characterized by a segmental arrangement even more striking (p. 38). It is interesting that the overlap between any two dorsal roots is very marked. Thus, if the middle one of three adjacent dorsal roots is severed, the overlap from the other two makes it difficult to detect a loss of sensation. *Hypesthesia,* not anesthesia, is found.

The fact that afferent fibers are collected into dorsal roots is

utilized clinically in spinal anesthesia. The introduction of an anesthetic, such as *procaine,* into the subarachnoid space is followed
by anesthesia of the sacral areas, then lumbar, and so forth, depending on the amount of anesthetic injected and the height to
which it is allowed to rise. Such anesthetics affect nonmyelinated
and small myelinated fibers first. Consequently, the sense of pain
disappears first, and that of pressure last. During an operation,
therefore, pain may be absent, but pressure sense may still be
present.

Nerve Components

The fibers contained within a nerve may be classified according
to the structures they supply. This has considerably simplified and
clarified our concepts of cranial nerves (see Chap. 15). In spinal
nerves, four types or components of fibers are present. These are
arranged in a manner relating to the position of the embryonic
sulcus limitans. It will be recalled that within the neural tube
those neuroblasts lying ventral to the sulcus limitans, that is, in
the basal plate, become efferent in nature. The dorsally placed
afferent fibers, on the other hand, enter the alar plate and synapse
with the cells developing there. The same relationship is found in
the adult.

Ventral roots contain large myelinated fibers supplying skeletal
muscle, and small myelinated fibers to spindle muscle fibers. These
are efferent fibers to somatic structures, hence are called *somatic
efferent fibers,* and their cells of origin are in the most ventral part
of the gray matter. Many ventral roots contain small myelinated
fibers destined for visceral structures. These *general visceral efferent* fibers are preganglionic axons of the autonomic system. The
reason for using the term "general" is explained in Chap. 15.
The cells of origin of these fibers are found just ventral to the
sulcus limitans.

Dorsal roots contain *general somatic afferent* and *general visceral
afferent* fibers, which supply somatic (skin, muscles, and so forth)
and visceral structures, respectively.

Spinal nerves, since they are formed by dorsal and ventral roots,
contain all four components. This is true of major peripheral
nerves, but branches of these vary in composition. Thus a nerve
to skin lacks somatic efferent fibers.

In the upper levels of the cervical spinal cord, large motor neurons are found in intermediate as well as in ventral gray matter. The axons of cells in the intermediate gray leave, not by way of spinal roots, but instead emerge laterally and form the spinal portion of the accessory nerve, ascending through the foramen magnum to join the medullary portion. These axons comprise a functional component which belongs with the brain stem (p. 265).

Peripheral Nerves

Nearly all major peripheral nerves include fibers from several spinal nerves, though not all of each one (p. 39). For instance, the femoral nerve in the thigh is derived from the second, third and fourth lumbar spinal nerves and supplies the skin over the anterior surface of the thigh and the extensor muscles of the leg. The obturator nerve is also derived from the second, third and fourth lumbar nerves, but it supplies a different skin area and the adductor muscles of the thigh. Thus these lumbar trunks are distributed by way of different peripheral nerves. Furthermore, the fourth lumbar nerve contributes to the sciatic nerve.

When a spinal nerve is severed, therefore, the effects are found in parts of several peripheral nerve areas. A lesion of the second lumbar spinal nerve, for instance, is followed by involvement of part of the femoral and part of the obturator nerve supply. A lesion of a peripheral nerve, however, involves part of several spinal nerves. These facts are of the utmost clinical value in determining the location of a lesion causing muscle paralyses or anesthesias, or both.

Peripheral nerve lesions are not uncommon in automobile and industrial accidents, as well as in wartime injuries. If a nerve is completely severed, all its fibers distal to the injury degenerate. The muscles supplied by the nerve undergo a sudden, complete flaccid paralysis. Reflexes as well as sensation are lost. The anesthesia covers an area less than the anatomical distribution because of the overlap from neighboring peripheral nerves. Without proper care the muscles will atrophy before regeneration occurs, and atrophy will inevitably follow if there is no regeneration.

As nerve fibers begin to regenerate, spontaneous pains may occur in the area of distribution of the nerve. This results from an irritation at the growing ends, and the pain is of a projection type. When connections are re-established, the muscles slowly regain their tone, atrophic changes lessen, and the field of sensory impairment gradually narrows and disappears. Pain and temperature return first, partly because small fibers grow faster, and partly because nonmyelinated fibers from neighboring normal areas grow into the denervated skin. The regeneration of the larger peripheral nerves may take a year or two.

A description of a radial nerve injury suffices to illustrate. This nerve supplies the extensors of the forearm, wrist and proximal phalanges, so that these muscles become paralyzed and a "wrist drop" results. The fingers tend to bend because the flexor muscles are unopposed. Sensory losses are slight because there is a considerable overlap; only a small area on the back of the hand between the thumb and first finger becomes anesthetic. If the cut ends are united, regeneration may occur in a year or less.

Summary

The spinal cord retains, to a certain extent, the segmental character of the neural tube. The gray matter has a basic arrangement which is modified by local changes in character and number of contained neurons. The white matter is arranged in funiculi which are also modified locally. Tracts, such as the lateral spinothalamic, are not anatomically demonstrable in normal material.

In the spinal cord the basic reflexes are coordinated in local and general movement patterns. These, such as stepping or walking, are spinal mechanisms, but cannot function autonomously. Certain higher centers must be present before the spinal cord can function normally.

Transection of the cord in man is followed by spinal shock, with complete flaccid paralysis and loss of sensations. Autonomic functions, such as sweating and evacuation of the urinary bladder, are restricted to local reflexes operating over cord levels.

Spinal nerves contain general somatic afferent and general visceral afferent components, which enter dorsal roots; and somatic efferent and general visceral efferent fibers derived from motor neurons by way of ventral roots. The major peripheral nerves likewise contain these components.

Lesions of spinal and peripheral nerves differ in their effects because (1) a spinal nerve reaches its area of supply through several different peripheral nerves and composes only part of each, and (2) a major peripheral nerve contains parts of several spinal nerves.

References

The physiology textbooks generally have sections on experimental studies of cord functions.

Creed, R. S., and others: Reflex Activity of the Spinal Cord. Oxford, Clarendon Press, 1932. Excellent experimental analysis of spinal cord functions.

Kuhn, R. A.: Functional capacity of the isolated human spinal cord. Brain, *73:* 1–51, 1950. A very thorough study, especially valuable because patients were observed for long periods of time, and cord transections were verified at surgery.

CHAPTER 15

The Brain Stem

SOME OF the morphological characteristics of the brain stem and cerebellum have been discussed in Chap. 2, and others with their functional correlations in chapters on motor and sensory paths. Because of the diversity of functions in these areas, further details must be added.

A number of features combine to differentiate the brain stem from the spinal cord. Most of the cranial nerves arise or terminate within the brain stem. The cerebellum forms massive connections throughout the whole region. The reticular formation contains neurons active in both visceral and somatic functions. The tracts running to and from the cord undergo rather marked rearrangements in their passage through the brain stem. The entire area may be considered a suprasegmental apparatus concerned with special senses, vital processes and other visceral and somatic functions, all of which may be modified by impulses entering over the cranial nerves and from the cerebellum and forebrain.

General Features of the Brain Stem

The Medulla Oblongata

The change from spinal cord to medulla oblongata at the level of the foramen magnum is more evident microscopically than grossly. The lower limit of the pyramidal decussation marks the transition. The nucleus gracilis and nucleus cuneatus soon appear on each side, and above this level the medial lemnisci become more and more prominent (Fig. 126). The bilaterally placed *olivary*

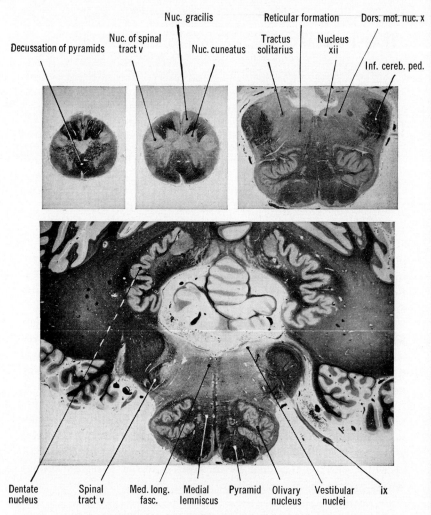

Figure 126. Photographs of cross sections of medulla oblongata and cerebellum.
Weigert stain.

nuclei, characterized by their crumpled shape, begin at the approximate level at which the medial lemnisci appear and extend upward to the pons.

In the dorsal part of the medulla oblongata, on either side of the midline, are the motor nuclei of the hypoglossal nerves. Lateral to each is the dorsal motor nucleus of the vagus. The nuclei of both nerves lie in the floor of the fourth ventricle (Fig. 126).

Dorsolaterally in the medulla oblongata on each side is an isolated bundle of myelinated fibers, the *tractus solitarius*. The spinal tract of the trigeminal nerve lies on each dorsolateral surface of the lower part of the medulla oblongata, while at higher levels it lies ventral to the restiform body.

The reticular formation constitutes a large part of the medulla oblongata. It is a mixture of white and gray matter which contains many types of neurons, as well as myelinated and nonmyelinated fibers (Fig. 126 and Fig. 17, p. 23). The term "reticular" is a general one and implies no functional specificity.

Cells subserving visceral and somatic functions may lie side by side. For example, the vagus, glossopharyngeal and accessory nerves supply striated muscles by axons derived from large neurons in the medulla oblongata and upper cervical cord. These neurons form a nucleus in the reticular formation, but one so difficult to locate, except under relatively high magnification, that it is called the *nucleus ambiguus*.

The reticular formation near the point of entrance of the eighth nerve is specialized as several nuclei in which the vestibular nerve terminates (Fig. 126).

The Pons and Midbrain

The dorsal portion of the pons is structurally and functionally an upward continuation of the medullary reticular formation. It also contains motor nuclei of the facial, abducens and trigeminal nerves, as well as the sensory nuclei of the trigeminal nerves. As the medial lemnisci enter the pons, they become oriented transversely instead of dorsoventrally and thus separate the ventral from the dorsal pons (Fig. 127). With this rearrangement there appears on each side of the dorsal midline the *medial longitudinal fasciculus,* which can be traced into the midbrain.

The ventral pons contains masses of cells, the pontile nuclei, the axons of which project laterally as the middle cerebellar peduncles. Between the cells and fibers are descending corticospinal fibers.

At the lower limit of the midbrain the fourth ventricle becomes continuous with the cerebral aqueduct. Dorsal to the aqueduct are the superior and inferior colliculi; ventral to it are the motor nuclei

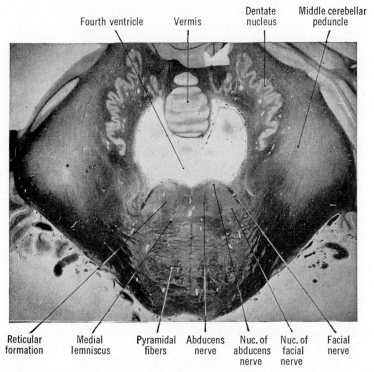

Figure 127. Photograph of cross section of the pons and cerebellum. Descending pyramidal fibers form small bundles in the ventral part of the pons. Weigert stain.

of the oculomotor and trochlear nerves. The red nuclei are landmarks in the upper part of the midbrain; ventral to them are the substantia nigra and the cerebral peduncles (Fig. 128 and Fig. 15, p. 22).

The inferior colliculi receive fibers from the ascending auditory paths. Cells in the inferior colliculi project to motor neurons of the brain stem by way of the *tectobulbar tracts* and to the spinal cord by way of the *tectospinal tracts*. *Tectum* refers to the roof of the midbrain; hence the name of any tract arising here carries the prefix *tecto*.

The superior colliculi and the area between them and the thalami receive fibers from the retinae by way of the optic nerves and tracts. These fibers are distinct from those which form the visual path to the cortex. Cells in the superior colliculi also project to the motor neurons of the brain stem and spinal cord by way of tectobulbar and tectospinal tracts.

The various cranial nerves and the upper cervical nerves are frequently coordinated in movement patterns. One of the important pathways in this connection is the bilaterally placed medial longitudinal fasciculus (Fig. 126), an association tract which appears early in the development of the nervous system. Each tract runs from the midbrain to the upper cervical cord and carries ascending and descending fibers which link the various motor nuclei.

The substantia nigra and red nuclei probably represent specialized portions of the reticular formation. In connections and function they are associated with the basal ganglia of the forebrain, and the red nucleus is also associated with the cerebellum. The substantia nigra is found in man and perhaps some of the other higher primates. Its dark appearance is due to the fact that its

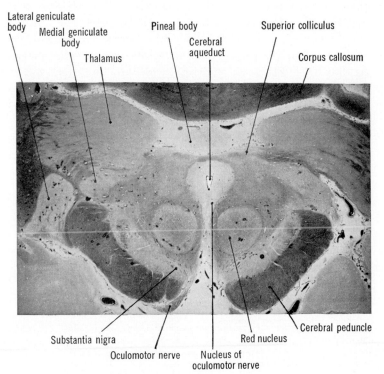

Fig. 128.   Photograph of cross section of the midbrain. Weigert stain.

constituent cells contain melanin pigment. In lower animals the cells in corresponding regions lack this pigment.

The red nuclei in animals such as the cat are composed of large motor neurons which project directly to the spinal cord by the *rubrospinal* tracts, and are under the influence of the cerebellum by way of the superior cerebellar peduncles. In animals higher in the evolutionary scale a smaller type of cell appears. In primates the larger motor neurons are greatly reduced in number, and in man the small-celled portion of the red nucleus is predominant. Impulses from it reach the spinal cord indirectly by way of rubro-reticular and reticulospinal tracts (Fig. 134, p. 283). For practical purposes, one may consider that in man the rubrospinal tracts are either nonexistent or are functionally unimportant.

Cranial Nerve Components

Some of the differences between cranial and spinal nerves were pointed out on page 41, and the functional components of the spinal nerves were discussed on page 255. Figure 129 illustrates the fundamental arrangement of cranial nerve components and indicates certain ones not found in spinal nerves. This diagram represents the condition not only in the medulla oblongata, but also in most of the brain stem. For each component the cells of origin or termination form a column which extends longitudinally in

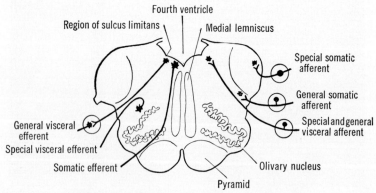

Figure 129. Schematic representation of cranial nerve components as found in the medulla oblongata. Afferent fibers are shown on the right, and efferent on the left. Also indicated are the approximate locations of the cells of origin and termination for the various components.

the brain stem. If any particular column is interrupted in some levels where certain nerves may not have this component, the cells above and below are nevertheless found in the same positions relative to medial and lateral planes.

What are the reasons for these added components? The questions relating to them have for the most part been answered by studies of amphibian forms, and the available evidence indicates that the arrangement is fundamentally similar in man.

Gills do not appear in the human embryo, but *branchial arches* do develop in the neck region (see embryology textbooks). The muscles derived from and associated with the arches are, therefore, said to be *branchiomeric*. Thus the muscles of mastication arise from the first arches and are innervated by fibers from the motor nuclei of the trigeminal nerves. The facial muscles arise from the second arch and are supplied by the facial nerves. The muscles of the pharynx and larynx arise from the third, fourth and fifth arches. Their nerve supply is from the glossopharyngeal, vagus and medullary portions of the accessory nerves—all fibers being derived from the columns formed by the nuclei ambigui. The spinal divisions of the accessory nerves supply those parts of the sterno-cleidomastoid and trapezius muscles which appear to be derived from branchial arches. Although the branchiomeric muscles are striated, many are functionally associated with the respiratory and alimentary systems. Others function in vocalization. Because of their association with visceral activities, the nerves supplying them have been designated *special visceral efferents*.

Taste is a special sense associated with visceral functions; so taste fibers are called *special visceral afferents*. The fibers travel centrally over the facial, glossopharyngeal and vagus nerves and enter the tractus solitarius in the medulla oblongata. *General visceral afferent* fibers from abdominal and thoracic viscera and from pharynx and larynx also enter this tract. These fibers convey impulses aroused by hunger, thirst, distention, changes in blood pressure and so forth.

The *special somatic afferent* component refers to other special senses. Thus the fibers in the acoustic and optic nerves are in this category.

Table 3 tabulates the cranial nerves according to their functional components.

Table 3.   Components of Cranial Nerves

Cranial Nerve	Component	Function
Olfactory........	Special visceral afferent	Smell
Optic...........	Special somatic afferent	Vision
Oculomotor......	Somatic efferent	Movements of eyeball
	General somatic afferent	Proprioception from extrinsic eye muscles
	General visceral efferent	Contraction of smooth muscle in iris and ciliary body
Trochlear.......	Somatic efferent	Movements of eyeball
	General somatic afferent	Proprioception from extrinsic eye muscle
Trigeminal......	Special visceral efferent	Movements of mastication
	General somatic afferent	General sensations from face and head
Abducens.......	Somatic efferent	Movement of eyeball
	General somatic afferent	Proprioception from extrinsic eye muscle
Facial..........	Special visceral efferent	Facial expressions
	General visceral efferent	Salivation and lacrimation
	Special visceral afferent	Taste
Stato-acoustic	Special somatic afferent	Hearing and equilibrium
Glossopharyngeal.	Special visceral efferent	Pharyngeal movements
	General visceral efferent	Salivation
	Special visceral afferent	Taste
	General visceral afferent	Visceral reflexes
	General somatic afferent	General sensations from small part of external ear
Vagus..........	Special visceral efferent	Pharyngeal and laryngeal movements
	General visceral efferent	Parasympathetic to thoracic and abdominal viscera
	Special visceral afferent	Taste
	General visceral afferent	Visceral reflexes
	General somatic afferent	Same as glossopharyngeal
Accessory.......	Special visceral efferent	Laryngeal and shoulder movements
	General visceral efferent	Same as vagus
Hypoglossal......	Somatic efferent	Tongue movements

Somatic Functions of the Brain Stem

The brain stem in Ambystoma, even in the adult, is the chief one controlling muscular activity. It acts in conjunction with the spinal cord, and its functions are modified by afferent impulses from the spinal cord, the inner ear and the cerebellum. This type of arrangement is found throughout the vertebrate scale. Even though higher centers develop, the brain stem region persists and is used by such centers in projecting to the spinal cord. It therefore forms part of the extrapyramidal system.

From work on the cat and higher animals, as well as Ambystoma and other lower forms, it has been shown that the brain stem cells concerned in the control of muscular activity are scattered throughout the reticular formation, particularly in the medulla oblongata and pons. Some of these cells constitute an inhibitory mechanism, since, when they discharge, the end result is an increase in threshold of motor neurons to which they project, or an actual inhibition or blocking of muscular activity. If, for example, one stimulates this region of the brain stem while knee jerks are being elicited, one finds that the contraction of the leg extensor either decreases in amplitude or else stops. Other regions of the nervous system, such as the cerebral cortex, may inhibit activity by causing the inhibitory brain stem mechanisms to act, or may increase activity by preventing the inhibitory brain stem level from discharging.

Other cells in the reticular formation constitute an excitatory mechanism, since, when they discharge, they facilitate or lower the thresholds of motor cells to which they project or cause them to fire off so that muscular contraction results. As in the case of the inhibitory mechanisms, other regions of the nervous system may either activate or block the excitatory system.

In lower forms, such as fishes, one of the principal mechanisms modifying brain stem functions is the inner ear. Impulses resulting from changes in position of the head reach the brain stem over the vestibular nerve. The fibers of this nerve terminate in the vestibular nuclei, which are specialized portions of the reticular formation. One of these nuclei, the lateral, gives rise to the vestibulospinal tract, which descends with the excitatory reticulospinal tract, mainly in the ventral part of the spinal cord. Functionally, this lateral vestibular nucleus and its tract are part of the excitatory mechanism of the brain stem. The other vestibular nuclei project to various cranial nerve nuclei. In higher animals this basic arrangement persists, and in man both vestibulospinal and reticulospinal tracts are to be found. One may consider therefore that in man, the extrapyramidal system mediates its effects upon the spinal cord by discharging through the phylogenetically older system, the reticular formation of the brain stem.

A number of brain stem functions are carried out on a reflex level. For example, one can demonstrate some of these in a subject who is sitting in a chair which is being rotated. The rotation stimulates semicircular canals according to the manner discussed on p. 216. With the proper optical system it can be seen that, when rotation begins, the eyes exhibit certain rhythmic movements called *nystagmus*. This is a reflex attempt to fix the eyes during movement. When the rotation reaches a steady state, nystagmus stops. But when rotation stops, nystagmus reappears and persists for fifteen to twenty seconds or more. This is a reflex result of post-rotational pressure in the semicircular canals. One may see nystagmus in people in an elevator, or in people in a train watching telegraph poles. Many other types of brain stem reflexes can also be demonstrated in normal subjects. Examples are the jaw jerk (reflex contraction of jaw-closing muscles in response to sudden stretch); the corneal reflex (blinking when a cornea is touched); blinking in response to objects appearing suddenly in the visual fields; and sudden muscular responses to noise.

Various types of reflexes can be studied in an animal in which the brain stem has been isolated from higher centers. It was pointed out on p. 251 that, after spinal cord transection in higher animals, reflex extensor activity decreases. This picture is changed, however, if brain stem mechanisms are superimposed on the spinal cord. This may be done by transecting the brain stem in the region of the midbrain, thereby producing a *decerebrate animal*. Most of the cranial nerves and many cerebellar connections are still intact. A decerebrate cat exhibits strong, maintained contractions in extensor muscles, so much so that, if placed upright with the proper support, the limbs can support the body weight. The animal cannot, however, carry out any locomotor activity. If pushed over, it falls and cannot right itself. It must be fed and, since temperature control is lacking, must be kept warm. Blood pressure is reflexly maintained, and respiration is slow and deep.

What are the reasons for such differences from a spinal animal? Certainly the inhibitory and excitatory mechanisms of the brain stem have been added, but why should certain postural features predominate? A concept rather generally held today postulates that excitatory brain stem mechanisms, especially those concerned with postural mechanisms, exhibit autonomous activity when connections with higher centers are lost. In other words, cells are continually discharging to the spinal cord. Inhibitory cells, on the other hand, are silent, and are activated only when impulses from the proper sources reach them. In a decerebrate animal, then, impulses are continually reaching the motor cells supplying antigravity muscles and either stimulating them or so facilitating them as to make them more susceptible to afferent impulses from muscles. Impulses also reach motor cells giving rise to gamma efferents. These impulses cause the spindle discharge rate to increase, thereby accentuating reflexes. The gamma system appears to be more easily influenced by impulses from the brain stem than are the large motor cells. Decerebrate rigidity can be abolished or greatly diminished by cutting dorsal roots or the descending motor tracts. Inhibition of muscular activity can also be carried out in a coordinated manner by the spinal cord (p. 250). If, after decerebration, the spinal cord is transected in the thoracic region, the stretch reflexes and the rigidity of the forelimb become even more marked. Evidently the lumbar portion of the cord had been inhibiting motor cells of the cervical region.

Decerebrate rigidity is not often seen in man. When it does occur, it resembles in many respects the situation seen in lower animals. Less severe motor disorders are common, however, and certain aspects of them are similar to decerebrate rigidity. For example, it was pointed out in Chap. 10 that in an upper motor neuron lesion, exaggerated deep reflexes and spasticity were characteristic findings. If the causative lesion is in the internal capsule, the result is akin to decerebration in that some of the connections between higher centers and the brain stem are cut so that the excitatory mechanisms become autonomous and the inhibitory ones relatively inactive. The spasticity which is seen is therefore similar to rigidity. Spasticity will also result from a spinal cord lesion when such a lesion destroys the inhibitory paths in the lateral funiculi, leaving the excitatory ones intact.

The predominance of extensor tone in a decerebrate cat makes fluidity of motion and walking impossible. These depend upon intact higher centers. Certain types of reflex responses can, however, be demonstrated in a decerebrate animal, including many of those demonstrable in normal animals. The reflexes are mainly of a static nature. Phasic types of reflexes are either not easily demonstrable in a decerebrate animal or else are fleeting in duration.

Static Reflexes in Decerebrate Rigidity

Local.   If a single extremity of a decerebrate animal touches the ground, it stiffens enough to offer support. The intrinsic mechanisms are stretch reflexes operating locally, initiated by stretch of antigravity muscles and pressure upon the foot. The local reaction may be illustrated in a somewhat different manner. If the animal is supported off the ground and the foot is touched, or slightly pressed, the limb extends. The extension continues as the finger is slowly drawn away, the foot appearing to follow the finger like a magnet. This is the *positive supporting reaction.*

Segmental and Intersegmental.   The classic example of the segmental reaction is the crossed extensor reflex (p. 249). This is obtained in a spinal as well as in a decerebrate cat. It may be accompanied by extension of the opposite forelimb, so that there is an intersegmental reaction forming a pattern resembling a phase of locomotion.

General.   This includes the reactions to changes in position of the head and neck. These are (1) the tonic neck reflexes and (2) tonic labyrinthine reflexes.

Tonic neck reflexes are best demonstrated after the labyrinths are destroyed. If the head is turned to one side, the limbs on that side increase in extensor tone, thus providing a mechanism for supporting the body on the side to which the cat is looking. The reaction depends upon proprioceptive impulses from the neck muscles being stretched, and from joints between the cervical vertebrae. Long propriospinal fibers conduct the impulses to the ipsilateral motor neurons.

Tonic labyrinthine reflexes are best shown after the cervical dorsal roots are cut so as to eliminate tonic neck reflexes. Changes in the position of the head are again followed by maintained reactions. If the cat is placed on its back with the head somewhat elevated, a maximal tone appears in the limbs, which become fully extended. In intermediate head positions, the tone is less than maximal. In this particular plane the maculae utriculi are maximally stimulated by the effects of gravity. Impulses reach the vestibular areas and thence the motor neurons of the spinal cord. Although these are static and not acceleratory phenomena, there is considerable evidence that the semicircular canals subserve some functions in this matter. If the maculae are destroyed, tonic labyrinthine reflexes may yet be demonstrated. This leads to the concept that acceleratory reactions are predominantly but not entirely vested in the canals, and static reactions predominantly but not exclusively in maculae utriculi. Since extensor tone is maintained as long as the head occupies a position under these conditions, Magnus (p. 277) has termed these responses *attitudinal reflexes*. Under most circumstances the tonic neck and labyrinthine reflexes operate together, producing coordinated reactions.

Functions of the Midbrain

The midbrain is a complex region having many incompletely understood functions. The superior collicular area, for example, is the main visual area in lower animals, and in birds it overshadows the rest of the brain stem. But in mammals the process of cephalization becomes more and more evident, and in primates the occipital lobes carry out nearly all the visual functions. The superior colliculi are mainly centers for visual reflexes which are possible by means of the connections mentioned on p. 262. An example of a common type of reflex is blinking in response to an object that appears suddenly in the visual fields. More generalized muscular responses may also occur in response to such a stimulus. Pupillary constriction in response to light shining on the eyes is another example of a visual reflex, although, strictly speaking, this is carried out by the region between the colliculi and the thalami. The colliculi, together with centers in the pons, may under certain circumstances carry out reflex conjugate movements of the eyes even when voluntary pathways for such movements have been destroyed. The colliculi themselves appear to be particularly concerned in vertical conjugate movements.

The inferior colliculi are centers for auditory reflexes. Thus a sudden noise may be followed by turning the eyes, the head or the body to the sound, or by a general startle reaction. These responses ordinarily depend upon impulses reaching the inferior colliculi by paths mentioned on p. 262.

There are certain midbrain structures which functionally are closely associated with the basal ganglia (see Chap. 17). These are the substantia nigra, the red nuclei, and probably certain tegmental nuclei as well. These structures, although relatively intact in a decerebrate animal, function mainly when their connections with higher centers are intact and are concerned in various phases of muscular activity. The red nuclei in addition are closely associated with the cerebellum.

Reticular Formation

The descending influences of the reticular formation have already been mentioned. It has been shown that stimulation of the reticular formation in unanesthetized animals leads to an arousal reaction, that is, a sleeping animal awakes. The ascending fibers appear to arise from the same part of the reticular formation that has descending excitatory functions. The arousal reaction is accompanied by a flattening of the waves in the electroencephalogram (p. 309). It is held that ascending sensory pathways, in their passage through the brain stem, give collaterals to the reticular formation, which then by a very diffuse system of ascending paths relays through subcortical centers to the cerebral cortex. The entire system has been called an activating system, and is thought to play an important role in wakefulness, conscious states and attention.

Destruction of midbrain reticular formation can produce enduring loss of consciousness. Similar conditions have been reported for man. Otherwise, there is as yet little direct evidence regarding the reticular activating system in man.

Visceral Functions of the Brain Stem

Many of the cells in the reticular formation are concerned with visceral activities. These cells are smaller than somatic motor neurons, but, like them, are scattered throughout the pons and medulla, so that cells subserving somatic and visceral functions may lie side by side. The visceral cells receive projections from the hypothalamus and in turn project to various cranial nerve nuclei and to the spinal cord.

Some of the cells are concerned in relatively simple mechanisms. For instance, certain ones scattered in the upper medulla and lower pons (*salivatory nuclei*) project as parasympathetic fibers to salivary glands by way of the facial and glossopharyngeal nerves. These fibers mediate excitation, and, therefore, control secretory processes in these glands. The cells may be reflexly activated by impulses resulting from taste or smell, or psychically by impulses from the cerebral cortex. The psychic influence is usually inhibitory, as, for example, dryness of the mouth in many emotional states. The salivatory system was extensively used by Pavlov (p. 278) in his studies of conditioned responses.

Many of the visceral cells function in more complex, integrated activities. Some of these, such as the control of blood pressure, were discussed in Chap. 13. Others are as follows:

Control of Respiration

Although the muscles of respiration are skeletal in type, the respiratory process itself is reflexly controlled. No one can voluntarily hold his breath to the point of asphyxiation. The following brief account of respiratory mechanisms is based mainly upon the cat, but there is reason to suppose that similar mechanisms occur in man.

Scattered throughout the reticular formation dorsal to the olivary nuclei are small neurons which project to the spinal cord. Here they synapse with the motor neurons of the cervical cord giving rise to the phrenic nerves supplying the diaphragm. They also reach cells in the thoracic cord whose axons supply the intercostal and abdominal musculature.

If the cells in the medulla are stimulated with electric currents, two different functions can be demonstrated. More caudally placed stimuli are followed by an inspiration which is maintained for the duration of the stimulus. Transection of the upper cervical cord prevents this, so that these cells apparently control the spinal supply of respiratory muscles. Collectively they form the bilateral *inspiratory centers*.

More cephalically placed stimuli cause an expiratory act, and the cells mediating this activity form *expiratory centers* which project to the same regions of the cord.

Inspiration is a fundamentally more important act than expiration, since in the latter case the intrinsic elasticity of the lungs is more significant than muscular action. This dominance is reflected in the medullary centers. If these are isolated from all afferent impulses, the inspiratory centers discharge continuously and the animal dies in a state of prolonged inspiration. Normal respiration is reflexly controlled by modifying the intrinsic activity of these centers.

Within the lungs are interoceptive receptors which are sensitive to the stretch resulting from the expansion of the lungs during inspiration. The nerve impulses which traverse the vagi increase

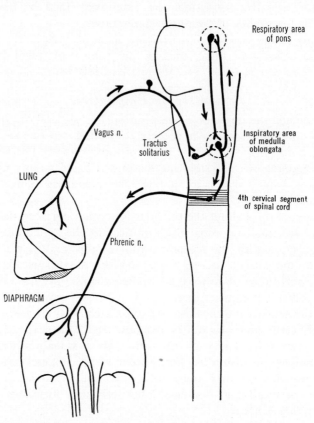

Figure 130. Schematic, simplified diagram of the pathways in a respiratory reflex. The terminals in the lung are stimulated by expansion during inspiration. See text for description.

in frequency as the expansion, and thereby the stimulus intensity, increases. The fibers carrying the impulses are of the general visceral afferent type. They enter the tractus solitarius of the medulla oblongata and are then relayed to the respiratory centers (Fig. 130). When the impulses reach a certain frequency, they inhibit the inspiratory and stimulate the expiratory centers. The most important result is the lessening of discharges from the former center. Inspiration, therefore, lessens and stops; expiration supervenes. The stimulation of lung receptors naturally decreases in intensity. Below a certain frequency the inhibition of inspiratory centers lessens, and they again resume activity.

If the vagi are cut, however, so as to prevent the entrance of vagal impulses, respiration slows and deepens, but does not stop. It stops only when the brain stem is transected just above the centers. In the pons there is a bilaterally placed respiratory center which receives fibers from the medullary centers and in turn projects to them. These pontile centers, upon receipt of impulses at or above a certain frequency, discharge to and inhibit the inspiratory centers. Expiration thus intervenes. Either vagal impulses or pontile centers can produce fairly normal respiration, but, if both are absent, the animal dies in prolonged inspiration.

That the cervical cord is unable to maintain respiration automatically is shown as follows: If the cord is severed just below the fourth or fifth cervical segment, respiration continues because the control of the diaphragm is intact. But if the transection is above this level, the fibers descending from the medulla oblongata are severed. Death rapidly follows because of the asphyxia resulting from failure of respiration. This explains why transections of the cord high in the cervical levels are rapidly fatal in man. It also explains why medullary lesions may be fatal if they involve much of the reticular formation.

The respiratory centers receive impulses from higher centers, so that their activity may be considerably modified, either voluntarily or in emotional states, but in neither case can reflex functions be completely suppressed.

The respiratory centers are directly sensitive to gaseous tensions in the blood flowing through them. Thus an increase in carbon dioxide in the lungs is followed by an increase of carbon dioxide in the blood and, consequently, by an increase in the rate and depth of breathing. This blows off the excess carbon dioxide which had raised the blood level of this gas.

At the bifurcation of each common carotid artery is a small tissue mass, the carotid body, containing receptors which are likewise sensitive to changes in gaseous tensions of the blood flowing by them. The impulses traverse the glossopharyngeal nerves to the respiratory centers and result in reflex mechanisms similar to those cited in the preceding paragraph.

Respiration illustrates a coordination of somatic and visceral systems which may likewise extend linearly in other mechanisms as follows:

Control of Movements in the Alimentary Tract

When food enters the mouth and is tasted and smelled, or even before it enters the mouth, saliva reflexly flows into the oral cavity. Its contained enzymes begin the digestion of certain constituents of the food.

Swallowing initiates other types of reflexes. The first part of swallowing is the voluntary thrusting of food into the oral pharynx by the tongue. The impact of the food upon the walls of the pharynx stimulates interoceptive receptors. The nerve impulses reach the medulla oblongata over the vagus and glossopharyngeal nerves, and there are distributed to special visceral efferent cells in the motor nuclei of these nerves. There is set into play a complex series of involuntary actions involving the branchiomeric muscles. The palate and upper part of the pharynx constrict so as to prevent food from entering the nasal cavity. The upper part of the larynx constricts so as to shut off the air passages to the lungs. The muscles just around the bolus of food contract, while those just ahead of it relax so as to receive it. The wave of contraction, preceded by a wave of relaxation, proceeds from the pharynx into the esophagus and thence to the stomach. The timing of this mechanism is even more intricate when one realizes that initially the activity involves striated muscle, but that in the middle of the esophagus the musculature becomes of the smooth type. Hence the impulses shift from the special visceral efferents of these nerves to the general visceral efferents of the vagus nerves (from the dorsal motor nuclei). Furthermore, sympathetic fibers are involved, because inhibition of the muscles, as evidenced by the wave of relaxation, is a function of the sympathetic system. Impulses descend from the medulla oblongata to the thoracic cord, then out to the sympathetic ganglia and eventually to the esophagus. This type of activity, in which there is a wave of relaxation preceding a wave of contraction, is known as *peristalsis,* and is one of the fundamental types of coordinated activity of the intestinal tract. The complexity of events is even more pronounced when one considers that secretory phenomena accompany intestinal movements, and in this the dorsal motor nuclei of the vagus nerves are important factors.

Gastro-intestinal movements may be reversed in vomiting. This is accompanied by simultaneous contraction of the external abdominal muscles and descent of the diaphragm, thereby increasing the intra-abdominal pressure and forcing intestinal contents orally. Whether or not vomiting results from activity of a special center is unknown. It may be reflexly induced by impulses resulting from irritation of gastric mucosa, from putrid odors, and so forth. There is a drug, *apomorphine,* which apparently acts directly on brain stem cells so that its administration induces vomiting. Likewise, increased intracranial pressure stimulates these cells so that otherwise unexplained vomiting is an important sign of such an increase.

Summary

The spinal cord becomes the medulla oblongata at the foramen magnum. Above this point the major tracts are topographically rearranged, and nuclei of cranial nerves appear. Functional components found in spinal nerves are also found in cranial nerves. In addition, there are others: special visceral efferent supplying branchiomeric muscles; special visceral afferent or taste; and special somatic afferent, including hearing, balance and vision.

The reticular formation, including the vestibular nuclei, contains motor neurons, some of which are excitatory in function and others inhibitory. A decerebrate animal is one in which the brain stem is sectioned between basal ganglia and reticular formation. The excitatory mechanisms become active, the inhibitory mechanisms relatively silent, and the result is increased, exaggerated postural activity, decerebrate rigidity. The reticular formation mechanisms are modified by impulses from the labyrinths, the paleocerebellum, the midbrain and the cerebral hemispheres.

Many cells in the reticular formation of the brain stem subserve visceral functions. The most important of these are the control of blood pressure, cardiac activity, respiration and alimentary movements.

Within the midbrain there are also areas concerned in auditory and visual reflexes. The inferior colliculi subserve auditory reflexes; the superior, optic reflexes.

Names in Neurology

Magnus, Rudolph (1873–1927)

For many years Magnus was Professor of Pharmacology at Utrecht. In 1908, shortly after a winter spent at Liverpool with Sherrington, he began the first of a series of investigations of postural mechanisms. In 1924 he published a classic monograph on animal posture in which he clearly described reactions in three dimensions.

Pavlov, Ivan Petrovitch (1849–1936)

Pavlov, a Russian physiologist, was director of the Institute for Experimental Medicine in Petrograd. He devised an operative procedure for gastric and pancreatic fistulas which left the nerve supply intact. In such animals, if the esophagus is severed, gastric reactions with and without food can be studied. Later he devised a fistula for salivary ducts and over many years carried out his famous experiments on conditioned responses. In 1904 he was awarded the Nobel Prize.

References

Refer to physiology and neuroanatomy textbooks for discussions of brain stem structure and functions.

The following are advanced reviews, monographs, or symposia, with excellent bibliographies.

Adrian, F. D., Bremer, F., and Jasper, H. H., in Delafresnaye, J. F., ed.: Brain Mechanisms and Consciousness. Springfield, Ill., Charles C Thomas, 1955.

Magoun, H. W.: Caudal and cephalic influences of the brain stem reticular formation. Physiol. Rev., 30:459–474, 1950.

Magoun, H. W., and Rhines, Ruth: Spasticity: The Stretch Reflex and Extrapyramidal Systems. Springfield, Ill., Charles C Thomas, 1947.

CHAPTER 16

The Cerebellum

THE CEREBELLUM is attached to the brain stem by three pairs of peduncles (p. 17). It is grossly divisible into two hemispheres and a midline connecting portion, the vermis. Fissures of varying depths subdivide the hemispheres and vermis. The cerebellum is connected with the spinal cord and cerebral hemispheres as well as the brain stem, and on the basis of these connections there has been devised a more functional subdivision, as follows: A small portion of the cerebellum, shown in Fig. 131, is the *archicerebellum,* which is closely associated with the vestibular nerve. A corresponding part is present in lower animals, but in man the archicerebellum is relatively unimportant. Most of the vermis and certain

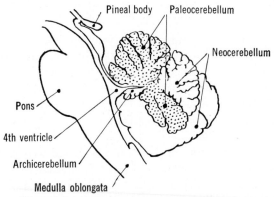

Figure 131. Outline sketch of a median section of the brain stem and cerebellum, after Fig. 11 (p. 19). The neocerebellum, which forms the bulk of this organ, is only partially visible in this view (see Fig. 6, p. 13).

279

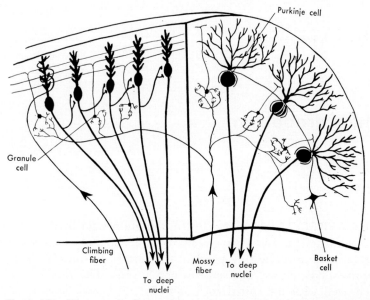

Figure 132.   Diagram of cells in a folium of the cerebellum. The Purkinje cells have a very large dendritic tree across the plane of the folium, hence in this view are much more extensive than in the plane parallel to the length of the folium. Mossy fibers synapse with many granule cells, and these in turn with many Purkinje cells. The axons of granule cells enter the molecular layer and divide, each branch running lengthwise in the folium. Climbing fibers synapse directly with Purkinje cells. Axons of Purkinje cells have recurrent branches to adjacent Purkinje cells. The molecular layer contains granule cell axons, Purkinje cell dendrites and basket cells. The afferents of the basket cells are unknown but their axons link Purkinje cells. Thus the entire arrangement is such that a few afferent fibers can activate a wide extent of cerebellar cortex.

parts of the cerebellar hemispheres form the *paleocerebellum,* which is present in vertebrates with limbs. The bulk of the cerebellum is the *neocerebellum,* so called because it (together with the cerebral cortex) is found in mammals and is best developed in man. These three subdivisions are rather arbitrary, but as an organization or basis for discussion they are useful.

The cerebellum, like the cerebral hemispheres, has a cortex of gray matter and an interior of both white and gray matter. The cortex has an inner or *granular layer* composed of many small neuroglial and nerve cells, a middle layer composed of a single row of large neurons called *Purkinje cells* (p. 289), and an outer or *molecular layer* consisting mainly of nerve cell processes, plus scattered nerve cells (Fig. 132).

The gray matter in the interior of each half of the cerebellum is composed of several nuclear masses, chief among which are the dentate nucleus and nucleus fastigius. The fastigial nuclei and several smaller ones form the so-called roof nuclei in the roof of the fourth ventricle.

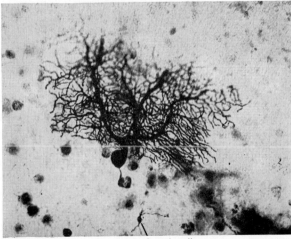

Granule cell

Figure 133.   Photomicrographs of Purkinje cells, Golgi stain. In the lower photograph a thin axon is seen extending downward from the cell body. This cell is incompletely impregnated. Hence the larger dendrites are less obscured than in the upper cell.

The nerve fibers going to and from the cerebellum form the peduncles. The entering (afferent) fibers reach the cortex and end in one of several ways. Some fibers (mossy fibers) synapse with granule cells. Others (climbing fibers) end on dendrites of Purkinje fibers. The cerebellar cortex is organized for *avalanche conduction,* that is, widespread discharge following relatively limited afferent input (Fig. 132). The reasons are 1) a mossy fiber connects with many granule cells, 2) a granule cell connects with many Purkinje cells, and 3) a Purkinje cell has recurrent branches that activate other Purkinje cells. Basket cells in the molecular layer provide for widespread connections, but their afferents are uncertain.

The axons of Purkinje cells form the output of the cerebellar cortex. Those axons synapse with cells in the cerebellar nuclei, and axons from the nuclei leave the cerebellum by way of the peduncles.

Connections with the Cerebral Cortex

The cerebral cortex is closely connected with the cerebellum, particularly with that part known as the neocerebellum, although the latter has, in addition, many connections in the brain stem. The corticocerebellar connections are in the nature of a circular or closed route, in that impulses which leave the cerebral cortex may ultimately return by way of the cerebellum (Fig. 134). Fibers destined for the cerebellum arise mainly from motor and sensory areas and descend in the internal capsule to the pons. Some are specifically concerned with the cerebellum and end in the pons. Others are major tracts, such as corticospinal, and the fibers give off collaterals as they descend through the pons. The direct fibers and collaterals synapse with nerve cells scattered throughout the ventral part of the pons. The axons of these cells cross the midline and collect to form the middle cerebellar peduncle (brachium pontis). Since the cerebral cortex and neocerebellum are relatively large in man, the ventral portion of the pons is correspondingly well developed. The fibers in the peduncles radiate to the cortex of the cerebellar hemispheres. Impulses leaving the cortex do so over axons of Purkinje cells, which conduct them to the dentate nuclei. Axons from the cells in these nuclei then ascend as the superior cerebellar peduncle, most of the fibers crossing the midline on reaching the mesencephalon. Some of the fibers ascend to the thalamus, which then relays impulses back to the cerebral cortex.

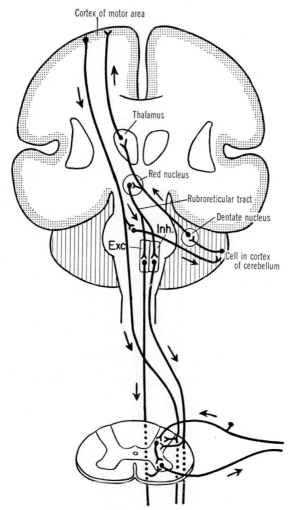

Figure 134. Diagram of some of the connections between cerebral cortex and cerebellum. Corticospinal fibers are represented as giving off collaterals in the pons. The cells with which they synapse give rise to the brachium pontis. The path ascending from the dentate nucleus is the superior cerebellar peduncle. In man, impulses from the red nucleus reach the spinal cord only by way of relays at brain stem levels.

Other fibers end in the red nucleus, which relays impulses to the brain stem and spinal cord.

Connections with the Spinal Cord

The cerebellum has long been regarded as a "head ganglion" or "proprioceptive organ" because it was thought that impulses reaching it from the spinal cord originated in neuromuscular spindles.

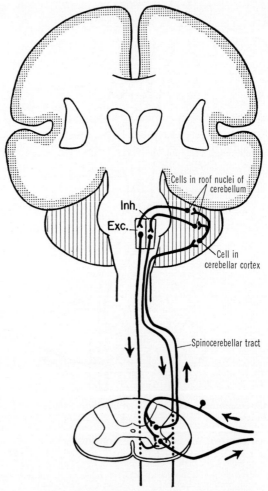

Figure 135.   Connections of the cerebellum and spinal cord. The spinocerebellar fibers actually enter the cerebellum by several routes rather than just the one shown here.

It is now known that impulses from skin, periosteum, joints and ligaments, as well as muscles and tendons, reach the cerebellum, and tactile projections are most prominent. The impulses that enter the spinal cord ascend by *spinocerebellar tracts* (anterior and posterior) that enter the cerebellum by the inferior cerebellar peduncle, and to a lesser extent by the superior cerebellar peduncle. There are other ascending tracts that relay in the brain stem before reaching the cerebellum. The various tracts are distributed mainly to the paleocerebellum. Axons of Purkinje cells then project to roof nuclei, and these in turn to the reticular formation of the brain stem. Accordingly, the functions of this part of the cerebellum are directed back to the spinal cord (Fig. 135).

Connections with Brain Stem and Cranial Nerves

That portion of the cerebellum known as the archicerebellum receives fibers from the vestibular nerve directly and also from vestibular nuclei. Its efferent fibers reach the vestibular nuclei and reticular formation.

Fibers from other cranial nerves, such as the trigeminal, also reach the cerebellum. These fibers are probably similar to those coming from the spinal cord in that they carry impulses originating in various peripheral receptors. The cerebellum also receives impulses from tracts carrying other special senses, such as hearing and vision.

The cerebellum is connected with other brain stem structures. Figure 126 (p. 260) illustrates the striking similarity of the dentate nuclei and the olivary nuclei. The latter are like the dentate nuclei and neocerebellum in that they are relatively largest in man. The olivary nuclei project to the cerebellar cortex by way of the inferior cerebellar peduncles probably mainly to the neocerebellum.

Localization in the Cerebellum

There have been numerous attempts to correlate cerebellar and body areas to determine, for instance, whether this or that part of the cerebellum is concerned with the upper extremity, and another part with the lower extremity. These efforts have been somewhat successful in lower animals, but in man the only localization known with any certainty is that relating a hemisphere to the same side of the body, and that the arm is represented in the cerebellum to a greater extent than the leg. Figure 134 illustrates that the right cerebellar hemisphere is concerned with the right side of the body. This ipsilateral control is a characteristic but not absolute feature of the cerebellum. This means that a lesion in the *left* cerebellum will cause signs on the *left* side of the body, in contrast to a lesion in the *left* internal capsule which can cause a *right* hemiplegia. A confusing situation results when there is a lesion in superior cerebellar peduncle after it has crossed in its ascent, in which case there are cerebellar signs contralateral to the side of the lesion. Thus it is not unknown for cerebellar signs to follow lesions in the frontal lobe, so that with a left-sided lesion the signs would be on the right side.

Functions of the Cerebellum

It has been difficult to analyze cerebellar functions, particularly in man, because data are largely restricted to those obtained from clinical disorders. These data and those obtained from animal experimentation indicate that the cerebellum has an important role in the coordination of muscular activity and that its functions are not at a conscious level.

This can be illustrated in the following manner. Suppose that in carrying out a movement such as flexion of the elbow, the flexor muscles contracted, but the extensors did not relax to a corresponding degree. This lack of relaxation would either prevent flexion or make it difficult to carry out smoothly. Suppose now that the extensors did relax, but not until flexor contraction had begun. The result would be a jerky type of movement.

These examples illustrate that an important part of muscular activity is timing, that even if muscle power and voluntary control are normal, if muscle groups do not contract in the proper time with respect to each other, movement will be jerky and awkward. The cerebellum seems to be largely responsible for coordinating and timing activity in various groups of muscles, both in static or postural and phasic or locomotor mechanisms. The functions of the cerebellum cannot be voluntarily modified. Actually, so far as is known, we are never directly conscious of the functions of the cerebellum, and defects resulting from cerebellar disorders cannot be voluntarily controlled or modified to any extent.

In order for the cerebellum to control or modify muscular activity, it needs information about position and movement. This information is derived from all receptors involved—skin, muscle, tendon, joint, labyrinth—and, since a very important feature of control of movement is visual, impulses from the retinae reach the cerebellum. Likewise, auditory impulses reach the cerebellum. It is very likely that those impulses from muscles which signal changes in muscle tension are mainly important at cord levels, but are less important than touch and vision at cerebellar levels. The cerebellum receives impulses from the cerebral cortex but, perhaps more important, its own discharges to the cerebral cortex serve to maintain or enhance the excitability of cortical neurons and thus facilitate and time discharges over motor tracts.

It is commonly stated that the paleocerebellum is primarily concerned in coordination of postural activity, and the neocerebellum in locomotor activity. This is based on the fact that in lower animals, such as the cat, it has been demonstrated experimentally that electrical stimulation of the anterior part of the cerebellum (paleocerebellum) may be followed by relaxation of antigravity muscles. Whether there is actually such a sharp distinction is open to question. For example, it is possible to obtain opposite effects merely by changing the frequency of the stimulating current.

Not much is known of the functions of the archicerebellum, and it is probably relatively unimportant in man. There is a malignant tumor, the *medulloblastoma,* composed of undifferentiated, rapidly growing cells, which occurs in children and frequently starts in this portion of the cerebellum. The earliest signs may be incoordination in trunk musculature. It has been deduced, therefore, that this part of the cerebellum is concerned in the coordination of the dorsal musculature of the trunk. The validity of these deductions is still uncertain.

So far as the deep nuclei of the cerebellum are concerned, little is known of the part they play in cerebellar functions.

The cerebellum is receiving increasing attention from experimenters and clinicians. With the knowledge that impulses from all types of receptors reach the cerebellum has come the realization that this structure is much more than a "head ganglion." It is undoubtedly implicated in a variety of nervous functions. For example, there is increasing evidence that the cerebellum is concerned in many visceral activities, such as respiration, the control of blood pressure, and others.

Disorders of the Cerebellum

In general, cerebellar defects are manifested as disorders in timing or coordination. This may result in jerky movements or *intention tremors*. The loss of timing may be particularly noticeable at the end of movement and result in *terminal tremor*. These defects may be elicited by asking the patient to put his finger to his nose. He may do so, but is often unable to stop his finger at his nose, or he may point much to one side of it. If elicited during walking, the resulting stumbling gait is known as *ataxia*. The defects may be pronounced during standing and may be elicited by having the patient put his feet close together, whereupon he sways severely and may fall over. Patients with lesions in the posterior funiculi of the spinal cord also have this difficulty, but mainly when the eyes are closed. They use vision to compensate for the loss of position sense. Cerebellar signs tend to be present whether the eyes are open or closed, although naturally much worse with the eyes closed. Cerebellar signs are compensated for rapidly, provided the lesion is not progressive. That is, symptoms may partially or completely disappear after several weeks or months. Perhaps vision is used to tell when muscular contractions reach the proper point, thus compensating for the loss of the more automatic mechanisms.

Another common cerebellar sign is *hypotonia*. This may be so great that the muscles are limp or actually flaccid, with decreased or even absent deep reflexes. This may be due to (1) decreased excitability of neurons in the cerebral cortex following loss of impulses from the cerebellum, and (2) decreased discharge from the red nucleus.

Summary

The cerebellum is a fissured structure attached to the brain stem by three pairs of peduncles. It has a cortex, composed of an inner granular layer, a middle Purkinje layer and an outer molecular layer. Fibers to the cerebellum reach the cortex and establish various types of connections. Axons of Purkinje cells leave the cortex and connect with the cells which form the cerebellar nuclei. These cells in turn project to other regions of the nervous system.

The cerebellum has widespread reciprocal connections with the cerebral cortex, particularly the motor and sensory areas. It has many connections with the spinal cord, chiefly with paths derived from peripheral receptors, and there are many connections with cranial nerves, particularly the vestibular, auditory, trigeminal and optic nerves.

The cerebellum is involved in timing or coordination of muscular activity. It receives information from peripheral receptors, and from motor and sensory regions of the cerebral cortex. It carries out its functions primarily through brain stem inhibitory and excitatory mechanisms, which it modifies, and also the motor cortex. The anatomical connections are such that each cerebellar hemisphere is concerned mainly with muscles on the ipsilateral or same side of the body.

Disorders of the cerebellum are manifested chiefly as defects in coordination of muscular activity.

Names in Neurology

Purkinje, Johannes (1787–1869)

Purkinje was a physician, born in Bohemia, who was the first to use a microtome in the preparation of microscopic slides and also developed many other aids for microtechnique. He was a man of widespread interests. In 1837, two years before formulation of the cell theory by Schleiden and Schwann, he pointed out the similarity of animal and vegetable cells. He studied nerve cells, glands, the heart and other organs. He described the specialized conducting fibers of the heart and the large nerve cells of the cerebellar cortex. He did not confine his interests to anatomy, but studied fingerprints, noted that deaf mutes could in some cases hear through the bones of the skull, and investigated the effects of opium, belladonna and other drugs.

References

Physiology textbooks generally have excellent sections on experimental studies of the cerebellum, but it is often difficult to relate such studies to man. For accounts of disorders of the cerebellum in man, see Grinker and Bucy, and Walshe (cited on p. 328).

CHAPTER 17

The Forebrain

THE FOREBRAIN is the primary brain vesicle from which the telencephalon and diencephalon differentiate (Chap. 5). In this section it is used as a general term to include the adult derivatives, such as the cerebral cortex, basal ganglia, thalamus and hypothalamus.

Human behavior is related to neurological structure and function just as is its counterpart in lower forms. Its infinite complexity is correlated with increasing development of the forebrain, particularly the cerebral cortex. Here reside the mechanisms governing language formation and use, emotional reactions and intelligence. Although our understanding of these mechanisms is extremely limited, this does not mean that there are no physiological processes forming the bases for such complex functions as memory or intelligence. Instead, it implies that they are not visible to the naked eye or detectible with present-day instruments.

Behavior is modifiable even in such simple forms as amebae. An ameba will not enter a beam of strong sunlight, and any portion of the cell that does so is immediately withdrawn. This behavior is known as a *tropic reaction*. After a few such local experiences, the entire cell takes part in a general avoiding reaction. The ameba then changes its direction of movement. The stimulus has not changed, but the local response has been followed by a spread of activity which depends upon some intrinsic protoplasmic organization. This rudimentary modification, however, is short-lived.

A paramecium ordinarily swims in wide spirals. In a strong avoiding reaction it may swim backward, but still spirally. If, however, it is placed in a small capillary tube which is too narrow to permit spiralling, the paramecium swims forward by a rotary movement to the end of the tube. Here it reverses the movement several times and finally turns around by a series of quick jerks. This reaction is never seen in normal unconfined behavior. It is "learning by experience" in a primitive manner.

As the synaptic type of nervous system appears in higher groups of animals, behavior becomes more complex and more modifiable. Fixed types are nevertheless present in any one species, and these usually predominate. In insects, for instance, the nervous system is almost fully formed before it begins to function. Hence modifiability is at a minimum. Ant colonies, for example, are complex phenomena because of the various types of ants within them, each with its own specific and relatively nonmodifiable function within the group.

Vertebrates also have fixed or "instinctive" types of behavior, for the most part determined by highly differentiated local patterns of nerve tissue which, however, do not function spontaneously. Some environmental factor is always needed to activate them. In ascending the vertebrate scale, "intelligent behavior" becomes more and more pronounced, attaining its highest development in man. This is correlated with the appearance of labile areas which have a large capacity for growth and differentiation even after they have started to function.

The structural features relating to lability of behavior appear to be on a hereditary basis. They are evident before the nervous system assumes its functions as a conducting mechanism. Hence they may be termed *preneural changes.* For instance, cranially located neuroblasts develop processes which extend downward and link with other cells at spinal levels. Spinal neuroblasts develop growing tips which push through the external surface of the neural tube and grow into areas of developing muscle (p. 64). At the same time, multineuronal sensory chains are being formed dorsally which give branches to the surface of the body. The sensory and motor chains are not connected commissurally, even when they begin to conduct. Hence experience due to influences of the external environment plays no part in exciting or influencing through nervous conduction the formation of these paths. The basic pattern of behavior is not determined by normal experience with the outside world.

Even after the longitudinal motor and sensory tracts take form and begin to function, there are preneural changes in higher areas. Neuroblast proliferation and differentiation becomes especially localized in forebrain areas. Optic centers differentiate before optic nerves enter them. The visual cortex is well defined in an eighteen weeks old human fetus at a time when body movements are simplest in form. Preneural and neural mechanisms thus overlap.

The characteristic feature of the cerebral cortex in primates is its tremendous early growth, even in the fetus. Long before it is needed or can be used, the adult pattern is formed. The cortex as well as the rest of the nervous system is composed of neurons, but the neuron concept as ordinarily presented creates the idea of rigid conducting patterns. It fails to account for the inherent capacity for change even after individual neurons are formed. Thus the adult pattern is unnecessary for the fetus at the moment, but provides a tremendous reserve for future learning. Growth is extensive even after conduction is possible. Neurons increase in length and size through fetal life, infancy and childhood. Comparisons of pyramidal and Purkinje cells at birth and in the adult show that marked changes in numbers and arrangements of dendritic processes have taken place in the intervening period.

Comparative Aspects of the Forebrain

The following brief account is intended to point out some features of the forebrain in different vertebrates.

Fishes

Correlative mechanisms are not well developed in fishes. Nearly all the central nervous system is devoted to fixed fundamental patterns, though coordinating centers such as the cerebellum are prominent. Even the forebrain is dominated for the most part by the olfactory system, and but a small part of it resembles a correlation center, that is, an area receiving impulses from more than one sensory system. This small part lies at the base of the brain in the thalamic region and is apparently the forerunner of the thalamus, corpus striatum and cerebral cortex of mammals. There is no true cerebral cortex in fishes.

The hypothalamic area of fishes is the dominant area for visceral mechanisms, while the midbrain subserves the same functions

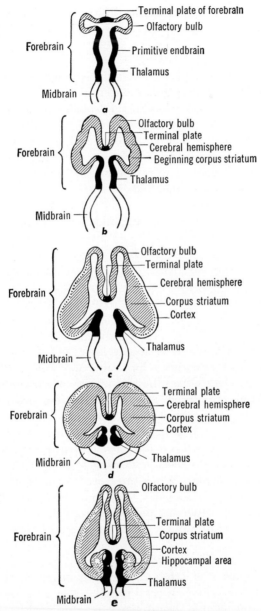

Figure 136. The forebrain in different vertebrates. Solid black indicates the primitive or unevaginated portion of the forebrain. *a*, Primitive vertebrate forebrain; *b*, frog; *c*, turtle; *d*, pigeon; *e*, rabbit. (Modified after Herrick.)

for somatic senses. Figure 136, *a,* illustrates a primitive vertebrate forebrain.

Amphibians

In amphibians part of the forebrain is evaginated into cerebral hemispheres that are devoted almost entirely to olfactory functions. But even in these forms two structural tendencies are evident. The cerebral hemispheres are complex because of (1) the local differentiation of functionally specific areas and (2) the presence of functionally diffuse areas. The first are represented by the corpus striatum, the second by the cerebral cortex. Thus, in the frog, a specialized amphibian, one finds a corpus striatum and a rudimentary cerebral cortex.

Figure 136, *b,* illustrates an amphibian forebrain.

Reptiles

Reptilian brains have fairly evident basal ganglia and a true cerebral cortex.

Figure 136, *c,* illustrates the forebrain of a turtle.

Birds

The corpus striatum is relatively large and complex in birds, whereas the cerebral cortex is primitive and scanty. The cerebral hemispheres are larger than those of reptiles, because of large basal lobes. Olfaction is reduced, as evidenced by the small size of the olfactory bulbs. The exteroceptive senses are well developed and are represented by a large midbrain. Birds are capable of highly complex behavior, but this is cast in stereotyped forms and instinctive responses. For instance, certain complex behavior cycles are really composed of parts which must occur in a regular sequence. If these cycles are interrupted, they must be renewed from the beginning and not from the point interrupted.

Figure 136, *d,* illustrates the forebrain of a bird.

Mammals

The development of cerebral cortex in mammals is associated with a relative reduction in basal ganglia. The cortex of the dorsolateral surfaces of the hemispheres is associated with somatic afferent and efferent mechanisms. Ventromedially, the cortex is linked with higher olfactory and visceral processes and is known as the *hippocampal area*. Just behind the olfactory bulbs is the *piriform area,* concerned with olfaction on a lower level. The last two areas are the phylogenetically older cortex or *archipallium,* whereas the remainder is the newer or *neocortex* or *neopallium.* The olfactory areas in each hemisphere are connected by a number of commissures, chief of which is the *anterior commissure.* In most mammals the neocortex on each side is connected by massive bundles of association fibers which form the corpus callosum.

Figure 136, *e,* illustrates the forebrain of a rabbit.

The neocortex throughout the mammalian scale becomes increasingly prominent and the archipallium relatively overshadowed, the latter having reached its maximal development in lower mammals. Olfaction is less important than vision in the arboreal habitat of primates. The progressive development of the neocortex in the latter forms is correlated, among other things, with the increasing importance of auditory, tactile and visual mechanisms.

Vision is one of the most important of these senses. Objects near at hand or far away may be recognized. Their precise location in space, their color, texture and form are discernible with great accuracy. The importance of these phenomena hardly needs emphasis. The development of the visual sense is accompanied by a reduction of the snout region, a lessening of the importance of smell, and by rotation of the eyes. In lower forms with pronounced noses, binocular or stereoscopic vision is not possible because the eyes look laterally, instead of forward. Even as the snout decreases and the eyes come to look forward, binocular vision is not possible until visual fields can overlap. This takes place when there is a concomitant change at the optic chiasm from a total to a partial decussation. Only with the latter can corresponding retinal points of two eyes project to one side of the brain. Finally there is a shift in visualization from the midbrain to the occipital lobes.

Upright posture in the primates is associated with skill in motor activities through the development of digital dexterity and an opposable thumb. The corticospinal tracts are most prominent in species with such digital facility. Cerebral dominance also becomes pronounced in the sense that most persons are right-handed, the handedness originating in the left cerebral cortex.

The facility of speech is associated with higher centers of the cerebral cortex and also with corticobulbar tracts to the motor nuclei concerned with speech. Likewise, binocular vision necessitates finer, more precise control of eye movements, associated with greater cortical control and with increasing complexity and differ-entiation in the oculomotor nuclei.

These functions are all related to the motor and sensory areas of the cerebral cortex which give rise to and receive projections. These areas are about the same size in man and in such lower primates as the great apes. Yet the brain of man is by far the larger because of the greater extent of association areas which are anti-mately connected with each other and with the motor and sensory regions.

The Basal Ganglia

The term "basal ganglia" is nonspecific; it refers to masses of gray matter in the interior of the cerebrum (Chap. 2). Those in the midbrain, the red nuclei and substantia nigra, are in a sense a junctional region between the other basal ganglia and more

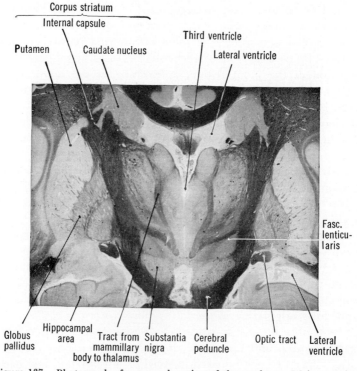

Figure 137. Photograph of a coronal section of the cerebrum. Weigert stain.

caudally placed reticular formation, and are anatomically and functionally connected with both. Although thalamus and hypothalamus could be termed basal ganglia, they are usually not considered basal ganglia. The term "subcortical" is non-specific, and is often used to refer to any non-cortical structure in hemisphere and diencephalon.

Connections of the Basal Ganglia. These are complex and poorly understood, hence only a very general survey will be made here. Most of the basal ganglia have connections with all sensory pathways, and they also receive fibers from the cerebral cortex, either directly or by relays through the caudate nucleus and putamen.

These are various motor paths leaving the basal ganglia. One of the most prominent tracts is composed of fibers leaving the globus pallidus, these fibers forming a tract called the fasciculus lenticularis (Fig. 137). This tract pierces the internal capsule (some loop around the capsule, as ansa lenticularis), and is distributed to the thalamus, by which impulses are returned to the cerebral cortex,

Internal capsule   Caudate nucleus   Corpus callosum   Thalamus

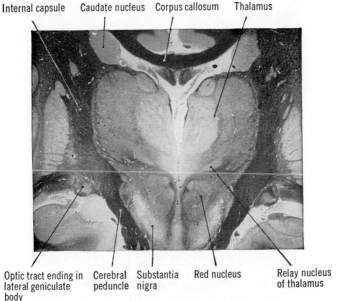

Optic tract ending in   Cerebral   Substantia   Red nucleus   Relay nucleus
lateral geniculate   peduncle   nigra   of thalamus
body

Figure 138. Photograph of a coronal section of the cerebrum. Weigert stain.

and to the reticular formation, by means of a series of short, descending paths involving other basal ganglia.

Motor Functions and Disorders of Basal Ganglia

It has been difficult to study the functions because basal ganglia are difficult to reach without destroying other parts of the nervous system. Electrical stimulation has on the whole yielded little infor-

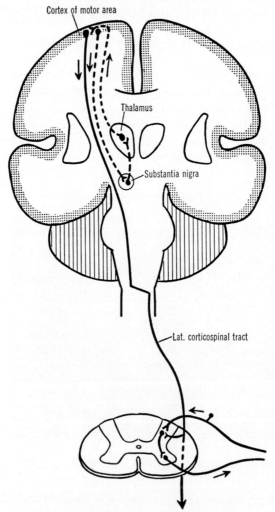

Figure 139.   A circular route from motor cortex through basal ganglia and back to the cortex to the origin of corticospinal fibers.

mation. Yet it is known that in lower forms, such as birds, well-coordinated behavior is carried out in the absence of cerebral cortex. Perhaps in mammals the functions of basal ganglia are obscured or overshadowed by the cerebral cortex.

Some facts appear fairly well established. Many of the so-called

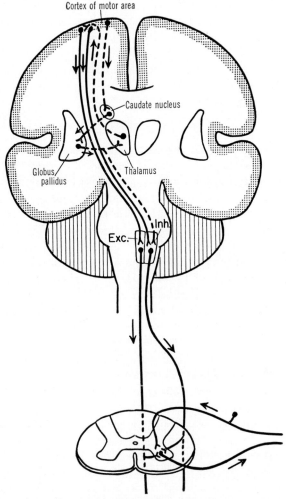

Figure 140. A circular route from motor cortex through basal ganglia and back to the origin of extrapyramidal fibers. The outflow from the globus pallidus is represented in part by the fasciculus lenticularis of Fig. 137. In addition, projections to brain stem inhibitory levels are shown coming from the globus pallidus as well as directly from the cerebral cortex.

extrapyramidal functions of the cerebral cortex are mediated through the basal ganglia. This seems to be particularly true of inhibitory functions. Stimulation of certain regions of the cerebral cortex may be followed by suppression of electrical activity of neighboring motor cortex and of any active movement going on at the time. These regions are associated with the circular routes through basal ganglia and with paths to the brain stem illustrated in Figs. 139 and 140. The fact that basal ganglia are involved in inhibitory mechanisms probably explains why direct stimulation of basal ganglia has often appeared to be ineffective. The basal ganglia are not, however, limited to inhibitory mechanisms. They are involved in much more complicated functions, as illustrated by the following discussion.

Dynamic Reactions

It was pointed out in Chap. 15 that a decerebrate animal is incapable of locomotor activity. If, instead of transecting the brain stem of a cat at the midbrain level, one severs it in the thalamic area in a manner which spares the midbrain and part or all of the thalamus and other basal ganglia, one has a *thalamic* or *midbrain* animal. Dynamic or phasic reactions can be demonstrated in such a cat. These consist in the ability to right itself or return to a standing position after changes in position and to carry out a fairly well-coordinated type of locomotion. In a normal animal the various reactions can be analyzed by excluding first one and then another of the various sensory and reflex fields. It must be emphasized that in the absence of cerebral cortex they can be carried out by the basal ganglia, by the cerebellum and perhaps by the hypothalamus, and that practically nothing is known of the manner in which the necessary integration is carried out.

Labyrinthine-Righting Reflexes. If an animal is blindfolded and placed in any position in space, the head returns to the normal horizontal position. The midbrain and the labyrinths appear to be essential for this reaction.

Body-Righting Reflexes Acting on the Head. The labyrinths must first be destroyed. If the blindfolded animal is then placed on its side, the head assumes a normal position. But this can be prevented if a board is placed on the upper surface of the body with enough pressure to equalize the pressure of the body weight exerted on that surface lying on the ground. The reflex depends then upon unequal stimulation of pressure receptors in the body.

Neck-Righting Reflexes. If the neck has once been turned in response to labyrinthine- or body-righting reflexes, proprioceptive receptors in the neck muscles are stimulated. This is followed by a reflex rotation which brings the body into line with the head and neck.

Body-Righting Reflexes Acting on the Body. In order to demonstrate these fully, the labyrinths must be destroyed and the animal blindfolded. If the forelimbs and shoulder are placed lateral to the ground, the hindlimbs tend to rotate to the horizontal position. This reaction can be prevented by equalizing the pressure with a board, as before.

Optic-Righting Reflexes. In the tests so far the animals are blindfolded to exclude optic-righting reflexes. These are important in the normal animal, but, since they depend upon the cerebral cortex, are absent in a midbrain animal. If the labyrinths are removed and cervical dorsal roots sectioned, the otherwise normal animal demonstrates righting reflexes with the eyes open, but not if blindfolded.

These reactions can be demonstrated in a thalamic cat or dog. In lower forms, such as birds, the basal ganglia are relatively much more important, and in the absence of cerebral cortex quite normal-appearing activity can still be carried out.

Primates differ from quadrupeds in that a midbrain primate, even though exhibiting righting reflexes, cannot stand. The cerebral cortex has become relatively much more important.

Motor Disorders

It has been postulated that some of the inhibitory functions of the cerebral cortex and basal ganglia are directed mainly against the pyramidal system, and others against the extrapyramidal system. If the first type were lost, uninhibited or spontaneous discharges from motor cortex over pyramidal fibers might occur and would be manifested as abnormal movements in muscles supplied mainly by this system. Such involuntary discharges do occur and are manifested as fine, rapid, involuntary contractions of digital and cranial muscles. These tremors disappear during sleep and tend to smooth out or disappear during a voluntarily induced movement. Hence they are frequently termed *tremors at rest.* The lay term is shaking palsy. The tremors are usually part of a disorder called *paralysis agitans,* frequently referred to as Parkinsonism (after James Parkinson, who first described it) (p. 310). It is not a definite disease entity, but a group of signs and symptoms referable to lesions of the basal ganglia, most pronounced in the substantia nigra. Other signs are commonly present, including rigidity in all muscles, loss of such associated movements as arm swinging when walking, loss of emotional expression in the face, and often a propulsive gait. There is no true paralysis. Movements are difficult mainly because of the associated rigidity.

If inhibition of extrapyramidal fibers were lost, the result might be spontaneous discharges from the motor cortex over these fibers. Clinically, such disorders occur and are manifested as *chorea,* in which involuntary movements are rapid, jerky, of wide range, and involve muscles all over the body; and *athetosis,* characterized by movements slower in rate, writhing or twisting in nature, and seen mainly in the extremities. These may be combined as *choreo- athetosis.*

Violent choreiform movements are seen in *St. Vitus' dance* (Sydenham's chorea) (p. 310). This is a disease of children which is related to rheumatic fever, probably as an involvement of the nervous system by that disease. *Huntington's chorea* (p. 310) is a hereditary disorder which, however, does not appear until adult life. It is characterized, not only by chorea, but also by speech diffi- culties and progressive dementia.

Recent clinical studies have shown that destruction of the medial part of the globus pallidus, by interruption of blood supply or by injection of a chemical, may relieve or abolish the motor signs described above. The relief is contralateral; that is, for tremor on the right side the surgeon would destroy the left globus pallidus. These findings are in conflict with some of the commonly held ideas about the functions of basal ganglia, and it seems likely that they will stimulate research and necessitate revision of ideas.

The Thalamus

Although the thalami have been studied mainly from the stand- point of their importance in sensation, they are closely connected with association areas of cerebral cortex, and are an important station in the projection of impulses from cerebellum, reticular system, and basal ganglia to the cerebral cortex. They therefore have multiple functions.

The various nuclei of which each thalamus is composed may be grouped according to their connections with other parts of the brain. Many nuclei, found mainly next to the third ventricle, connect with subcortical structures, such as hypothalamus. Another group of nuclei comprises the ventral portion of the thalamus and is associated with afferent paths for special and general senses. These nuclei relay impulses from these paths, as well as from cerebellum, reticular system, and basal ganglia, to the cerebral cortex. The bulk of the thalamus is relatively new phylogenetically—it is the *neothalamus*. Its nuclei receive no fibers from lower centers (at least no direct ones are known), but instead are connected to the cortical association areas, which themselves form most of the cerebral surface.

Many of the connections found by anatomical methods have been confirmed by physiological and pharmacological methods. These have dealt mainly with the classical afferent pathways and nuclei. Only in recent years have there been major attempts to decipher the connections of other nuclei.

Certain thalamic nuclei are called non-specific, in the sense that although they project to cerebral cortex, they are not confined to one cortical area. Stimulation of these non-specific thalamic nuclei produces remarkable changes in the electrical activity of the brain, such that the record consists of large, relatively slow synchronized waves that in some instances resemble the petit mal discharges of epilepsy.

Emotional and Visceral Functions of Subcortical Centers

An emotion is difficult to define. It may be expressed in terms of a way of acting and a way of feeling. All bodily activities may be involved in emotional states. Fear is an emotion. In it, respiration may increase, blood pressure rise, sweating may occur. The skin may pale, muscles tense, blood sugar may rise, and intestinal movements stop. Yet the same reactions may be present in anger, and an observer may find it difficult to distinguish the two states.

Facial muscles are extremely important in the expression of emotion. It is known that upper motor neuron lesions may interfere with or destroy voluntary control of facial muscles, yet not affect reflex facial movements. In such instances it is not uncommon to find that all types of facial expressions occur during emotional states, in spite of the paralysis of voluntary movement. Conversely, subcortical lesions in the region of the thalamus may abolish facial movements in emotions, although voluntary control is retained. In

other words, the arrangement of motor responses in affective behavior seems to be a function of regions other than the cortical
motor areas. For instance, emotional speech may occur voluntarily
in a patient with motor aphasia (p. 340).

The fact that stimulation of the hypothalamus is followed by
responses similar to those seen in emotional states has led to a
concept that the hypothalamus is concerned with motor components
of emotion. An animal with its cerebral cortex removed may fly
into *sham rages,* and these may be reproduced by electrical stimulation of the hypothalamic region. These rages subside when the
stimulus stops, and there is no indication that they are accompanied
by changes in affective tone. Patients deprived of objective emotional responses because of hypothalamic lesions may nevertheless
subjectively experience the emotions. The feeling of an emotion is
a function of other parts of the nervous system, including the cortex
of the frontal lobe (p. 345).

A single sense or group of senses cannot be identified with affective tone. Pain is a definite sense. But considered subjectively, it
may be associated with pleasure. For example, some people gain
pleasure from having pain inflicted on them (*masochism*), whereas
others may derive satisfaction in inflicting it (*sadism*).

Not only are the frontal lobes concerned in emotion, but so are
the temporal lobes, and certain basal ganglia. It was formerly
thought that the so-called rhinencephalon, including the hippocampus, dealt with smell, but it now seems that it has little to do
with smell, being concerned instead with emotion. The exact regions, their connections and functions, are still uncertain, but the
hippocampus and its connections seem to be especially important,
as do the amygdaloid bodies. In man, lesions of the temporal lobe,
particularly lesions involving the medial, basal cortex, cause emotional disturbances. Symptoms may include hallucinations, disordered recognition and memory, disturbances of reality, dream
states, clouding of consciousness, sensory fits (sudden, subjective
smell or taste, often unpleasant), and psychomotor epilepsy. Surgical removal of part of the temporal lobe has been performed for
psychomotor epilepsy. Surgical lesions in the temporal lobes of
wild or otherwise unmanageable animals may tame them. Bilateral
removal of temporal lobes may result in complete absence of emotion and, interestingly enough, increased sexual activity. The latter
seems to be related to the amygdaloid bodies, bilateral removal of

which may lead to hypersexuality or abnormal sexual behavior, possibly with changes in uterus and ovaries. The amygdaloid bodies consist of a number of nuclear masses, the connections and functions of which are still uncertain.

It has been possible in man and experimental animals to place electrodes into the brain and leave them there, so arranged as to be able either to stimulate with or record from these electrodes in the conscious, unanesthetized state. Some of the information mentioned above has been obtained with such methods. For example, stimulation of some regions (especially hippocampus and its connections) may cause widespread electrical convulsive activity in the cerebral hemispheres.

It has also been shown that electrical stimulation of some subcortical regions in animals affects these animals in a way such that they appear to be gaining pleasure from it. In such instances, on being trained to activate the electrical circuit and thus to stimulate themselves, the animals may keep up the self-stimulation for hours or days.

The importance of the various subcortical centers, and especially their possible importance in psychiatric disorders, is now generally realized. But our knowledge of these regions is still quite fragmentary.

Structure of the Cerebral Cortex

In spite of the functional differences between species, extensive studies have led to the conclusion that the neurons of the cerebral cortex are arranged in a similar pattern in all animals which have a cortex. These conclusions are based on the fact that by studying sections stained for Nissl substance, the cell bodies of the cortical neurons appeared to be grouped into six layers.

By using stains for nerve fibers, it has been shown that nerve fibers projecting from the cerebral cortex (such as corticospinal) arise mainly from cells in the fifth layer, that nerve fibers entering the cortex end mainly in the fourth layer, and that the cortex is chiefly composed of interneurons which provide for intracortical connections. The most numerous interneuron in the fourth layer is the *granule cell;* hence the first three layers are called *supragranular layers.*

The basic pattern of cortical connections (Fig. 141) is similar to patterns of connections described for gray matter generally (p. 122).

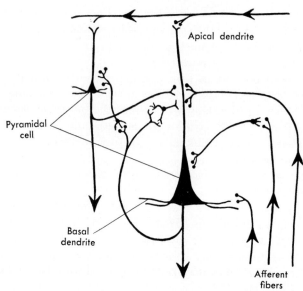

Figure 141. Schematic representation of some cells and their connections in the cerebral cortex, based on Golgi staining. Microscopic studies using Nissl stains (thus showing only cell bodies) do not reveal the connections of nerve cells. Some nerve fibers entering the cortex relay through small cells to the body of the large pyramidal cell, activation of which leads to a discharge over the axon with provision for reactivation through the recurrent branch of the axon. Most synapses are with the dendrites of the pyramidal cell and not the cell body. Dendritic activation is accompanied by large, slow potential changes, by lack of an absolute refractory and by prolonged depolarization. The latter two factors make it possible for successive impulses reaching dendrites to maintain them in a depolarized state. In turn, current flow from dendrites very likely can depolarize the cell body and cause it to discharge. Thus, prolonged activity and repetitive discharges are dependent not only on conduction through various chains of neurons (as shown in more detail in Figure 70), but also on dendritic activation by connections shown in above figure. Note also that the apical dendrites of pyramidal cells can be linked together by axons in the outer layer of cerebral cortex (cell body not shown). (Based on Clare and Bishop, Am. J. Psychiat., vol. 111, 1955.)

Figure 141 is a gross oversimplification. The interneurons which link the afferent and efferent fibers and also various units (not shown in the figure) are numbered in the billions. Actually, our knowledge of cortical structure is so fragmentary that any attempts to compare these units to man-made electronic feedback circuits are purely speculative.

The earliest studies of the cerebral cortex led to the naming of lobes, convolutions, gyri, fissures and sulci. Subsequently, investigators of cortical lamination developed a system of numbering (also lettering), each area being given a number as it was studied, and each one supposedly structurally different from other numbered areas. As the studies continued, more and more numbered areas were delimited, several hundred now being described. Many of these studies are based on Nissl stains, which give no information about cell processes. Actually, few of the studies have established any objective criteria for critical distinctions between cortical areas, and few have taken any account of individual variations.

The naming and numbering of areas, and the use of diagrams, unfortunately, give the impression of clear-cut, sharp distinctions between areas. This is not so. Actually, except in a few instances, numbered and named areas are neither functionally nor structurally specific. The present tendency is toward a simplification of numbering, with more attention to physiological correlates in the intact organism. This does not mean that there are no structural or functional differences between different regions of the cerebral cortex. There probably are, but the criteria ordinarily used today do not demonstrate them satisfactorily. Some of the structural differences are mentioned in Chap. 18 in connection with motor and sensory regions.

Electrical Activity of the Brain

The electrical activity of the brain can be detected and recorded much in the same manner as electrical activity of the heart or a peripheral nerve is recorded. Electrodes are placed on the subject's scalp, and the voltages across the electrodes are magnified or amplified by means of a vacuum tube amplifier. Finally, the voltage changes are recorded with an ink writer or oscillograph. In normal subjects there is a characteristic pattern made up of waves of varying frequency and magnitude. Such a changing pattern represents the algebraic sum of the potentials of billions of cortical neurons. The record obtained is an *electroencephalogram* or *EEG,* and the oscillations recorded are popularly known as "brain waves."

The electroencephalogram is obtained with the subject at rest, in a darkened room or with the eyes closed. Although the pattern of the electroencephalogram varies from one person to another, in many normal persons moderate deflections occurring ten to twelve times a second are often visible. These are the *alpha waves* (Berger rhythm) (p. 310).

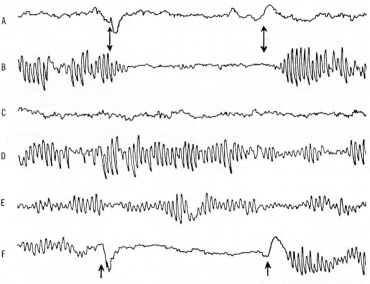

Figure 142. Normal electroencephalograms of a medical student. *A*, Record from right and left frontal regions and, *B*, from right and left occipital regions, taken simultaneously. The first arrow indicates opening the eyes. Note the subsequent deflection in the frontal record. This is an artifact due to the movement. Note that the activity in the occipital leads is suppressed. The second arrow indicates eye closing, again followed by an artifact, with a reappearance of occipital activity. *C* and *D*, Continuations of *A* and *B* to give an idea of variations in activity. The frontal records are mainly low voltage, relatively fast or *beta* activity. The occipital records are mainly higher voltage, 10 to 12 per second *alpha* activity. Alpha activity by definition decreases or disappears upon opening the eyes, as it did in *B*. *E*, Record between right occipital and right frontal, continued in *F*, in which the opening and closing of the eyes, indicated by arrows and blinking artifacts, is accompanied again by suppression of alpha activity.

Smaller faster deflections, the *beta waves* (Fig. 142), may be superimposed on the alpha waves, especially when recording from frontal regions. Waves slower than five per second are frequently termed *delta waves;* these are not found in the normal person except during sleep.

Mental activity or opening the eyes causes the alpha waves to disappear (Fig. 142). Changes in the normal rhythm occur during sleep, especially during deep slumber, when slow waves of three a second or more duration appear. In moderately deep sleep there may be bursts of fast activity, the sleep *spindles,* superimposed upon the slow waves.

Anesthetics and metabolic changes frequently alter normal rhythm, this being correlated with variations in the excitability of the cerebral cortex. In certain disorders the wave form deviates from the normal. The presence in an electroencephalogram of abnormal waves, especially if slow and large, often aids in the diagnosis of these disorders. The electroencephalogram has found its most useful clinical function in the localization of certain types of surface tumors or lesions and in studies of epilepsy (p. 326).

What the electroencephalogram represents is not yet known. It is true that there are regional differences, the alpha rhythm appearing to come mainly from the occipital cortex, while the frontal region shows mainly beta activity. The waves can be modified by various sensory and pharmacological procedures. But they cannot yet be interpreted with any accuracy in terms of what is known regarding fiber conduction and cellular activity. Nor can one assume that the waves are primarily cortical in origin so far as spontaneous activity is concerned. There is considerable evidence that stimulation of brain stem reticular formation alters the brain wave pattern. The reticular activating system mediates the arousal reaction, with desynchronization or flattening of the EEG. Reduction of afferent impulses to the cerebral cortex has a profound effect. For example, the cerebral cortex of a decerebrate animal, a cortex which receives impulses only from the olfactory and optic nerves, has a pattern resembling that of sleep. In certain paroxysmal states electrical patterns of the cortex may be "driven" by the thalamus. These examples give some idea of the complexity of events under study, and the section on volume conduction (p. 103) points out the difficulties involved in studying conducting tissue when the components of this tissue are not linear, parallel conductors.

Summary

Instinctive behavior consists in stereotyped patterns which are mainly dependent upon highly differentiated local arrangements coordinated by spinal cord and brain stem centers. Intelligent behavior is related to labile, relatively nonspecific areas of the forebrain.

Forebrain arrangement in the vertebrate scale is in two general trends: (1) toward the appearance of basal ganglia, which in birds attain their maximal development relative to the rest of the brain; (2) toward the appearance of a cerebral cortex, which is maximally developed in mammals.

The cortex develops along olfactory and nonolfactory lines, the latter overshadowing the former with progression toward primate forms. In the latter, cortical development is correlated with the appearance of upright posture, opposable thumb, binocular vision, and higher mental processes.

Cortical structure can be illustrated by a fundamental vertical unit, but only a few regions of the cerebral cortex show consistent structural differences.

Electrical activity of the brain can be recorded and is a spontaneous type of activity known as brain waves or the electroencephalogram. This activity can be modified by various physiological and experimental procedures, but it cannot be interpreted in terms of peripheral nerve electrophysiology.

Names in Neurology

Berger, Hans (1873–1941)

Berger, a neurologist in Jena, was the first to record the electrical activity of the brain in the human subject. He studied the electroencephalogram extensively, and one of the basic patterns or rhythms bear his name.

Huntington, George (1850–1916)

Huntington, an American physician, was the first to describe hereditary chorea.

Parkinson, James (1755–1824)

Parkinson, an English physician, in 1812 described the first recognized cases of paralysis agitans. He was noted for his studies of fossil remains, being an able geologist and paleontologist, but was perhaps better known during his time as a radical reformer and political agitator.

Sydenham, Thomas (1624–1689)

Sydenham was an English physician who published first-hand accounts of many diseases, including gout, scarlatina, measles, bronchopneumonia, hysteria, chorea, and others. Some of his descriptions are unsurpassed classics.

References

In addition to the following volumes, attention is called to the references on pp. 328 and 347. See also Brain Mechanisms and Consciousness (cited on p. 278).

Child, C. M.: Physiological Foundations of Behavior. New York, Henry Holt and Company, 1924.

Herrick, C. J.: Neurological Foundations of Animal Behavior. New York, Henry Holt and Company, 1924.

Clark, W. E. LeG.: Early Forerunners of Man. Baltimore, William Wood and Company, 1934. This is a skilled general discussion of evolutionary changes in primates.

Gibbs, F. A., and Gibbs, E. L.: Atlas of Electroencephalography. 2nd ed. Cambridge, Mass., Addison-Wesley Press, Inc., 1950. This atlas presents representative records of normal subjects and of patients with various disorders. See also Clinical Examinations in Neurology (cited on p. 150) for an excellent, short chapter on electroencephalography.

CHAPTER 18

Motor and Sensory Functions
of the Cerebral Cortex

THE MOTOR functions discussed in this chapter are those carried out by the regions of the cerebral cortex from which the motor paths arise. The sensory functions are those carried out by regions in which afferent paths end, that is, the primary receptive areas.

Motor Areas

There are several regions of the cerebral cortex the electrical stimulation of which is followed by some type of muscular activity. These regions are the ones from which the descending motor paths arise. Most of those known at the present time lie anterior to the

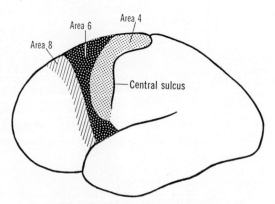

Figure 143. Diagram indicating the approximate locations of the motor areas on the lateral surface of the frontal lobe.

Central sulcus

Cortex of
Postcental
Gyrus

Cortex of
Precentral Gyrus

Layer of
Large
Pyramidal
Cells

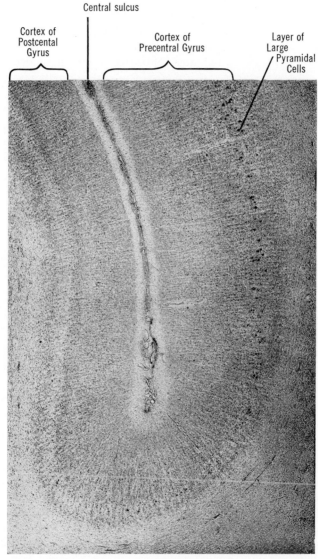

Figure 144. Photomicrograph of Nissl-stained section of central sulcus with motor cortex (precentral gyrus) on the right and the sensory cortex (postcentral gyrus) on the left. Note large pyramidal cells in the motor cortex. The central fissure between the two is filled with pia mater, arachnoid and blood vessels.

central sulcus and form the precentral motor cortex, a region which is usually subdivided into several numbered areas (Fig. 143). The cerebral cortex of this region is rather thick (Fig. 144). It receives many fibers from the thalamus, and these fibers end largely in layer IV. There are many pyramidal-shaped cells of various sizes in the fourth and fifth layers; as a consequence, the fourth layer is obscured, to the extent that motor cortex is often spoken of as *agranular cortex*. These pyramidal cells contribute to the corticospinal and extrapyramidal tracts. There are no sharp lines of demarcation between the numbered subdivisions of the motor cortex, either grossly or microscopically. Figure 143 merely illustrates their approximate locations. In a brain exposed at operation it is practically impossible to be sure what area is in the operating field. Arachnoid, pia mater and blood vessels obscure surface landmarks, and there is great individual variation in the relation of surface landmarks to bony landmarks.

There are regions of the cerebral cortex other than the classical precentral which are also motor areas. Motor paths having to do with eye movements arise from the occipital cortex. A second motor area has been found on the medial surface of the hemisphere. Various parts of the frontal lobe, particularly medial and basal surfaces, give rise to paths having to do with visceral activities.

The cortical motor areas have little function at birth. A newborn infant shows little voluntary or coordinated activity and has reflex patterns ordinarily not seen in an adult. For example, a grasp reflex is easily demonstrated by placing one's finger in a baby's hand. A Babinski response is present and only gradually disappears when walking begins. One can argue that the withdrawal which a Babinski reflex represents would conflict with walking and that it consequently is inhibited when the cortex begins to function. At least it disappears and in an adult is elicited only in upper motor neuron disorders, in fatigue or in deep sleep. The newborn infant also shows static and dynamic responses, reflex patterns much like those of a thalamic animal. Not until the child begins to walk does the fine coordination characteristic of more complete cortical functioning begin its development.

Stimulation

If the precentral motor cortex is explored with a stimulating electrode, an inverted representation of movements is found, such that movements in the lower extremity follow stimulation of the upper or dorsal part of the region; movements in the upper extremity when the middle of the region is stimulated; and movements in the head and neck muscles following stimulation of the lower or ventral part of the region. This is anything but a specific pattern, however. Figure 145 helps to illustrate what might be called overlap. For example, if one stimulates a spot on the motor cortex with a single electrical pulse, a muscle or a few muscles will twitch on the opposite side of the body. If the strength of the stimulus is increased, other muscles will also respond. And if

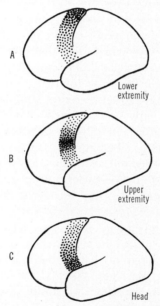

Figure 145. Diagram of the manner in which movements are represented in the cerebral cortex. *A,* Stimulation of the heavily shaded area usually, or most easily, elicits movements in the lower extremity. Stimulation anywhere else in the motor cortex can also elicit movements in the lower extremity, but less easily, and the degree of shading is some indication of the degree of response. *B,* Similar situation for upper extremity and, *C,* for head and neck. If these three drawings were superimposed so as to represent the actual situation, then in any one region (even a very small region) of motor cortex, all types of movements would be represented, but some one type much more so than any other. Conversely, destruction of a part of the motor cortex would have its greatest effect on one type of movement, so that there might be weakness or paralysis of a muscle or group of muscles in this particular movement, but the same muscles might be used effectively in other movements.

the same spot is stimulated with 60-cycle current of the same strength, many more muscles contract. It is known that in the so-called arm region, nerve cells for the arm muscles have the lowest threshold, that is, are most excitable, other muscles in the body being represented by nerve cells with a higher threshold. Likewise, in the leg region, nerve cells to leg muscles have the lowest threshold.

One might suppose that contraction of a leg muscle when the arm area is stimulated is due to spread of the stimulus to the leg area. Actually, however, it is possible so to isolate the stimulated region surgically as to leave only connections to subcortical centers. Stimulation of just one spot can still yield multiple patterns of response. The results are such that one can only conclude that even in very small parts of the motor cortex all types of movements all over the body are represented, and that some of them are pre-dominantly represented, that is, more easily elicited by stimulation. Figure 145 simply illustrates predominant representation.

It must be emphasized that electrical stimulation is an artificial procedure, and that only by the merest chance would such a pro-cedure activate a pattern of cells in the same manner as would a physiological stimulus. The results depend, not only upon the strength of the stimulus, but also upon the frequency. Contraction may occur in one group of muscles during stimulation at one fre-quency, and in another group during stimulation at another frequency.

The results also depend upon posture. That is, if a muscle or group of muscles is placed in a particular position, the result of stimulation may be different than if the muscles had been placed in another position.

Impulses from skin, muscles, and joints have a profound effect upon the result of cortical stimulation. The interpretation of cortical stimulation may be complicated by secondary movement. If one observes a pattern of activity in response to stimulation, one cannot assume that the entire pattern was a direct result of the stimulus. It is possible that some muscles contracted after stimula-tion, and that this contraction reflexly induced activity in still other muscles, independently of the cerebral cortex. Visual obser-vation is extremely misleading in study of muscular activity. Con-scious human subjects on whom stimulation experiments are carried out report that any movements which result seem quite beyond their control and without any sense of being willed or initiated. It is interesting that stimulation of the precentral gyrus sometimes causes tingling or other sensation rather than movement.

The multiplicity of representation is encountered clinically. A surface tumor may irritate a small part of the motor cortex and thereby cause involuntary movements or convulsions on the opposite side of the body. The convulsions start in those muscles which are predominantly represented in the affected area and then rapidly involve other muscles. These spreading seizures, without loss of consciousness, are often called *jacksonian* convulsions (p. 327).

The threshold, or excitable level, of the cerebral cortex varies greatly. For instance, after stimulation of a cortical focus there may be a long period during which no response can be obtained. This is a subnormal period. The threshold may also vary according to metabolic activities. A shift in hydrogen ion concentration toward the alkaline side is followed by an increase in excitability which may be recorded as fast activity in the electroencephalogram. The alkalinity can be produced by hyperventilation, during which carbon dioxide is blown off. Even in normal subjects, continued overbreathing may be followed by such an increase in excitability that spontaneous involuntary twitchings or tremors appear.

The division of the precentral motor cortex into Areas 4, 6 and 8 has been made mainly on the basis of stimulation studies and to some extent on extirpation and on microscopic studies. Movements are most easily elicited by stimulation of Area 4, and the inverted representation of the body is most pronounced here. The area is practically coextensive with the precentral gyrus. Area 4 is often subdivided, the basis being the presence within its fifth layer of large pyramidal cells. Some are so large as to be called giant pyramidal cells. These large pyramidal cells are most numerous in the upper part of the gyrus, that concerned primarily with the lower extremity. Their size is probably only a reflection of the distance which their axons travel (to the lumbar and sacral cord). Large pyramidal cells are often found in many other areas, including sensory cortex.

Stimulation of Area 6 is frequently without effect. It has been concluded that inhibitory fibers arise more strongly here than they do from Area 4, and it is known that fibers from this region reach the reticular formation of the brain stem by direct paths and by relays through basal ganglia. Area 8 is often called the frontal eye field, since its stimulation is often followed by conjugate eye movements as well as by various head and neck movements. It is quite similar to Area 6, and there is much doubt as to its distinctness.

Many experimenters have reported that specific regions of the cerebral cortex are concerned with inhibitory mechanisms. These regions are usually small and often form a strip of cortex. One, said to lie between Areas 4 and 6, is called Area 4S (a strip or suppressor area). This region is said to project by way of basal ganglia, and also by direct paths, to the brain stem. Although there is much evidence supporting these views, many investigators do not believe that such specific strips exist. One factor that has to be considered is that even minor trauma during study, or exposure of cerebral cortex to room temperature, often results in a spreading depression. This is characterized particularly by decreased electrical activity and decreased sensitivity to stimulation, and the spread is not dependent upon nervous pathways.

Visceral as well as somatic responses may follow cortical stimulation. Thus there is increased blood flow through muscles active in cortically induced movements, and the impulses mediating this vasomotor reaction probably originate in the cortex. Changes in systolic blood pressure and heart rate may also occur. Strong stimulation of Area 8 may be followed, not only by conjugate eye movements, but also by the formation and flow of tears, and by changes in pupillary diameter. There is a cortical zone anterior to Area 8, near the inferior surface of the frontal lobe, stimulation of which results in marked inhibition of many visceral activities.

Recent work indicates that motor responses may follow stimulation of a region on the medial surface of the hemisphere and that such responses may involve any muscle of the body. The significance of this second motor area is unknown.

Extirpation

Many of the functions of the motor areas have been deduced by studying the loss of function following cortical destruction. If a small metal disk, heated to the proper temperature, is placed on part of the motor cortex, the first three or four cell layers will be destroyed, but stimulation of the area so treated is still followed by movements. However, if the temperature is such as to kill the first five layers, responses are no longer obtained, indicating that projections arise from the fifth cell layer. This again indicates the artificial nature of the electrical stimulus. The great numbers of small cells beyond any doubt are of the greatest importance, yet removing them makes little difference in the response to stimulation.

With destruction of part or all of a motor area, either experimentally or by disease, upper motor neuron types of disorders occur. In general, the more widespread the destruction, the more pronounced and enduring is the weakness or paralysis. The degree to which functions can be assessed, however, is limited, because it is difficult to destroy one area precisely without affecting neighboring ones. This is especially true of pathological processes, which rarely limit themselves to one region.

Spasticity, hyperactive deep reflexes and pathological reflexes often accompany weakness, especially with widespread lesions. Complete paralysis is rare, once there is recovery from the sudden onset of a disorder. Even weakness is only relative with cortical lesions, and this is clearly shown when such lesions are small. A muscle may for all practical purposes be paralyzed when attempts are made to use it in one type of movement pattern, and yet the same muscle may be used easily in another movement pattern. For example, with loss of part of the arm area, a patient may be unable to extend his wrist on command. Yet the wrist may extend when making a fist. This illustrates again the multiplicity of representation, that any one small part of the motor cortex deals with many movements, and that any one movement is represented in many parts of the motor cortex.

Weakness and even paralysis are also relative as to time, because with proper training, practice, and lapse of time, motor deficits from cortical lesions (and even subcortical ones) may practically disappear.

Certain types of pathological responses appear to be characteristic of large lesions of the motor cortex. For example, the grasp reflex and groping response seem to follow large defects, particularly those involving Area 6 or the supplemental motor area on the medial surface of the hemisphere. The *grasp reflex,* seen normally in infants, is the reflex grasping of an object placed in the hand, a reflex initiated by the pressure of the object and carried out by the cerebral cortex. It has been postulated that Area 4 is responsible for carrying out this reflex and that Area 6 inhibits it in the adult. The *groping response* is more complex. Contact with an object by the fingers is followed by reflex reach toward and grasping of the object. Tactile, pressure and proprioceptive afferents are necessary for the initiation of the response, which, like the grasp, is carried out by the cerebral cortex.

These responses are most apt to follow clear-cut surgical or other traumatic lesions. Other types, such as tumors or inflammatory processes, are much more liable to produce swelling and diffuse, widespread damage, so that any resulting signs and symptoms are much less specific.

Comparable reactions in lower forms, such as the cat, are hopping and placing reactions. In the *placing reaction,* if the paw of a blindfolded cat is touched to the edge of a table, that paw is almost instantly placed upon the surface of the table. The initiating factors are tactile stimuli. The response is dependent upon both sensory and motor cortex. Destruction of one motor cortex is followed by loss of the placing reaction in contralateral paws. *Hopping reactions* are similar. If the dorsal surface of a paw is dragged along the surface of a table, the animal makes repetitive placing movements, each of which is a pattern initiated by tactile impulses.

Removal of the motor cortex in man, either partially or completely, does not cause any memory loss. The patient still knows how to carry out even the most complex maneuvers he has ever learned and, if he has a usable extremity left, can attempt learned patterns with that extremity. In other words, the defects are just in the execution of motor activity.

Relation to Sensory Areas and the Cerebellum

Experimental work on lower animals has shown that motor and sensory cortices are interdependent, and clinical evidence indicates that this is also true in man. This was mentioned in connection with the hopping and placing reactions, which are initiated by tactile stimuli and are abolished by lesions of either the motor or sensory cortex.

As was pointed out previously, discharges from, or results of stimulation of, the motor cortex are modified, or even determined, by the state of contraction or activity in the muscle group supplied by the stimulated region. Even passive alteration of the position of a muscle may alter its subsequent response, or even abolish it.

In other words, the proprioceptive impulses reaching the cerebral cortex condition the motor cortex.

The motor cortex is closely associated with the cerebellum, particularly as regards timing mechanisms (p. 286). These relationships were discussed in Chap. 16.

Sensory Areas (Primary Receptive Areas)

In considering sensory mechanisms, we may arbitrarily assign to certain portions of the cerebral cortex the function of initial perception of a primary modality of sensation; and to other regions, the localization, discrimination and integration of the primary modalities and the integration of these mechanisms into learning. Such a method is useful in considering the symptoms resulting from destruction of different parts of the cortex, but so far as normal functions are concerned the various parts are so integrated that their separate functions are not subjectively recognized or differentiated. From the standpoint of organization it seems desirable to consider certain features of perception here and also in the next chapter.

The primary receptive areas were discussed briefly in Chap. 11,

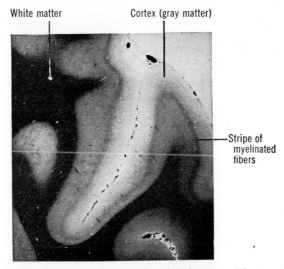

Figure 146. Photomicrograph of a section of occipital cortex. The entering visual fibers form a band or stripe as they end in the fourth cell layer. Weigert stain.

where it was pointed out that afferent paths project to them by way of thalamic relay nuclei. The cortex of these areas is generally thinner than that of the motor areas and has definite granular layers (Fig. 144). The afferent fibers that enter these areas form bands that are often visible to the naked eye, especially in the occipital cortex (Area 17) (Fig. 146). If a portion of cerebral cortex is destroyed, there is a characteristic reaction of the thalamus to cortical injury. The thalamic fibers ending in the injured cortex undergo retrograde degeneration to the extent that chromatolysis of the cells of origin is not reversed. The cells die, and the thalamic nuclei containing these cells atrophy. There is, therefore, no "pure" cortical lesion, because any cortical lesion is followed within a few months by death of some portion of the thalamus. This thalamic reaction to cortical injury has been widely used to determine anatomical relationships between the thalamus and the cerebral cortex.

Stimulation

The primary areas have been artificially stimulated, but the resulting sensations are not those normally experienced. Electrical stimulation of the visual cortex gives rise to sensations of flashes of light. One would not expect it to be otherwise, unless by chance the stimulation affected a group of neurons which would normally be activated by objects in the visual fields. Such stimulation is just as artificial as that which simultaneously activates all the fibers of a peripheral nerve.

Stimulation may also result from the actions of certain drugs. If, for example, strychnine is applied to the cortex of the postcentral gyrus of cats, the resulting excitation evidently is accompanied by subjective sensations, because the animal scratches, bites or licks those parts of the body which are represented in the stimulated part of the cortex. It is interesting that for cutaneous senses the subjective responses occur on both sides of the body. It should be emphasized that the cerebral cortex is insensitive. The sensations resulting from stimulation are projected sensations, perceived by the patient as if they were in some part of the body, and without any sensation directly referable to the surface of the brain.

Stimulation may also result from pathological processes. Tumors may stimulate sensory cortex much as they do motor cortex, and the patient experiences subjective sensations. The sensory cortex may also be implicated in epilepsy (p. 325).

Electrical Activity

It is possible to record the electrical activity of sensory cortex in a manner that gives a clue to representation of different parts of the body. If brain waves are suppressed with a drug, such as a barbiturate, and a sense organ or a nerve then stimulated, the arrival at the cerebral cortex of the resulting impulses is indicated by a well-defined, surface-positive spike potential. Studies of this kind on lower animals indicate that impulses from the lower extremity enter the upper part of the gyrus; those from the face, the lower part of the gyrus. The available information, particularly that derived from clinical studies, indicates that a similar arrangement is present in man.

Recent studies indicate that there are secondary somatic areas, and perhaps tertiary, according to a terminology which lists the postcentral gyrus (and sensory cortex in lower animals) as Somatic Area I and the second somatic area as Somatic Area II. Impulses from sense organs all over the body reach the second somatic areas bilaterally. The location of Somatic Area II varies according to species, and it seems likely that one is present in man above the lateral fissure, near the foot of the central fissure. The significance of these secondary areas is not known.

Extirpation

Results indicate that for general senses, the thalamus and postcentral gyrus are the primary receptive areas (Fig. 147). The inter-

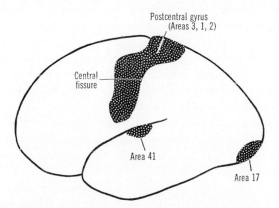

Figure 147.   Diagram indicating the approximate locations of primary receptive areas. The postcentral gyrus is often subdivided into Areas 3, 1 and 2, although no functional significance has been attributed to this subdivision.

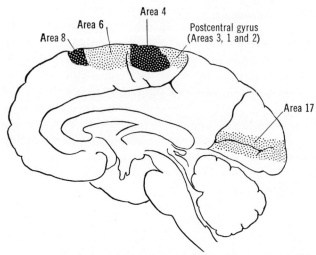

Figure 148. The motor and sensory areas on the medial surface of the cerebral hemisphere.

relationships of these two are still uncertain. If the thalamus is destroyed, the effect is the same as if all the afferent pathways were severed. Lesions of the postcentral gyrus, however, are not followed by such marked losses. Position sense is severely affected, touch less so, and pain and temperature relatively little, at least as far as perception is concerned. But in such cases a patient may recognize that he has been touched and yet have difficulty in distinguishing degrees or intensities of stimulation. Furthermore, there is evidence from clinical cases that a considerable degree of recovery from such defects is possible.

The primary receptive areas for vision are in the occipital lobes (Fig. 148). If both these areas are destroyed, the patient is as blind as if both optic nerves had been severed. This illustrates again the perceptive functions of these areas.

The primary receptive areas for hearing are in the temporal lobes (Fig. 147), each receiving impulses from both ears, so that destruction of one such area will not produce total deafness.

Pain

Pain, although but one of the general senses, is mentioned separately here because of its great clinical importance. It is one of the most common presenting complaints of patients, and its alleviation

is always a problem. The psychological, physiological and pathological properties of this sensation constitute an extensive phase
of neurophysiological research. The alleviation of pain by organic
means may be carried out by a variety of methods, including
surgery (Fig. 97, p. 178; see also p. 345). The advance of medicine
has been due in great part to the fact that a variety of chemical
compounds can alleviate, abolish or prevent pain, and one of the
most important groups of this type is the anesthetics.

Anesthetics may be local in action—that is, they may block conduction in peripheral nerve fibers—or they may have central actions
and in some way prevent subjective interpretation of afferent impulses reaching the brain. Ether is a centrally acting drug, for
example, that is given by inhalation, so that it reaches the nervous
system by way of the blood stream. Anesthetic effects are proportional to the rate and time of administration.

Epilepsy and the Convulsive States

The term "epilepsy" is applied to any disorder in which convulsions or fits occur, and of itself is not specific. Most epilepsies
are associated with motor or sensory cortex. For instance, tumors
growing in or near the motor areas may so irritate the neurons
that they discharge and thereby initiate jacksonian convulsions.
Irritative phenomena resulting from inflammatory processes may
likewise cause convulsions if the motor areas are affected. *Post-
traumatic epilepsy,* a not infrequent complication of severe head
injuries, may be the result of irritation by scar tissue formation
in the region of the injury. Sensory fits may also occur if the irritative processes involve sensory cortex.

There is, however, a classical symptom complex of unknown
etiology with which the term "epilepsy" has been associated. It is
called *idiopathic epilepsy,* also known as the "falling sickness." In
its most severe form there are convulsions preceded by periods of
unconsciousness. These are known as *grand mal attacks.* The more
common and less severe attacks with only momentary losses of
consciousness are *petit mal attacks.*

There is no evidence that the cerebral cortex is primarily at
fault in idiopathic epilepsy. It is possible that the cortex is "driven"
by discharges from subcortical structures. The abnormal increase
in excitability is not limited to the motor effects, because there
may be epileptic fits of a sensory type; that is, instead of having

a

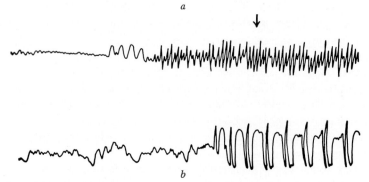

b

Figure 149. *a,* Electroencephalogram of a nine-year-old boy. Tonic-clonic seizure with fast, high voltage waves. Arrow indicates appearance of clinical evidence of seizure. *b,* Petit mal attack, with staring, blinking, and loss of consciousness. Characteristic wave and spike discharge in electroencephalogram. (Reproduced from Gibbs and Gibbs: Atlas of Electroencephalography, courtesy of Lew A. Cummings Co.)

muscular convulsions, the patient may experience peculiar or perverted sensations, such as itching or disagreeable odors.

The diagnosis can often be made from the history and from direct observation of attacks. In suspected cases, breathing deeply for a short time may initiate a convulsion. This hyperventilation decreases the amount of carbon dioxide in the lungs and leads to an alkalinity of the blood, so that the increased excitability may trigger an attack. Electroencephalograms taken during grand mal attacks show prominent high voltage waves (Fig. 149). At other times, and also during petit mal attacks, the records frequently show abnormal waves of the type pictured in Fig. 149.

Summary

The motor areas are those which give rise to the descending motor tracts. Most of them are found in the frontal lobes (precentral motor cortex). They are often called agranular cortex because of the large numbers of pyramidal cells in the granular layer. Electrical stimulation reveals an inverted, multiple representation of movements in different parts of the body. The type of motor response to stimulation depends upon the strength and frequency of stimulation.

The precentral motor cortex is divided into Areas 4, 6 and 8

Area 4 is practically coextensive with the precentral gyrus and has the lowest threshold and most definite inversion of body representation. Stimulation of Area 6 more often yields inhibitory responses. When movements do result, they are often more complex than in the case of Area 4. Area 8 is called the frontal eye field because stimulation primarily results in eye, head and neck movements. Removal of motor cortex yields upper motor neuron types of disorders, the severity of which depends upon the extent of destruction. When Area 6 is involved, the grasp reflex and groping response are often characteristic signs in the adult.

Motor and sensory cortex are interdependent in function. Afferent impulses reaching the cerebral cortex, particularly tactile and proprioceptive impulses, condition the responses of the motor cortex.

The sensory cortex (primary receptive areas) includes those portions of the brain in which afferent paths end. These areas have to do with the perception of primary modalities of sensation, a function which is lost when a primary receptive area is destroyed. Electrical stimulation does not yield normal sensation. Recording of evoked electrical activity enables one to map out the termination of afferent paths.

The cerebral cortex is involved, although not necessarily primarily at fault, in various types of epilepsy. These are motor or sensory fits of various kinds, often characterized by an abnormal electroencephalogram.

Names in Neurology

Jackson, John Hughlings (1834–1911)

Jackson was an English physician and a clinical neurologist whose concepts of the nervous system were so far advanced for his time that to a large extent they were not appreciated. From clinical and postmortem studies of epilepsy, aphasia and paralysis, he concluded that certain cortical areas were concerned in motor activities, sensory mechanisms and language, and he accurately located the regions concerned. He pointed out that positive signs in neurological disorders are often the result of release of lower centers from the control of higher centers. His studies were the forerunner and often the basis of subsequent investigations of the brain.

References

Physiology textbooks generally have sections on experimental studies of cortical functions (for the advanced student); see also Bucy (cited on p. 171).

Brain, R., and Strauss, E. B.: Recent Advances in Neurology and Neuropsychiatry. Boston, Little, Brown and Company, 1955. Valuable up-to-date summaries in many phases of neurology.

Cobb, S.: Foundations of Neuropsychiatry. 5th ed. Baltimore, Williams and Wilkins Company, 1952. The first seven chapters are general surveys of the nervous system, clearly written, well organized, and recommended for both the beginning and the advanced student.

Franz, S. I.: How the Brain Works. University of California at Los Angeles, 1929. In this lecture given to the faculty, Franz points out the general features of his work on re-education of paralyzed patients and discusses the relation of nervous tissue to learning in animals.

Grinker, R., and Bucy, P. C.: Neurology. 4th ed. Springfield, Ill., Charles C Thomas. 1949. This is probably the best of the current American textbooks of clinical neurology because of the manner in which structure and function are correlated with neurological disorders. Although the material is clinical, many sections will be valuable to the advanced student.

Penfield, W., and Jasper, H. H.: Epilepsy and the Functional Anatomy of the Human Brain. Boston, Little, Brown and Company, 1954. This is a valuable reference dealing as it does with clinical research into the problems of epilepsy.

Walshe, F. M. R.: Diseases of the Nervous System. Edinburgh, E. and S. Livingstone, Ltd., 1949. A relatively short, well-written account by an outstanding clinical neurologist.

CHAPTER 19

Associative Functions

of the Cerebral Cortex

MENTAL AND emotional events or processes form what may be termed the psychological level of the organism, that is to say, the "mind." Although one cannot consider the mind as substance, there is no doubt that it is resident in the nervous system. This is corroborated by the almost vegetable-like existence which follows complete decortication or decerebration, and by the effects on mental processes of various insults or damage to the cerebral cortex. In spite of the fact, then, that the mind is a concept, it is a concept which depends upon physical structures and, in that sense, *is* physical.

The most important parts of the nervous system as regards mental and emotional processes are those portions of the cerebral cortex known as association areas. As Fig. 150 indicates, these regions occupy the greater part of the lateral surfaces of the occipital, parietal and temporal lobes, and of the frontal lobes anterior to the motor areas. They are connected with each other and with the neothalamus by innumerable fibers passing through the corpus callosum and the white matter of the hemispheres.

There are several methods by which mental and emotional processes have been studied. The ability to learn and the retention of learned patterns of behavior have been investigated in normal subjects and have also been correlated with the destruction of part

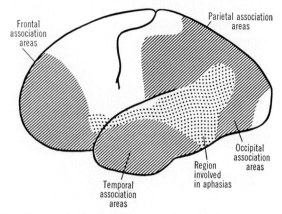

Figure 150.   Diagram indicating the extent of association cortex on the lateral surface of the cerebral hemisphere. The strippled region is often involved in aphasic disorders, but there is no definite demarcation between it and the remaining association cortex.

or all of the cortex, both experimentally and in man after neurological disorders and surgical operations. The relation of learning to the conditioning of responses is another valuable approach, and there are many other psychological studies of normal subjects which may be carried out. The results of these investigations are often difficult to analyze because the occurrence of a defect following a cortical lesion does not necessarily indicate that the opposite of the defect is a function of the removed area. Furthermore, if no defect follows a cortical lesion, one cannot conclude that this area has no function. A brick can be removed from the foundation of a column; but if the column does not fall, one does not conclude that the brick served no purpose.

Mental and emotional events are extremely complex and cannot be broken down into a series of definite, separate performances. It follows that no separate, specific functions can be assigned to separate, specific parts of the association cortex. Rather, this cortex functions as a whole, and defects resulting from damage to it are complex. In many instances the severity of such defects is related to the extent or amount of cortex damaged and relatively little to the location of the lesion. In other words, the more cortex removed, the greater and more complex the defect. This does not mean that various parts of the association cortex do not function differently. They undoubtedly do in the sense that these parts contribute something different to performances carried out by the whole cortex. What should be emphasized is that different parts cannot be regarded as functioning in an isolated manner.

The term "associative" which heads this chapter is probably a poor one, but it is in common use and, for want of anything better, is used here.

Learning

Learning is a general term used to indicate an attribute which is highly developed (relatively speaking) in man. The mechanisms involved in learning take years to develop, and the process as yet is beyond our comprehension. Learning includes, in the form of memory, relationships between neural processes which may last over scores of years. The time differential cannot be explained by any known physiological data or anatomical structure. There is no specific region of the brain responsible for learning, no specific region which, when destroyed, results in inability to learn, and no specific anatomical or physiological characteristics of learning. There is no good evidence that fixed neural paths or connections in the cerebral cortex are necessary for learning. There is, in fact, evidence that they are not necessary.

Learning and Sensorimotor Functions

In this particular discussion certain features of afferent paths are included because of their importance in psychological mechanisms.

Motor. Although the movements resulting from stimulation of motor cortex may give an idea of the functions of this part of the brain, the movements are, nevertheless, artificial. Stimulation may be followed by contractions of certain muscles, but not by patterns such as threading a needle, writing, or playing the piano. At present, the concept is that no one area of the brain specifically directs motor activities.

In spite of such nonspecificity, however, considerable information of clinical importance has been derived from the study of *apraxias*. Apraxias are defects in movement patterns or purposeful acts resulting from lesions of association cortex. A purposeful act may be an acquired automatism such as walking, or driving a car, or it may be threading a needle, lighting a cigaret, playing the piano or operating a typewriter. In any event it is an arrangement of muscular activity into some meaningful or purposeful sequence. For any such pattern there is a period during which the component movements are laboriously learned. But finally all are arranged as a modal sequence which one thinks of as a total act. In driving a car there is usually no conscious awareness of component movements. In fact, if asked to describe just how all the necessary actions are carried out, one might be hard put to do so. What has been learned and retained is a total pattern.

The learning and performance of such types of motor behavior are related to handedness. In right-handed persons the left hemisphere is said to be the major one. In terms of neurological lesions this dominance is important for the following reasons: Lesions of association cortex in the major hemisphere may be followed by apraxias, whereas similar lesions in the minor hemisphere may cause no noticeable symptoms. There is no one specific part of association cortex which has to be involved in order to cause an apraxia. For example, destruction of the major supramarginal gyrus in one patient may cause an apraxia characterized by inability to play the piano (when such an ability had been present before), as well as difficulties with other movement patterns. Yet in other patients similar apraxias may follow lesions elsewhere, or lesions in this gyrus may cause other types of disorders.

There are various kinds of apraxias. In some the patient loses his concept of how to carry out a pattern. In others he may remember quite well, but be unable to perform it properly. It must be emphasized that these patients are *not* paralyzed unless the lesion has also involved motor areas or pathways. The muscles which cannot be used to light a cigaret properly may be used to thread a needle. The tongue which cannot be protruded on command may be used in talking.

Sensory. A typewriter is a familiar object because it has been seen and perhaps used. But it is not necessary to see it in order to revisualize it, either as an object or as a functioning mechanism. The sound of a typewriter in another room is sufficient to identify it as a typewriter. It can be recognized, if one is blindfolded, merely by handling it. By watching a typewriter in use, one might learn to operate it, though certainly not skillfully at first. The sensory phenomena involved are extremely complex. Although nearly all the senses may be involved in any one of the examples cited, the final result or experience is not a group of separately recognized senses, but a perception, the component factors of which are not consciously distinguished. One does not say, "Here is something which feels like this, looks like this, sounds like this, and is named a typewriter." It is simply a typewriter.

So it is with most sensory phenomena. While it is true that the various senses may be individually detected or experienced under certain conditions, perception nevertheless depends upon quantitative differences in sensory fields. The stimulation of a single tactile spot is perceived because of differences in excitation of this and surrounding spots. Warmth is perceived only because of a difference in temperature from that of the body. An object may be colder than another object, yet both may be warmer than the body.

Nearly all environmental changes involve several primary modalities and result, therefore, in what are called *compound sensations*. When the base of a vibrating tuning fork is placed over a bony prominence, the resulting sensation is a combination of touch and pressure at a rather high mechanical frequency. A hot object is thought by many investigators to stimulate receptors of warmth and pain, a compound stimulation interpreted as hot. It is well known that if an object is very hot, only pain is felt. Likewise, cold is said to be compounded of pain and coolness. The fact that a subject whose eyes are closed can tell that two points of a compass are touching him (two-point or tactile discrimination) depends, not on the presence of special receptors and fibers for this quality, but upon the fact that impulses from tactile receptors in two different areas are recognized, localized and discriminated by the cerebral cortex.

This synthesis of primary modalities is given the general term *eugnosia,* and appears to be a function of association cortex. Those parts of the cortex adjacent to the primary receptive areas receive fibers from these areas and in turn are connected with each other and with the rest of the cerebral cortex.

If a lead pencil is examined manually, the average subject recognizes it even with his eyes closed. The individual modalities are integrated into factors of size, weight, shape, texture and temperature. Past experience relates these qualities to a lead pencil. This *stereognosis* usually proceeds rapidly and, for familiar objects, is completed almost immediately without the conscious intervention of the component qualities.

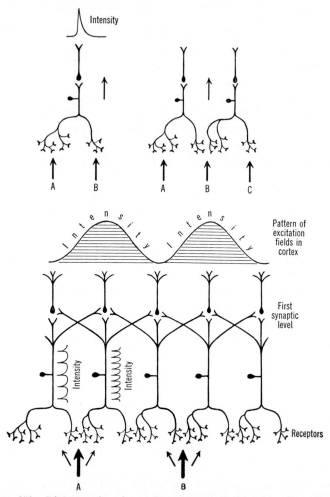

Figure 151. Diagram of various afferent mechanisms. *Upper left:* The conventional scheme. Stimulation of a touch spot at *A* is not distinguishable from stimulation at *B*, since the impulses traverse the same fiber. The electrical activity recorded on arrival at the cortex is represented as a spike of activity in a restricted field. *Upper right:* The touch spot at *B* is derived from two dorsal root fibers. Stimulation here is localizable, but not distinguishable from simultaneous stimulation of either *A* or *C*. In either case there would be a single field of cortical activity. *Lower:* The simplest arrangement for two-point discrimination. Stimulation at *A* results in a higher frequency of impulses over the second neurons, since it contributes more endings to the touch spot and is therefore more intensely stimulated. The same situation obtains for the fourth neuron giving endings to *B*. The interconnections at the first and subsequent synaptic layers (omitted from the diagram) allow a spread of excitation. The recorded cortical response is over a wide area and is a field of algebraic summation of many spikes, more pronounced in the center because of the higher frequency of entering impulses. With two such fields, two-point discrimination is possible.

334

The quality of rapid synthesis is especially marked in visual phenomena. If the picture of an airplane is flashed upon a screen, a certain time is necessary to determine its type, purpose and nationality. If the time upon the screen is gradually reduced, it is not long before a fraction of a second suffices for identification. This is recognition of a total pattern and not of a collected group of qualities.

Similar functions obtain in regard to hearing. Dropping a lead pencil might or might not produce a characteristic sound, but dropping a coin on a hard surface certainly would. A subject could not only recognize that a coin produced the sound, but might very well be able to tell its denomination. For both vision and hearing, eugnostic mechanisms appear to be a function of the major hemisphere.

Agnosias may follow lesions of the association areas. Agnosia literally means "without knowledge." Here it is used in the sense that knowledge or recognition of objects is impaired or impossible. There are many grades and types of agnosias, and many of them cannot be related to specific cortical areas.

One type is *visual agnosia*, which often follows a lesion of the occipital cortex on the lateral surface of the major hemisphere. Previously familiar objects are seen but not recognized. A lead pencil may mean nothing unless the patient is allowed to handle it, recognition then being related to stereognosis. A bunch of keys is not recognized until they are shaken; their characteristic sounds are then the determining qualities.

Lesions of the parietal lobes may be followed by *astereognosis,* the loss of the normal quality of stereognosis. If the lead pencil is held in the hand opposite to the involved lobe, it is not identified, even though the primary modalities are relatively intact. If the eyes are open, recognition is possible because of visualization.

Afferent Paths and the Cerebral Cortex.   Sensory functions are difficult to study because of the lack of objective responses which can be recorded, and because fluctuations at the cortical level may either enhance or depress subjective interpretation. It is well known that a painful injury received in the heat of play or some other activity may go unnoticed at the time it happens. The concern of the brain with the activity of play enables it to ignore or suppress the afferent impulses reaching it. Yet if the same injury were deliberately inflicted upon someone with his fore-knowledge, then the subjective interpretation of the afferent impulses is nearly always exaggerated.

A number of methods of investigation, however, have yielded considerable information. These include studies of receptors as regards their distribution and response to stimuli; the anatomical connections of the afferent paths; the recording of electrical activity in these paths and in the cortical areas; and the correlation of these with psychophysiological studies in the intact human subject.

The conventional diagrams of receptors and their afferent paths are useful in indicating anatomical configuration and location, but they are much too schematic to enable one to correlate structural and functional properties.

Let us first consider receptors, using the tactile type as an example. A dorsal root fiber does not enter a small skin area and there form but a single group of Meissner's corpuscles. If this were true, the simultaneous stimulation of adjacent tactile spots could not be differentiated, for there would be no unstimulated spot in between to form a neutral background. Perception always consists in the recognition of a figure against a background. The background may represent stimulation, but if its activity is generally less than that of some contained point or area, then a comparison is possible and configuration appears.

Anatomical studies have shown that a dorsal root fiber branches over a relatively wide area, probably hundreds of square millimeters or more. If such an area were supplied by but a single fiber (Fig. 151), one could detect differences in intensity of stimulation. An increase in intensity causes an increase in frequency of impulses traversing the afferent path and reaching the cerebral cortex (p. 137). Localization, however, is not possible, because stimulation of one side of the area causes impulses in the parent fiber similar to those resulting from excitation on the other side. So far as the cortex is concerned, the impulses might be arising anywhere in the area.

The actual situation is that any one skin area is supplied by several fibers, and in a single touch spot there are receptors derived from several parent fibers. The simplest possible arrangement which accounts for tactile localization is shown in Fig. 151. Stimulation of a single touch spot results in impulses traversing two different fibers, thus allowing the cortex a comparison between these and nonlocalizable impulses from other parts of the area. But this arrangement does not correlate with the electrical activity recorded at the cortex under such conditions. Such activity is found over a relatively wide expanse and is of greater magnitude in the center of what might be called a field of activity. When even a small skin area is touched, there is no true point stimulation. The skin is bent or depressed, and the receptors in the center of the depression are more intensely stimulated than those at the periphery. Impulses starting here are therefore of a higher frequency. If, as shown in Fig. 151, one fiber gives more receptors to a touch spot than another fiber, the result is a higher frequency of impulses following stimulation. Consequently, there arrives at the cerebral cortex a group of impulses which activates a field or region of cortex. Impulses in the central part of this group are more frequent; the resulting activity of the central part of the cortical field is therefore more intense. Localization of a stimulated spot is therefore a matter of intensity discrimination.

With a two-neuron arrangement, however, tactile or two-point discrimination is not possible. In order to account for two-point discrimination, at least five neurons are necessary, as indicated in Fig. 151. Stimulation of two separate spots in their receptor pattern results in two fields of cortical activity. Regional variations in sensitivity (two-point discrimination is more exact in the skin of the hand than in that of the back) appear then to be at least partially explained by differences in pattern and zonal distribution of fibers and receptors.

The appearance of fields of cortical activity in response to peripheral point stimulation is enhanced by interconnections at synaptic levels of the afferent paths (Fig. 151). At any level, cord, medullary or thalamic, a single fiber may synapse with cells upon which other fibers of the same path impinge. Excitation, therefore, tends to spread laterally at synaptic levels and thus in the end activates a greater extent of cerebral cortex. The extent of spreading is exemplified in the visual system. With stimulation of a circular area in the fovea 5 microns in diameter, activity can be recorded from the occipital cortex in a region at least one hundred times as wide (0.5 mm.), the area being ten thousand times greater.

How may subjective interpretations be related to these facts? Can any correlation be made or law derived? There is a certain relationship between subjective sensation and intensity of stimulation. Suppose that to an object of a certain weight the arbitrary unit of 100 is assigned, and the same unit to the subjective sensation of weight. Then it is found that an object just enough heavier to be subjectively detected (101) has the weight of 110. The next subjective increase (to 102) necessitates an object of weight 121. These arbitrarily selected units indicate that the stimulus increases logarithmically while the sensation increases arithmetically—the *Weber-Fechner law* (p. 346). So far as peripheral receptors and afferent paths are concerned, increasing intensity of stimulation results in higher frequency of impulses. Frequency of impulses entering the cerebral cortex must therefore be of great importance in perception. The Weber-Fechner law, however, holds mainly for moderate intensities of stimulation.

Learning and Language Mechanisms

The use of symbols is highly developed in man, but is also seen in other primates. Symbolization is the form of speech by which ideas are expressed verbally and manually; it is also a part of internal symbolization or thinking. The degree to which this is possible is directly related to the intellectual development of an individual. A person may be illiterate for a number of reasons, and yet be innately intelligent, that is, possess the capacity for development if given the opportunity. But the degree of symbolization nevertheless affords the best index of intelligence, so much so that it is difficult to estimate intelligence in the presence of illiteracy.

One can indicate the complexity of symbolization by tracing its formation and development from infancy. A baby hears certain sounds which gradually become associated with objects he sees, and, by trial and error, his first attempts at vocalization gradually evolve into spoken words. Subsequently, the acquisition of new words is by a process of conditioning, the words being associated with objects, situations, and the like. Soon he is able to put words together as phrases, and later as sentences. By these he can express wishes and, perhaps, have desires gratified. These visual and auditory functions are associated with increasingly complex movements: namely, the more and more precise coordination of muscles of the abdomen, thorax, larynx, pharynx, tongue, lips and cheeks.

In other words, he learns that he can make different sounds by using these muscles in different ways. There is certainly no conscious selection of a particular muscle or muscles, but rather a trial and error method which, when successful, is facilitated by repetition and added to by conditioning.

At some time in his young life he becomes introduced to symbols in another form, that is, writing or printing. He may be shown the letters of the alphabet one by one and taught the sound of each. When he learns how letters are put together to form words, he identifies the printed words "mama" or "mother" with the sound of these words and with the person. Or he may be introduced to the word as a whole without any breakdown into component letters. After the visual introduction to letters and words the child can be taught to write these symbols. This introduces a new element of motor coordination—the use of digital muscles in symbolization.

In succeeding years these elements are gradually improved and expanded. More than this, he improves his phraseology and learns to group sentences so as to express emotions, ideas and wishes. All his emotional and intellectual processes become colored by symbolization.

As can be seen, symbolization is a complex phenomenon or, rather, is a matter of complex phenomena. While one cannot say that speech is located in this or that part of the brain, there is a considerable body of information derived from the study of speech defects following cortical lesions. In such cases cerebral dominance is important, since, as a rule, defects only follow lesions of the major hemisphere. Furthermore, most such defects follow damage to a general area indicated in Fig. 150.

These defects are called *aphasias*. Various kinds of aphasias have been described, and in each, certain symptoms appear to predominate, but careful examination nearly always reveals widespread or generalized involvement of symbolization. This region functions as a whole in such a manner that interference with a part tends to disrupt the entire mechanism.

The extent to which lesions of association cortex may disrupt symbolization may be illustrated by brief discussions of the resultant defects. Lesions may be the result of various neurological disorders. Thus a thrombosis of the left middle cerebral artery may be followed by softening and destruction of most of the cortex on the lateral surface of the hemisphere. Traumatic injuries, tumors, abscesses, and a number of other disorders often involve part or all of this general region.

The term "aphasia" literally means "without speech," but the term as used today refers to many different types of defects. The following is a general classification.

Expressive Disorders of Speech (Verbal, Motor or Broca's Aphasia) (p. 346). The patient has difficulty in speaking or writing, or both, although he usually knows fairly well what he wants to say and may understand what is said to him. He may be able to use only a few words, and when he does speak he tends to repeat again and again those words which he does not wish to say. He is, according to Jackson, "not wordless, but speechless." Surprisingly enough, under the stress of emotional situations he may speak fluently, in some cases almost as well as before the injury. But when the emotion subsides, the inability to speak reappears.

The disorder is usually not restricted to the expressive side. Other phases suffer as well, though to a lesser extent. There may be diminution in understanding of written and spoken commands. Comprehension of situations may also deteriorate. This type of aphasia is said to follow lesions in the anterior portion of the region illustrated in Fig. 150.

Receptive Disorders of Speech (Sensory, Auditory or Wernicke's Aphasia) (p. 346). These are characterized by difficulty in understanding what is said or read. Symbols may be recognized as objects; words are heard as sounds. But to the patient they are a foreign language. If he is asked to do something, he cannot, because the directive words are meaningless. The lack of understanding prevents the patient from recognizing or knowing what he himself says. Consequently, what he speaks and writes is frequently a meaningless jargon. Other phases of symbolization suffer as well, but to a lesser extent. Receptive disorders often follow lesions in the temporal or parietal regions.

Expressive-Receptive Disorders (Total Aphasias). With extensive lesions, there may be combinations of expressive and receptive disorders. These are incapacitating because patients cannot speak or write, or understand what they or anyone else reads or says. But there is no paralysis, no deafness, no blindness, and no loss of general sensations, unless other parts of the nervous system are affected.

Amnesic Aphasia (Nominal Aphasia). The outstanding symptom is an inability to use words as nouns. Such a patient may know that the object with which he is confronted is "to write with," but cannot say "pen." The resulting speech disorder is, therefore, great.

It is almost impossible to assign an involvement of a definite area in this aphasia, but the temporal lobe and even part of the parietal are usually involved.

Aphasias on a Higher Level. In the previously discussed aphasias there is an inability to associate symbols with objects or acts. But in higher levels there is a loss of the *significance* of symbols. They may be recognized, but their meaning is not understood. This may constitute a *semantic aphasia,* or it may be combined with other aphasias as a semantic defect. In the aphasic type, patients can understand and can read and write; but when one speaks to them, simple words must be used, and these must be spoken slowly. Often, in going from one sentence to the next, they lose the gist of what they are reading. Naturally, the inability to comprehend situations or ideas is present to a varying degree in all "normal" persons, so that, without a knowledge of previous intellectual level, the diagnosis of semantic aphasias and defects may be difficult, if not impossible.

The aphasias may be relatively easy to detect, but their analysis is often difficult. The intellectual level which a subject attains during life determines in part the degree of any aphasic disorder. Furthermore, just as in normal life, aphasic responses vary from day to day, and repeated examinations may be necessary.

Aphasias are not always the result of destructive lesions. As Nielsen (p. 347) emphasizes:

> There is hardly an element of agnosia, apraxia, or aphasia established as resulting from organic lesions that has not been noted in purely functional states. Fright may cause a temporary mutism just as thoroughly as that seen in motor aphasia. The inability to understand spoken words and the inability to perform purposeful acts as seen in postepileptic states may be as complete as acoustic verbal agnosia or apraxia due to organic lesions. The psychic blindness and deafness seen in hysteria and the inability to recall names of familiar persons so common in normal individuals may be as great in degree as similar symptoms in organic disease. If such symptoms can result from purely functional states, one cannot deny that functional states play an important role when organic lesions are present.

The foregoing discussions pointed out that aphasias are complex, variable defects, rather than clear-cut clinical syndromes. In most cases it is doubtful that the aphasia can be correlated with specific lesions in specific, small portions of the cortex. In the first place, lesions, even if surgically performed, are rarely sharp and clean. Usually they are diffuse, and their extent is seldom realized unless adequate microscopic examination is made at autopsy (many cases of aphasia do not come to autopsy until a long time after the defect occurred). Secondly, there is at present no way of assessing the function of the supposedly normal cortex remaining after damage to the brain. In other words, the separation of aphasias into types is of great value in localizing a neurological disorder to a general region and, what is especially helpful, to one side of the brain. But it is doubtful that aphasias tell us much about the actual mechanisms of symbolization.

The supposedly silent side or minor hemisphere is of clinical importance in the recovery from aphasic defects. Positive training may lead to partial or complete recovery. The minor hemisphere and the cortex remaining in the major hemisphere are probably both important in this matter.

Learning and Conditioned Responses

The modification of behavior on the basis of past experiences is primarily a function of the cerebral cortex. Everyone is familiar with the fact that the sight or smell of food may be just as potent a stimulus for salivation as taste. The objective response—salivation—is mediated by a nervous pattern already established at birth. The newborn infant salivates in response to the taste of food. Only later do visual and olfactory stimuli induce salivation. Salivation in response to taste is an *unconditioned reflex,* just as is the knee jerk, which may be elicited in an infant.

Many unconditioned reflexes may be modified by, or adapted to, new stimuli. Pavlov (p. 278) made use of this fact in extensive studies of behavior. The sound of a bell is not ordinarily followed by salivation. Pavlov showed that, if an animal is given food, or acid is placed in its mouth, so that salivation occurs, and if this is accompanied or shortly preceded by another stimulus, such as the sound of a bell, after repeated trials the sound alone may induce salivation. This is a *conditioned response*—a salivatory reaction to an auditory stimulus. It may be that the nervous connections which make this possible are established at birth, but they are not innately functional as are those in the unconditioned reflex arc. This further exemplifies the functional reserve and plasticity of nervous systems of higher forms.

Although Pavlov used salivation as an objective index, more recent techniques have turned to striated muscle because of the rapidity of its response and the greater ease with which such response can be recorded. Thus the blinking of an eye to a puff of air can be conditioned to a light flashed in the eye. These studies have definitely established that conditioned responses are not completely identical with unconditioned reflexes. Conditioned responses are, instead, more of an anticipatory reaction, somewhat akin in latency of response to voluntary activity, and form part of a general pattern.

The neurophysiological factors in conditioning are not definitely established. It has been shown, however, that responses resulting from electrical stimulation of motor pathways cannot be conditioned by simultaneous sensory stimuli of an auditory or visual type. On the other hand, conditioned responses to visual stimuli may be obtained when the unconditioned responses result from electrical stimulation of afferent pathways. This indicates that there is a mechanism for forming the pattern or association of conditioning, and that it resides in the central nervous system elsewhere than in the longitudinal pathways. The association areas are the most likely locations.

Removal of part or all of the cortex does not abolish conditioned responses or the ability to form new ones, but these are never as precise as in a normal animal. Whereas flexion of a limb might be the conditioned response in the normal, general escape movements of a diffuse type constitute the response in a decorticate animal. Subcortical areas thus appear to be able to function in this regard, but for precise or discrete activity the association areas are indispensable.

Conditioned responses, once established, are not invariable. They may gradually disappear if continually elicited without periodic reinforcement by the unconditioned stimulus, or if associated with extraneous stimuli. For a more extensive discussion of these variations, see the references at the end of the chapter.

It is important to note that the so-called involuntary processes may be easily conditioned. Marked changes in salivation, blood pressure, respiration and many other visceral activities may become associated with many types of stimuli. The devastating effects of stage fright may well be conditioning of this type. Of interest is the *psychogalvanic reflex,* which can be conditioned. This is an increase in sweating during emotional states. In areas where it occurs, such as the hands, the resistance to the flow of an electric current decreases and can be measured, thus furnishing objective data of such changes.

It is also important to note that conditions resembling neuroses may be produced in animals by eliciting in them a conditioned response to a stimulus such as a circle which must be differentiated from an ellipse. If the ellipse is gradually changed until it resembles a circle, the animal is confronted with an impossible situation. In one of Pavlov's experiments a dog thus trained exhibited the symptoms of an acute neurosis.

The ultimate explanation of conditioning is lacking, just as it is in other types of learning, in memory, and in intelligent behavior. The fundamental difficulty is this: The time scale is too great to be adequately explained by present data. Our scanty knowledge is insufficient to explain the months and years over which these conditions last.

Frontal Association Areas

These areas form a rather wide expanse of cortex anterior to motor areas, and to them various functions have been attributed. They are intimately connected with the thalami and probably with the hypothalamus as well. The frontal areas, like the rest of the brain, exhibit the property of functioning as a whole. They are dealt with specifically here because in recent years they have been vigorously attacked surgically, for a variety of reasons.

Removal of these areas in animals is followed by definite signs. Among these is *hyperactivity,* the appearance of which is separated from the operative period by a short-lived depressed state. This hyperactivity is a maintained or driven state of muscular activity, such as walking which has no immediate purpose and which appears almost maniacal. This may be the result of release of diencephalic levels from cortical control.

Another result of such lesions is an interference with temporally arranged acts. Animals cannot learn problems which demand a retention of facts for more than a few seconds, such as remembering in which of two cups food has been placed. "Immediate" or "recent" memory is lost, but abilities which the animal has as a result of previous training are not. The latter are performed or regained shortly after the operation. This indicates again the diffuseness of cortical function. A habit pattern may be formed in the frontal lobes and then shifted elsewhere for long-term retention.

Another factor in the inability to learn temporally arranged patterns is a *distractibility*, which may be so pronounced that an animal can be deviated from any line of activity by extraneous stimuli.

At present it appears that intelligence is not markedly deranged in frontal lobe disorders, either in man or in lower animals.

The Affective Component of Behavior

It has been observed, especially in man, that frontal lobe lesions are characterized by alterations in emotional reactions. Such changes have been most extensively studied in connection with surgery of the frontal lobes.

Certain severe neurotic and psychotic states have been treated by cutting the connections between the frontal association areas and other regions, such as the thalamus and hypothalamus. Emotional states may be so altered that the result has been somewhat inaccurately termed a reversal of personality. The results are actually much more complex, and so variable from one patient to the next that no prediction of results should ever be made. The most striking changes or characteristics are lack of self-consciousness, and ease and freedom in social relationships, often to an aggressive or embarrassing degree.

Similar operations have been carried out for relief of intractable pain and are sometimes successful. Pain is not actually lost; the patients still feel pinpricks. The pain no longer bothers them. It is still present, but has relatively little psychic effect.

Summary

Cephalization in evolutionary processes is especially characterized by the increase in amount of association cortex, which in man makes up the bulk of cerebral cortex, and by an increasing complexity of cortical structure and function. This cortex functions as a whole in those complex mental and emotional processes which we conceive of as mind.

Learning is a process for which there is no physiological and anatomical basis, other than that it is a function of the nervous system. It is a process which, with symbolization, is one of the most characteristic attributes of the human brain and which can be altered by disorders affecting the brain. There are no specific regions of the brain which carry out specific phases of learning. The brain tends to function as a whole.

Names in Neurology

Broca, Paul (1824–1880)

Broca is considered to be the founder of modern brain surgery in France. In a famous case study he postulated that the third left frontal convolution was concerned in speech, a theory previously advanced by Gall. Broca's patient was later shown to have a lesion involving much of the left side of the brain. He was the first to trephine the skull for a cerebral abscess located by symptoms relating to his theory of localization of function.

Fechner, Gustav Theodor (1801–1887)

Fechner was a professor of physics at Leipzig who wrote the first treatise on psychophysics. He carried out extended experiments on cutaneous and muscle senses and restated Weber's law in its logarithmic form.

Weber, Ernst Heinrich (1795–1878)

Weber was a distinguished professor of anatomy and physiology at Leipzig (1812–1866) and professor of anatomy until 1871. In 1825, he collaborated with his brother, Eduard Friedrich Weber (1806–1871), on the hydrodynamics of wave motion and showed the velocity of the pulse wave. In 1845 he discovered the inhibitory effects of the vagus nerve. He studied sensory phenomena and stated that the just detectable increment in the intensity of a sensation is some constant proportion of the stimulus intensity itself. A third brother, Wilhelm Eduard Weber (1804–1891), a professor of physics at Göttingen, collaborated with Eduard in a study of the mechanics of human locomotion.

Wernicke, Carl (1848–1905)

Wernicke was a German physician who studied sensory aphasias and clearly described a variety of these defects. He also studied diseases of the internal capsule and other portions of the nervous system.

References

The following references are intended to cover a wide variety of special phases of investigation of the nervous system. They are chosen to give different viewpoints on certain points, such as the question of localization in the cerebral cortex. In addition, nearly all contain extensive bibliographies which should aid in more detailed studies of specific phases.

Adrian, F. D., Bremer, F., and Jasper, H. H., in Delafresnaye, J. F., ed.: Brain Mechanisms and Consciousness. Springfield, Ill., Charles C Thomas, 1954.

Association for Research in Nervous and Mental Disease: Inter-Relationship of Mind and Body. Baltimore, Williams & Wilkins Company, 1939.

Freeman, W., and Watts, J. W.: Psychosurgery in the Treatment of Mental Disorder and Intractable Pain. 2nd ed. Springfield, Ill., Charles C Thomas, 1951.

Hilgard, E. R., and Marquis, D. G.: Conditioning and Learning. New York, Appleton-Century, 1940.

Lashley, K. S.: Brain Mechanisms and Intelligence. Chicago, University of Chicago Press, 1929.

McGeogh, J. A.: Psychology of Human Learning. New York, Longmans, Green & Co., 1942.

Murchison, C., ed.: Handbooks of General Experimental Psychology. Worcester, Mass., Clark University Press, 1934.

Nielsen, J. M.: Agnosia, Apraxia, Aphasia. 2nd ed. New York, Paul B. Hoeber, Inc., 1946.

Pavlov, I. P.: Conditioned Reflexes, translated by G. V. Anrep. London, Oxford University Press, 1927.

Penfield, W., and Rasmussen, T.: The Cerebral Cortex of Man. New York, The Macmillan Co., 1950.

Weisenberg, W., and McBride, K.: Aphasia. New York, Commonwealth Fund, 1935.

Young, P. T.: Emotion in Man and Animal. New York, John Wiley and Sons, Inc., 1943.

CHAPTER 20

Chemistry of the Nervous

System

THE FOLLOWING is a brief summary of some major trends and problems in a field that is rapidly assuming increasing importance. Chemical studies of the nervous system were pioneered primarily by J. L. W. Thudichum. Following his death in 1901, however, anatomical and physiological aspects dominated investigations of the brain. Research in neurochemistry lagged behind biochemical studies of other regions of the body. Only in relatively recent years has there been a resumption of interest in the biochemistry of the nervous system, due to the realization of its basic importance and practical significance.

General Metabolism

The metabolism of the nervous system in general is high. While the rate of respiration, that is, oxygen consumption, is about the same in resting peripheral nerve as it is in resting muscle, that in the central nervous system is about thirty times as great.

Central Nervous System. The brain contributes more to the basic metabolic rate, relative to its proportion of body weight, than do most tissues and organs. Oxygen consumption is higher in gray matter (more cells) than in white, and is higher in the brain (more gray matter) than in the spinal cord. Most nerve cells, especially those in higher centers, cannot survive more than a few minutes' deprivation of oxygen. The survival time may be prolonged if the temperature of the brain is lowered, and this has been taken advan-

348

tage of in certain surgical procedures in which body temperature is deliberately lowered so as to allow, if necessary, a longer interruption of blood supply to the brain.

In the intact brain the ratio of oxygen consumed to carbon dioxide produced, that is, the respiratory quotient, is about unity, suggesting that the brain uses *glucose* as its primary source of energy. Unlike other major organs, however, it is especially dependent upon this sugar. Thus, in hypoglycemia following excessive amounts of insulin, the musculature derives its energy from "secondary" sources, while the brain, obliged to use glucose and unable to get it, can no longer function normally.

Peripheral Nervous System.   Information about the metabolism of the nervous system has also been obtained by studying isolated peripheral nerves. Such studies show that peripheral nerves differ from the central nervous system in that their respiratory quotient is 0.8 instead of 1, indicating that they utilize noncarbohydrate as well as carbohydrate. For example, if a peripheral nerve is removed and placed in a moist chamber, oxygen consumption may continue at the usual rate, and the ability to conduct may persist for hours, even after the utilization of carbohydrate has stopped. An active peripheral nerve is not metabolically restricted to glucose, but may derive energy from some as yet unknown metabolite.

Exogenous glucose likewise seems to be the main substrate for resting metabolism in sympathetic ganglion cells. However, although glucose utilization is accelerated during activity, the substrate for activity metabolism is not glucose. The significance of increased glucose utilization during activity is uncertain.

Intermediary Metabolism

During the past quarter of a century there have been rapid strides in our understanding of the general metabolism of the carbohydrates, proteins, and lipids. Foremost has been the recognition that living cells degrade metabolites in well-ordered steps involving the formation of intermediate compounds, many of which have now been isolated and studied. Each such step requires the presence of an organic catalyst (enzyme) produced by the cell, and often other essential substances (cofactors) upon which the catalyst itself depends. Our knowledge of intermediary metabolism in the nervous system also has increased. As a consequence, many neurological disorders can now be recognized as deficiencies or aberrations in

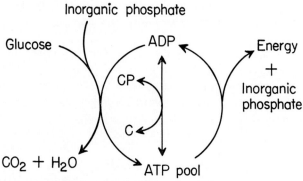

Figure 152.   A schematic representation of the transfer of energy from glucose metabolism. Energy latent in the glucose molecule is evolved in the form of a high energy phosphate group. The hydrolysis of most common organic phosphate esters evolves 2000 to 4000 calories per mole, while certain of the organic phosphates produced in glucose metabolism yield 10,000 to 16,000 calories per mole. These high energy phosphate groups are used by the cell in the form of the nucleotide, adenosine triphosphate (ATP), which is synthesized by the cell from adenosine diphosphate (ADP), inorganic phosphate and energy. Although a pool or reserve supply of ATP is available, the cell calls upon a secondary energy carrier, creatine phosphate (CP), during sudden bursts of activity. In the resting state some ATP is used to synthesize CP, which is then reconvertible to ATP at the appropriate time. Thus, slices of guinea pig cerebral tissue show a loss of CP following electrical stimulation, and a concomitant rise of inorganic phosphate, while ATP remains normal. When stimulation stops, CP and inorganic phosphate return to their normal levels.

essential enzyme systems, with the result that the normal sequence of events is slowed or interrupted. Interference with metabolic processes can reduce the production of energy and inhibit the synthesis of substances necessary for the conduction of impulses, for the maintenance of polarization of nerve membranes, and for the repolarization after conduction.

Carbohydrates.   To date, little is known about the way in which energy is used in the nervous system, but considerable information is at hand about the way in which it is made available. To release the potential energy of carbohydrate, the nerve cell degrades glucose ultimately to carbon dioxide and water by a series of intermediate steps. A general scheme for this process is given in Fig. 152. The energy is collected in the form of a special high energy phosphate group which combines with *adenosine monophosphate* (AMP) to produce *adenosine diphosphate* (ADP). With an additional high energy phosphate group, *adenosine triphosphate* (ATP) is formed. ATP is directly involved in the utilization of energy by cells. Thirty-eight molecules of ATP are produced in the total oxidation of a molecule of glucose to carbon dioxide and water. Most of these are formed as a result of the activity of the *cytochrome* system, which is centered in the mitochondria (Fig. 153). Each step in the degradation of glucose requires the presence of specific enzyme systems. These steps have been determined mainly from studies of muscle and liver tissue, but many of the enzyme systems have now been identified in nervous tissue. Some of the enzyme systems need cofactors, a number of which have been found to contain vitamins.

Thus it is understandable that in vitamin deficiencies the essential metabolic chain leading to energy production is broken and neurological disorders result. For example, in the anaerobic oxidation of one glucose molecule to two molecules of *pyruvic acid,* four atoms of hydrogen are released in combination with the cofactor that contains the vitamin *nicotinic acid* (dementia in pellagra from nicotinic acid deficiency). Pyruvic acid is either reduced to lactic acid or oxidized to carbon dioxide and water by an aerobic process, the tricarboxylic acid cycle. The first steps in the breakdown of pyruvic acid involve the cofactor that contains the vitamin *thiamine,* otherwise known as *vitamin B_1* (mental depression and neuritis from thiamine deficiency). Cofactors that have been reduced enter an oxidation-reduction system called the cytochrome system, an essential component of which is *riboflavin,* otherwise known as *vitamin B_2.*

Proteins and Amino Acids. Disturbances in the utilization of proteins and amino acids may also be implicated in or cause neurological disorders. The dicarboxylic amino acid, *glutamic acid,* and its amide, *glutamine,* constitute almost half the non-protein nitrogen in the mammalian brain. This high concentration implies an important physiological role, but the nature of this role is yet to be established. Although glutamic acid is structurally related to one of the substances formed in carbohydrate metabolism, it does not increase the production of high energy phosphate in cerebral tissues, and it depresses the electrical excitability of the tissues under study. Correlation of *in vitro* with *in vivo* sudies is difficult because glutamic acid does not enter the central nervous system from the blood stream (blood-brain barrier, p. 54). Attempts have been made to influence mental processes by giving glutamic acid. It seems to reduce petit mal attacks (perhaps by a nonspecific alteration of electrical activity). It is said to aid mentally retarded children and adults, but this work is largely unconfirmed.

Other amino acids may be involved in neurological disorders. There is a congenital error of metabolism characterized by inferior mental ability, in which there is an accumulation of *phenylalanine* in the blood and excretion of *phenylpyruvic acid* in the urine (*phenylketonuria* or *phenylpyruvic oligophrenia*). Apparently, the enzyme that converts phenylalanine to *tyrosine* is missing. Why this block in phenylalanine metabolism leads to mental retardation is unknown, but it may be more than fortuitous that tyrosine is the precursor of the nerve impulse transmitters, adrenaline and noradrenaline.

Lipids.   Defects in lipid metabolism also can be cited. There is a degenerative condition (*Tay-Sachs disease*) in which a lipid-carbohydrate complex known as a *ganglioside* accumulates in the brain. The symptoms are progressive mental deterioration, blindness, and paralysis. Another example is the disease in which the lipid *sphingomyelin* accumulates in nerve cells (*Niemann-Pick disease*). These and other lipid disorders are due to faulty functioning of some essential enzyme system.

Clinical Importance.   A better understanding of metabolic reactions in nervous tissue and their relation to nervous activity can lead to such practical matters as diagnosis and therapy, as well as the advancement of ancillary fields such as anesthesiology. At present, anesthetics are used on an empiric basis so far as their effects on the nervous system are concerned. Their modes of action remain unknown, although it is highly probable that they affect the permeability of nerve membranes, or alter or inhibit the chemical reactions at synaptic junctions. Ether, for example, produces surgical anesthesia by acting mainly on higher centers. Barbiturate compounds, of which there are a variety, may have more general effects, and their use is often accompanied by a more profound depression of vital centers in the medulla oblongata and spinal cord. Local anesthetics such as *procaine* block conduction of impulses at the site of application.

Chemical Composition

The study of the various components of cerebral tissue, begun by Thudichum, has led to the discovery of a multitude of exotic substances. It is not within the scope of this chapter to deal with their chemical structure.

In general, cerebral tissue has a fairly constant water content; water forms 85 per cent of gray matter and 70 per cent of white matter. The brain is unique in its high total lipid content, 12–15 per cent. To help in correlating general chemical composition with the morphology of the nerve cell, reference should be made to Fig. 153.

Most of the lipids, lipoproteins, and proteins of nerve cells are fixed or insoluble, or have a relatively slow turnover. Soluble or labile constituents of nerve cells include enzymes, cofactors, carbohydrates, amino acids, labile organic phosphate compounds, and minerals. Of the last, potassium and sodium are among the most important and are discussed elsewhere (p. 97). Other minerals are present, but their functions are largely unknown. Iron is present in nerve cells, and there are regional differences in its concentration. Copper is also present, and there are indications that it has an important function. There is a degenerative disease of the liver and the basal ganglia (*Wilson's hepatolenticular degeneration*), in which there is abnormal excretion of amino acids, and copper is found in especially high concentrations in the liver and the basal ganglia. There is also evidence that an abnormality of copper metabolism may be concerned in certain demyelinating diseases affecting sheep. Copper is usually associated with a particular protein in the blood, *ceruloplasmin,* elevated levels of which are claimed to be associated with schizophrenia.

Myelin. Myelin is believed to be composed of alternating concentric layers of lipid and protein. The chief lipids in myelin are *cholesterol, cerebrosides,* and *sphingosides.* The last two are complex esters of fatty acids, phosphoric acid, and the unsaturated amino alcohol, sphingosine. Cerebrosides are complicated by the presence of a molecule of hexose in their structure. Also present in the lipoproteins of myelin are a number of the simpler *phospholipids.*

The nature of proteins in myelin is largely unknown. Perhaps they are *neurokeratins,* the proteins in myelin having solubility properties similar to those of the keratins of the skin and hair, although their amino acid content is different.

Golgi Apparatus. The Golgi apparatus, which includes the Golgi bodies or *lipochondria,* is chemically very complex. The lipo-

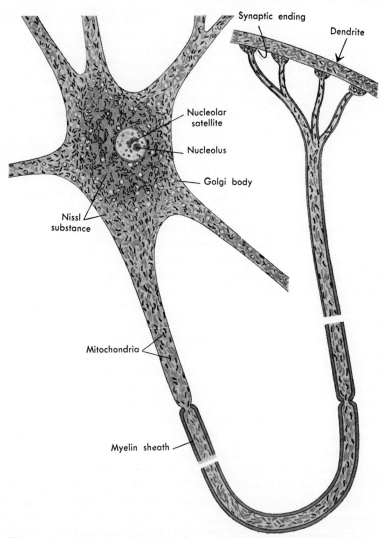

Figure 153. Some structural features of nerve cells as determined by bio-chemical, cytological and electron microscope studies. The nucleolus is composed largely of RNA. The nucleolar satellite is a basophilic structure containing DNA. It is larger in neurons from females, and probably represents sex chromatin derived from the X chromosome. Spherical bodies present within the nucleus may be pre-cursors of lipochondria. The nuclear-cytoplasmic membrane is up to 40 milli-microns thick and is of varying density, probably reflecting areas of differing per-meability. RNA probably passes through the membrane into the cytoplasm where, with other nucleic acids, it is present mainly in the Nissl substance of the cell body. Although the usual stains indicate that Nissl substance is limited to the cytoplasm

chondria contain phosphatides (phospholipids), as well as the class of carbohydrate-containing lipids known as *glycolipids*. The Golgi apparatus may be associated with certain enzymatic processes. After an axon is cut, many small spheres (lipochondria?) are seen near the nucleus.

Nucleoproteins of Nucleus and Cytoplasm. Nucleoproteins are conjugated proteins associated with the nucleic acids, *ribose nucleic acid* (RNA) and *desoxyribose nucleic acid* (DNA). RNA is present in the nucleolus, small quantities are found in chromosomes, and it is present in large amounts in the Nissl substance. DNA is found only in the nucleus, where it forms the nucleolar satellite (Fig. 153). Nucleic acids in general are large polymers of sub-units or nucleotides, which in turn are composed of a pentose unit, a purine or pyrimidine base, and phosphoric acid. Nucleoproteins are apparently depleted during intense activity of the nerve cell, are depleted or altered during chromatolysis, and are involved in some way in regenerative processes. Possibly they are associated with protein synthesis, because cytological evidence indicates a local increase in nucleic acid during regeneration. For example, nucleoli enlarge when regeneration begins after section of an axon.

Mitochondria. Mitochondria are distributed throughout the cytoplasm (Fig. 153). They are concerned in many metabolic activities. They carry practically all of the cytochrome oxidase system, and other enzymes as well. Mitochondria have been shown by electron microscopy to be surrounded by double membranes that consist of two protein layers separated by a double layer of lipids.

Hormones. Special hormones may also be important constituents of certain nerve cells. Thus, there are neurosecretory cells in the hypothalamus (p. 237). These cells form a substance that passes down their axons to the neurohypophysis and is there released as posterior pituitary hormones.

Transmitters. Transmitters are released at the synaptic and motor endings of nerve fibers (p. 146). These substances, acetylcholine, adrenaline, and noradrenaline (Fig. 154), are probably closely related to the general metabolism of carbohydrates and

of cell body and dendrites, nucleic acids are nevertheless present in axons as well. Electron microscopy shows the Nissl substance to be arranged as narrow tubes covered with fine granules. The Golgi apparatus of the cytoplasm is chemically very complex. It includes spheres called lipochondria. Mitochondria are numerous in the cell body and dendrites, and at synaptic and motor endings. Fewer are found in the axon. (From Young, J. Z.: Endeavour; vol. 15, 1956.)

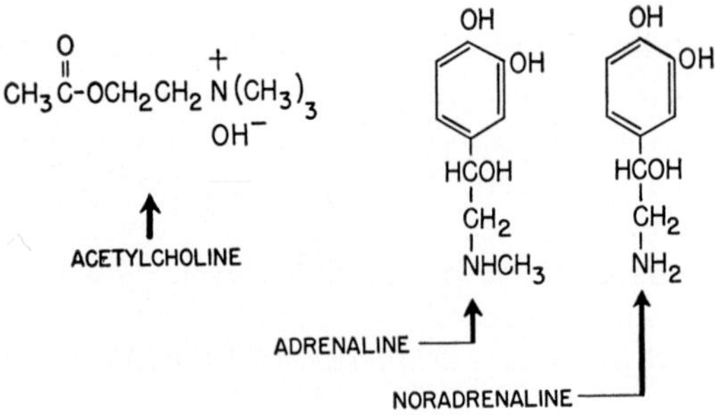

Figure 154.   Formulae of the transmitters.

amino acids. Adrenaline and noradrenaline are related in structure to the amino acid tyrosine while acetylcholine probably derives its component structures from both amino acid and carbohydrate metabolism.

Chemistry and Behavior

Recent work relating chemical to behavioral processes is of special interest. For example, *serotonin (5-hydroxytryptamine)*, which causes smooth muscle to contract, has been found in considerable amounts in the brain. Recent studies suggest that it is concerned in maintaining normal mental function.

Many compounds produce profound mental disturbances, including hallucinations and psychotic episodes. *Lysergic acid diethylamide* (LSD) is one such drug. When given even in the most minute quantities, it causes severe disturbances, including hallucinations. It is not yet known how either serotonin or LSD act, but there is evidence of a complex antagonism between them.

In recent years, several compounds have been discovered that affect emotional behavior. These compounds have in common the property of relieving the emotional tension or anxiety that may accompany or be a part of mental illness. These compounds are, therefore, called "tranquilizers" or "ataraxics." Of the three most widely known and used, one is derived from the root of the plant *Rauwolfia serpentina*. Its active principle has been named *reserpine*. The other two, *meprobamate* and *chlorpromazine,* have been synthesized. The clinical use of these drugs has facilitated the treatment of some mental disorders, has shortened the time of hospitalization, and has made patients more accessible to other forms of psychiatric treatment, such as psychotherapy.

The mechanism of action of these and other drugs is under active study in clinical practice and in the laboratory. Tranquilizers apparently do not influence the functions of the cerebral cortex. They produce no clouding of consciousness nor do they alter the normal mechanisms of perception and response to external stimuli. These compounds most likely affect the subcortical centers, particularly in the case of chlorpromazine. This is the most potent of the three, and clinical and experimental evidence indicates that it acts on the activating systems of diencephalon and midbrain. It must be emphasized that it is not yet possible to evaluate the long-term effects of these tranquilizers.

Names in Neurology

Thudichum, J. L. W. (1828–1901).

Generally called father of the chemistry of the brain, Thudichum, a London physician of German birth, first practiced medicine and then, in 1864, began the study of what are now called lipochromes or carotinoids. He and his assistants then carried out the first systematic attempts to isolate and characterize the chemical composition of the brain. The results of their work were published in 1884 as "A Treatise on the Chemical Constitution of the Brain," revised in 1901. Thudichum clearly recognized the importance of his contributions, but decades were to elapse before extensive study in the field began again. Thudichum actively practiced medicine, mainly in ear, nose, and throat work, he studied gallstones and later in life he wrote two books, one on cookery and one on wines.

References

Elliott, K. A. C., Page, I. H., and Quastel, J. H., eds.: Neurochemistry, Springfield, Ill., Charles C Thomas, 1955. An advanced work, consisting of review chapters by various authors.

Grenell, R. G., and Mullins, L. J., eds.: Molecular Structure and Functional Activity of Nerve Cells. Washington, D.C., Am. Inst. Biol. Sc., 1, 1956. See especially the articles by Larrabee and Horowicz on oxygen utilization in sympathetic ganglia, and by Mullins on nerve cell membranes.

Korey, S. R., and Nurnberger, J. I.: Progress in Neurobiology: I. Neurochemistry. New York, Paul B. Hoeber, 1956. Specialized, advanced articles by a series of contributors.

McIlwain, H.: Biochemistry and the Central Nervous System. Boston, Little, Brown and Company, 1955. A treatise of an advanced nature, with considerable factual data.

Page, I. H.: Chemistry of the brain. Science, 125:721–727, 1957. An interesting, well-written, short review of past events, present status, and future trends in neurochemistry.

Whitelock, O., and Furness, F. N.: The pharmacology of psychotomimetic and psychotherapeutic drugs. Ann. N. Y. Acad. Sc., 66:417–840, 1957. A comprehensive and valuable collection of articles of an advanced nature covering various aspects of the field. Some are in the nature of reviews.

Young, J. Z.: The organization within nerve cells. Endeavour, 15:5–19, 1956. This is a very fine summarizing article, linking structure and metabolic processes, with excellent illustrations.

Glossary of New Terms

MANY OF the terms used are listed here to show their derivation from the Greek or Latin and to indicate how they apply to the particular structure or function.

Abducens: L., *abducere*, to draw outward, away from the median axis. The muscle which the abducens nerve supplies turns the eyeball outward, that is, abducts it.

Acoustic: Gr., *akoustikos*, relating to hearing, from *akouein*, to hear.

Afferent: L., *ad*, to, plus *ferre*, to bear or to carry. In physiology, bearing or conducting inward to a part or organ.

Agnosia: Gr., ignorance, from *a*, without, plus *gnosis*, a knowing, denoting cognition or recognition. Loss of ability to recognize familiar objects.

Anatomy: Gr., *anatemnein*, to cut up. The science or branch of morphology which treats of the structure of animals.

Anesthesia: Gr., *an*, not, plus *aisthesis*, feeling. Loss of feeling or sensation.

Anterior: L., comparative of *ante*, before. Before or toward the front.

Aphakia: Gr., *a*, without, plus *phakos*, seed of a lentil (referring to lens). Absence of lens, as by surgery.

Aphasia: Gr., from *aphatos*, speechlessness, or not spoken, from *a*, not, plus *phanai*, to speak. Impairment of symbolization.

Apraxia: Gr., *a*, without, plus *praxis*, a doing. Therefore, inactivity; impaired ability to perform purposeful acts.

Arachnoid: Gr., *arachnoeides*, like a cobweb, from *arachne*, spider or spider's web. One of the meninges is so called because the delicate network of the tissue resembles a spider's web.

Archicerebellum: Gr., *archein*, to be first, plus *cerebellum*. The oldest part of the cerebellum, that is the part appearing first in the evolutionary scale.

Archipallium: Gr., *archein*, plus *pallium*. The first or oldest portion of the cerebral cortex.

Artery: Gr., *arteria*, air containing. So-called because the Greeks saw arteries after death when contractions had forced blood into the veins. Hence, they supposed them to contain air.

Asphyxia: Gr., *a*, without, plus *sphyxia*, pulse, throb. Deprived of blood (pulseless) and therefore of oxygen.

359

Astrocyte: Gr., *aster,* from *astron,* star, plus *kytos,* cell. A neuroglial cell so named because of its star shape.

Ataxia: Gr., *ataktos,* out of order, from *a,* not, plus *taktos,* ordered. Absence of arrangement or orderliness; ataxic movements are disordered.

Atherosclerosis: L., from Gr., *atheroma,* groats, meal, plus *sklerosis,* hardness. A degenerative process of arteries with fatty degeneration of the inner coats which in later stages may harden because of calcification.

Athetosis: Gr., *athetos,* set aside, not fixed, from *a,* not, plus *tithenai,* to place.

Atrophy: Gr., *atrophia,* from *a,* not, plus *trephein,* to nourish. A wasting away from want of nourishment.

Autonomic: Gr., *autos,* self, plus *nomos,* law; acting independently. So named because that part of the nervous system is concerned with visceral (involuntary) processes.

Axon: Gr., *axon,* axis or vertebra. An axon is long, slender and relatively unbranched.

Brachial: L., *brachium,* from Gr., *brachion,* arm. The region between the shoulder and elbow.

Brachium Conjunctivum: L., from Gr. *brachion,* plus L., *conjunctivus,* connective. A connecting arm. So called because the two peduncles cross each other.

Brachium Pontis: L., from Gr., *brachion,* plus L., *pons,* a bridge. So called because these two peduncles resemble a bridge between the cerebellar hemispheres.

Branchiomeric: Gr., *branchia,* gills, plus *meros,* part or portion. Relating to the visceral arches.

Calvarium: L., *calvaria,* a bare skull, from *calvus,* bald. Refers to the skull cap.

Capillary: L., *capillus,* a hair or minute tube. So called because of the minute size of these vessels.

Carotid: Gr., *karotides,* from *karos,* heavy sleep. Named because of the supposition that pressure and obliteration of the carotid arteries interferes with the blood supply of the brain and produces unconsciousness.

Cauda Equina: L., *cauda,* tail, plus *equus,* horse. The lumbar and sacral spinal roots form a cluster in the lower spinal canal which resembles the tail of a horse.

Caudal: L., *cauda,* tail. Toward the tail or posterior end.

Cerebellum: L., diminutive of *cerebrum,* brain; therefore, little brain.

Cerebrum: L., *cerebrum,* from Gr., *kara,* head. All the central nervous system above the line separating the midbrain from the hindbrain is referred to as cerebrum.

Chiasma: Gr., *chiasma.* Two lines placed crosswise, from *chiasein,* to make a mark with a *chi* or X.

Chorea: L., *choreia,* a choral dance. So named because of the fancied resemblance of the involuntary, choreic movements to those of a dance.

Chorioid: Gr., *chorion,* a delicate membrane, plus *eidos,* form. Therefore, like or resembling a delicate membrane.

Chromatolysis: Gr., *chroma,* color, plus *lysis,* solution. To lose or dissolve color, and in neurology refers to the loss of Nissl substance.

Chronaxie: Gr., *chronos,* time, plus *axia,* value. A value of time.

Clonic: Gr., *klonos,* violent, confused motion. A forced series of alternating contractions and partial relaxations of the same muscle or muscles.

Cochlea: L., *cochlea,* from Gr., *kochlias,* snail, from Gr., *kochlos,* a shell fish with a spiral shell. So named because of the coiled or spiral arrangement of the cochlea of the internal ear.

Colliculus: L., *colliculus,* mound, diminutive of *collis,* hill. Therefore, little hill. So called because each colliculus forms a small, rounded eminence or hill.

Congenital: L., *congenitus,* present at or dating from birth.

Conjugate: L., *conjugare,* to unite. In physiology, refers to muscles working in unison, as the eye muscles.

Cornea: L., *corneus,* horny.

Coronal: L., *coronalis,* of or pertaining to the crown or corona. In the plane of the coronal suture of the skull, the frontal plane.

Corpus Callosum: L., *corporis,* body, plus *callosum,* hard or indurated.

Cortex: L., *cortex,* bark of a tree, akin to *corium,* leather. Anatomically the term applies to the outer or superficial part of an organ, as the outer layer of gray matter of the cerebrum.

Cranial: Gr., *kranion,* the skull, akin to *kara,* head. Pertaining to or toward the skull or head.

Crista: L., *crista,* crest or cock's comb or ridge. So called because the crista of the semicircular canals are in the form of elevations or ridges.

Cuneatus: L., from *cuneus,* wedge. The fasciculus cuneatus is so named because it is short and wedge-shaped.

Cytoplasm: Gr., *kytos,* a hollow (cell), plus *plasma,* thing formed.

Dendrite: Gr., *dendrites,* of a tree, from *dendron,* tree. Dendrites are nerve processes which are numerous and branch repeatedly near the cell, forming a tree-like arborization.

Diabetes: Gr., *diabainein,* to pass through. Refers to the persistent and excessive discharge of urine in this disease.

Diastole: Gr., from *diastellein,* to put asunder, from *dia,* through, plus *stellein,* to set or place. The expansion or dilatation of the heart cavities as they fill with blood.

Diencephalon: Gr., *dia,* through or between, plus *enkephalos,* brain; the between-brain.

Diplopia: Gr., *diploos,* double, plus *ops,* eye. Double vision.

Distal: L., *distare,* be separate or distant from. Away from the center of the body.

Dorsal: L., *dorsum,* back. Pertaining to or situated near the back of an animal or one of its parts.

Dura Mater: L., *durus,* hard, plus *mater,* mother. In ancient times the meninges were thought to give rise to all the membranes of the body; it is the tough, outer meningeal layer.

Ectoderm: Gr., *ektos,* outside, plus *derma,* skin. The outer, investing cellular membrane of multicellular animals; applies especially to the outer germ layer of embryos.

Efferent: L., *effere,* to bear or carry out or away from. In physiology, conveying outward or discharging.

Electrode: Gr., *elektro,* from *elektron,* amber (rubbing or friction of which produces static electricity), plus *hodos,* way. Either terminal of an electric source.

Embryo: Gr., *embryon,* to swell in or teem in, from *en,* in, plus *bryein,* to swell, teem. In the human being, the period of development up to the third month *in utero.*

Encephalon: Gr., *enkephalos,* from *en,* in, plus *kephalos,* head. Refers to the brain.

Endocrine: Gr., *endon,* within, plus *krinein,* to separate. Secreting internally.

Entoderm: Gr., *entos,* within, plus *derma,* skin. The inner germ layer.

Ependyma: Gr., *ependyma,* an upper garment. Refers to the cloak or lining of the ventricles.

Epilepsy: Gr., *epilepsia,* a seizure, from *epi,* upon or besides, plus *lambanein,* to take.

Exteroceptive: L., *exterus,* outside, plus *capere,* to take. To receive from the outside.

Facial: L., *facies,* the face. Of or pertaining to the face or facial nerve (so called because of its distribution to the facial muscles).

Fasciculus: L., diminutive of *fascis,* bundle. Therefore, a little bundle. Commonly applied to a slender bundle of fibers, either nerve or muscle.

Fetus: L., *fetus,* fruitful, offspring. In the human being, the child in that period of development from the third month *in utero* until birth.

Flaccid: L., *flaccidus,* flabby, from *flaccus,* lack of firmness or stiffness.

Foramen: L., *forare,* to bore or pierce. An aperture or opening.

Fovea: L., *fovea,* a small pit; probably akin to Gr., *cheie,* a hole.

Frontal: L., *frontale,* a forehead ornament. Of or pertaining to the region of the forehead.

Funiculus: L., *funiculus,* diminutive of *funis,* cord. Therefore, a little cord, band or bundle of fibers. As applied to nerves, is less specific functionally than a fasciculus.

Ganglion: Gr., *ganglion,* swelling or enlargement. An enlargement or mass of nerve tissue containing nerve cells, usually outside the central nervous system.

Geniculate: L., *geniculum,* diminutive of *genu,* knee. Therefore, little knee or bend. So called because the lateral geniculate body is bent or angled like a knee.

Glossopharyngeal: Gr., *glossa,* tongue, plus *pharynx,* chasm or throat. The ninth cranial nerve, so called because of its distribution to these structures.

Gracilis: L., *gracilis,* slender, thin. The fasciculus gracilis is so named because it is long and slender, extending throughout the length of the spinal cord. Likewise, the gracilis muscle in the thigh is long and slender.

Grand Mal: Fr., *grand,* large or great, plus Fr., *mal,* from L., *malum,* an evil. The convulsive episode of epilepsy.

Gyrus: L., *gyrus,* from Gr., *gyros,* circle, circular or spiral form. On the surface of the brain, a convoluted ridge between grooves.

Hemianopia: Gr., *hemi,* half, plus *a,* without, plus *ops,* eye. Loss of vision in half of each eye.

Hemiplegia: Gr., *hemi,* half, plus *plege,* stroke. Paralysis or weakness of one side of the body.

Hippocampus: Gr., *hippos,* horse, plus *kampos,* sea monster. A part of the brain next to the temporal horn of the lateral ventricle.

Histology: Gr., *histos,* web (denotes tissue), plus *logia,* discourse. The science which treats of the structure of tissues.

Homeostasis: Gr., *homoios,* like or similar, plus *stasis,* a standing still. A state of dynamic equilibrium in bodily processes.

Hydrocephalus: Gr., *hydor,* water, plus *kephale,* head. Excessive amount or pressure of cerebrospinal fluid.

Hypesthesia: Gr., *hypo,* beneath or less than, plus *aisthesis,* feeling. Lessened or diminished sensation.

Hypoglossal: Gr., *hypo,* below, plus *glossa,* tongue. So named because the nerve courses below the tongue to reach the muscles it supplies.

Hypothalamus: Gr., *hypo,* below, plus *thalamos,* thalamus.

Idiopathic: Gr., *idios,* individual, plus *pathos,* suffering. A peculiar or individual characteristic or affection; a primary disease of unknown cause.

Incus: L., *incus,* anvil. One of the three ear ossicles which in shape resembles an anvil.

Inhibition: L., *inhibere,* to restrain or check.

Interoceptive: L., *inter,* between or within, plus *capere,* to take. To receive stimuli from within.

Labyrinth: Gr., *labyrinthos,* an intricate passageway or maze. Refers to the inner ear because of the intricacy of structure of this region.

Lateral: L., *lateris,* side or flank, akin to *latus,* broad or wide. In a direction or position opposed to median.

Lemniscus: L., *lemniscus,* a ribbon hanging down, from Gr., *lemniskos,* fillet. A band of nerve fibers; usually applied to a collection of fibers of second order neurons.

Lesion: L., *laesus* or *laedere,* to hurt or injure. Any morbid change in tissues due to disease or injury.

Macula: L., *macula,* a spot or stain. Any structure forming a spot, as the macula of the utricle or of the retina.

Malleus: L., *malleus,* hammer. The ear ossicle whose shape resembles that of a hammer.

Median: L., *medius,* middle. Situated in the middle.

Medulla Oblongata: L., *medulla,* marrow or essence, plus *oblongata,* oblong. The most caudal part of the brain stem.

Meninges: L., *meninges,* from Gr., *meninx,* membrane. A general term for any of the membranes covering the brain.

Mesencephalon: Gr., *mesos,* middle, plus *enkephalos,* brain. Therefore, midbrain.

Metencephalon: Gr., *meta,* after, plus *enkephalos,* brain. The afterbrain, part of the hindbrain.

Microglia: Gr., *mikros,* small, plus *glia,* glue. A small neuroglial cell.

Micron: Gr., *mikros,* small, petty. Also 10–6, or one millionth of standard units of measurements, and by itself is one millionth of a meter.

Microtome: Gr., *mikros,* plus *tomos,* cutting. An instrument to cut thin sections.

Microvolt: Gr., *mikros,* plus volt, the unit of electrical force. One millionth of a volt.

Millivolt: L., *mille,* thousand, plus volt. One thousandth of a volt.

Monoplegia: Gr., *monos,* one, plus *plege,* stroke. Paralysis of a single limb or part

Morphology: Gr., *morphe,* form, plus *logia,* science. Science of form and structure of animals.

Muscle: L., *musculus,* diminutive of *mus,* mouse. Therefore, little mouse. So called because of the fancied resemblance of movements of the biceps brachii to the movements of a mouse.

Myasthenia Gravis: Gr., *mys* or *myos,* muscle, plus *aistheneia,* weakness, plus L., *gravis,* heavy. A disease of the muscles causing fatigue and eventually paralysis.

Myelencephalon: Gr., *myelos,* marrow, plus *enkephalos,* brain. The marrowbrain; refers especially to the medulla oblongata.

Myofibril: Gr., *mys,* muscle, plus L., *fibrilla,* a little fiber. Therefore, a little fiber within a muscle.

Myotatic: Gr., *mys,* muscle, plus *tasis,* stretching. Refers to stretch reflex.

Neocerebellum: Gr., *neos,* new, plus *cerebellum,* little brain. The newest or latest portion of the cerebellum in evolutionary processes.

Neopallium: Gr., *neos*, new, plus L., *pallium*, cloak or mantle (refers to cortex). The newest portion of the cerebral cortex in evolutionary processes.

Nerve: L., *nervus*, akin to Gr., *neuron*, sinew or nerve.

Neurilemma: Gr., *neuron*, nerve, plus *lemma*, skin or peel. The outer skin or cell layer around a nerve fiber.

Neuroblast: Gr., *neuron*, nerve, plus *blastos*, germ. Means nerve forming and refers to embryonic cells which give rise to nerve cells.

Neuroglia: Gr., *neuron*, nerve, plus *glia*, glue. Means nerve glue and refers to the cells which support or hold nervous tissue together.

Neurology: Gr., *neuron*, nerve, plus *logia*, science. The science which treats of the nervous system in all its aspects. In a more restricted sense it is often used to refer to disorders of the nervous system.

Nucleolus: L., diminutive of *nucleus*, from *nucis*, nut. Therefore, a little nut. A rounded, often conspicuous body within a nucleus.

Nucleus: L., *nucleus*, kernel, from *nucis*, nut. A central mass or point, as the nucleus of a cell.

Occipital: L., *occipitus*, back of head, as opposed to forehead.

Oculomotor: L., *oculus*, eye, plus *motor*, motion. Moving the eyeball. The nerve supplies muscles which move the eyeball.

Olfactory: L., *olfacere*, to smell. Refers to the sense of smell or to structures subserving this function.

Oligodendroglia: Gr., *oligos*, small or few, plus *dendron*, tree, plus *glia*, glue. A neuroglial cell with a few small branches.

Optic: Gr., *optikos*, akin to *opsis*, vision. Of or pertaining to vision and the structures subserving this function.

Orbital: L., *orbita*, track or circuit. Pertaining to the skull cavity in which the eye and appendages are located.

Ossicle: L., *ossiculum*, diminutive of *os*, bone. Therefore, little bone.

Paleocerebellum: Gr., *palaios*, old or ancient, plus cerebellum. A phylogenetically older portion of the cerebellum.

Paralysis: Gr., *para*, beside, plus *lyein*, to loosen, dissolve or disable. Hence, to disable on a side.

Paresis: Gr., *paresis* or *parienae*, to let go. In neurology, means weakness or incomplete paralysis and is also used to indicate the involvement of the cerebral cortex in syphilis.

Parietal: L., *paries*, a wall or plate of a part or cavity. The parietal bones of the skull form part of the sides and roof of the calvarium.

Pathology: Gr., *pathos*, suffering or disease, plus *logia*. The science treating of diseases, their nature, causes, development and changes.

Peduncle: L., *pedunculus*, diminutive of *pes*, foot. Therefore, little foot. A stem or narrow part by which some part is attached to another, as the cerebellum to the brain stem.

Peristalsis: Gr., *peristaltikos*, clasping and compressing, as in the peculiar wavelike motions of the intestines.

Petit Mal: Fr., *petit*, small, plus *mal*. The less violent of the episodes of epilepsy.

Phagocyte: Gr., *phago*, I eat, plus *kytos*, cell. Phagocytic cells ingest and destroy other materials, including cells.

Physiology: Gr., *physis*, nature, plus *logia*. The branch of biology dealing with the processes and activities of living organisms.

Pia Mater: L., *pius*, tender or kind, plus *mater*, mother. The more delicate and closely investing of the three meningeal layers.

Pineal: L., *pineus,* a pine cone. The pineal body in shape and attachment resembles a pine cone.

Plexus: L., *plexus,* a turning or braid. Refers to the interweaving of nerves as they form a plexus.

Pons: L., *pons,* a bridge. The pons consist of fibers which bridge across the brain stem to the cerebellum on either side.

Posterior: L., *posterus,* from *post,* behind or after. At or toward the hind end of the body; in a tailward or caudal direction.

Proprioceptive: L., *proprius,* one's own, plus *capere,* to take. Receiving stimuli produced by tension in tissues, as muscles.

Prosencephalon: Gr., *pros,* toward or near, plus *enkephalos.* The first or foremost of the primary brain vesicles.

Protoplasm: Gr., *protos,* first, plus *plasma,* thing formed. Originally designated formative material of young animal embryos. Now refers to the essential substance of cell body and nucleus.

Proximal: L., *proximare,* to come near. Next to or nearest, as to the point of attachment of a limb to the body.

Psychiatry: Gr., *psyche,* the mind, plus *iatreia,* healing. Although literally meaning mind-healing, it is really the science of behavior, including behavior disorders.

Psychology: Gr., *psyche,* mind, plus *logia.* The science which treats of mental and behavioral processes.

Pudendal: L., *pudendus,* that of which one ought to be ashamed, from *pudere,* to be ashamed. Anatomically, refers to the region of the external sex organs.

Reflex: L., *re,* back, plus *flectere,* to bend. To turn or refer back.

Restiform: L., *restis,* rope, plus *forma,* form. Ropelike; these peduncles are so named because of their ropelike or cordlike shape.

Retina: L., *rete,* a net. The light-sensitive membrane of the eye.

Rheobase: Gr., *rheos,* current, plus *basis,* base or foundation. The basic or minimal current required to excite.

Rhinencephalon: Gr., *rhis,* nose, plus *enkephalos.* The olfactory or smellbrain.

Rhombencephalon: Gr., *rhombos,* equilateral parallelogram with oblique angles, plus *enkephalos.* The hindbrain, so named because of its shape.

Saccule: L., diminutive of *saccus,* sac. Therefore, a little sac. A small membranous bag in the inner ear.

Sagittal: L., *sagitta,* an arrow. Of or pertaining to the sagittal or midline suture of the skull and any plane parallel to this suture.

Spastic: Gr., *spastikos,* from *span,* to draw. To cause convulsions.

Sphygmomanometer: Gr., *sphygmos,* pulse, plus *manometer,* an instrument for measuring pressure. An instrument for measuring blood pressure.

Substantia Nigra: L., *substantis,* substance, plus *nigra,* black. So called because of the dark or black appearance of this area, resulting from the presence of melanin-containing cells.

Synapse: Gr., *synapsis,* a conjunction or union.

Syncytium: Gr., *syn,* with, plus *kytos,* cell. A multinuclear cell or aggregation of imperfectly separated cells.

Systole: Gr., *systellein,* to contract. Refers to the contraction of the heart.

Tactile: L., *tactilis,* tangible, from *tactum,* to touch.

Telencephalon: Gr., *telos,* end, plus *enkephalos.* The far or endbrain.

Temporal: L., *temporalis* or *temporal,* the temples. Of or pertaining to the region of the temples.

Thalamus: Gr., *thalos* or *thalamos,* inner chamber or anteroom.

Thrombosis: Gr., *thrombosis,* coagulation or curdling. Refers to the clotting of blood.

Tonic: Gr., *tonikos, tonos,* tone. To stretch or strain.

Transverse: L., *transvertere,* to turn or direct across.

Trigeminal: L., *trigeminus,* born three together, from *tri,* three, plus *geminus,* twin. Pertaining to the trigeminal nerve with its three branches.

Trochlear: L., *trochlea,* block or pulley. So called because the muscle which this nerve supplies has a pulley for its tendon.

Tympanum: L., *tympanum,* drum. This membrane is stretched tightly across the end of the external ear canal, like the skin of a drum.

Utricle: L., *utriculus,* diminutive of *uter,* sac or vesicle; a skin bag.

Vagus: L., *vagari,* wandering. So called because of the long and extensive course of this nerve.

Vein: L., *vena,* akin to *vehere,* to convey.

Ventral: L., *ventralis,* from *venter,* belly. Anything pertaining to or toward this part of the body, as opposed to dorsal.

Ventricle: L., *ventriculus,* diminutive of *venter,* belly. A chamber or cavity.

Venule: L., diminutive of *vena,* vein. Therefore, a little vein.

Vermis: L., *vermis,* a worm. So called because of the narrow, wormlike appearance of the midpart of the cerebellum.

Vestibular: L., *vestibulum,* passage, hall or chamber.

Viscera: L., *viscus,* to turn or wind, as the internal organs.

Index

367

Axon(s), in central nervous system, 80
  membrane of, 97
  motor units and, 141
  myelinated, 77–82
  nonmyelinated, 77–82
  outside central nervous system, 79–80
  postganglionic, 143, 230, 231, 232
  preganglionic, 143, 230, 231, 232
  structure of, 77–79
  synopsis and, 82, 83
Axoplasm, 97, 101

Babinski, J., 128
  reflex (response), 126–127, 168, 314
Balance, 215–220
Band (stripe) of Gennari, 204
Barbiturate suppression of brain waves, 323
Bard, P., 115
Basal dendrite, 73, 306
Basal ganglia, 21, 296–302
  and dynamic reactions, 300–301
  connections of, 297–298
  disorders of, 301–302
  functions of, 298–301
Basal plate, 60
Basilar artery, 15, 16, 45, 46, 50
Basilar membrane, 210
Basket cells, 280, 282
Beevor, C., 171
Behavior, 291
  affective component of, 291, 345
  and chemistry, 356–357
  instinctive type, 211
  reflexes and, 124–125
Békésy, G. v., 224
Bel, unit of power, 211
Bell, A. G., 211
Berger, H., 310
  rhythm (alpha waves of EEG), 307, 308
Bernard, C., 244
Best, C. H., 115
Beta waves of EEG, 308, 309
Biceps brachii, 126
Biceps jerk, 126
Binocular vision, 204–207
Bipolar cells, 66, 67, 77
  of cochlea (spiral ganglion), 210
  of olfactory mucous membrane, 221
  of retina, 193
  of vestibular ganglia, 215

Birds, forebrain of, 293, 294
Bishop, G. H., 115, 150, 306
Bitter, as primary taste quality, 220
Bladder, urinary, in spinal man, 253–254
Blind spot of eye, 193
Blindness, 206, 324
  color, 203–204
Blood, 44
Blood-brain barrier, 54
Blood-cerebrospinal fluid barrier, 54
Blood flow, and body temperature, 225
  in cranial cavity, 50–51
Blood pressure, control of, 239–241
  diastolic, 240
  systolic, 240
Blood supply, 44–52
  clinical importance of, 51–52
  of brain, 45–47
  of meninges, 47
  of peripheral nerves, 49–50
  of spinal cord, nerves, and roots, 48–49
Bloom, W., 94
Body(ies), amygdaloid, 21, 304, 305
  carotid, 275
  Golgi (Golgi apparatus), 58, 72, 353–355
  mammillary, 16, 19
  pineal, 16, 19, 263
Body areas, and cerebellum, 285
Body-righting reflexes, 300, 301
Body temperature, and blood flow, 225
  control of, 225–226, 237
Bone, temporal, 210
Bouton de passage, 83
Boutons terminaux, 82
Boyd, J. D., 70
Brachial plexus, 34, 37, 40
Brain, 10–24
  blood supply of, 45–47
  electrical activity of, 307–309
Brain, R., 328
Brain stem, 11, 259–278
  and autonomic nervous system, 229–230, 239–242
  association paths of, 263
  cerebellar connections of, 285
  excitatory mechanisms, 268
  functions of, 266–277
    somatic, 266–272
    visceral, 272–277

Every day is a gift

MY BOOK OF GRATITUDE

BELLE
CITY
GIFTS

Belle City Gifts
Savage, Minnesota, USA

Belle City Gifts is an imprint of BroadStreet Publishing Group LLC.
Broadstreetpublishing.com

Every day is a gift

978-1-4245-6092-9

Composed and compiled by Michelle Winger.

Design by Chris Garborg | garborgdesign.com
Edited by Michelle Winger | literallyprecise.com

Printed in China.

20   21   22   23   24   25   26   7   6   5   4   3   2   1

*E*very day is truly a gift from God. We are encouraged in His Word to give thanks in all things. When we choose to focus on that which we are grateful for, our satisfaction with life increases and we become happier in general.

This guided journal will encourage you to focus on things that bring life and joy, reflect on Scripture and quotes that give peace and comfort, and evaluate each day in the light of truth.

Take time to ponder the gift of another day and thank God for it!

When do you feel the happiest?

_____

_____

_____

_____

_____

_____

_____

_____

_____

_____

_____

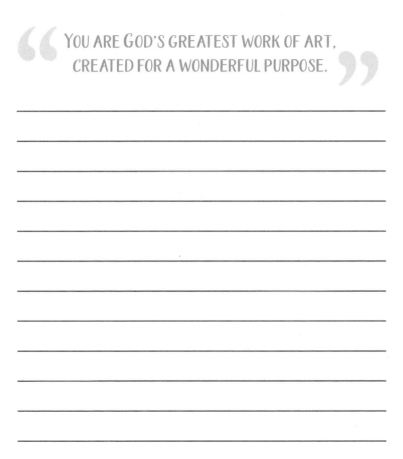

> YOU ARE GOD'S GREATEST WORK OF ART,
> CREATED FOR A WONDERFUL PURPOSE.

Life is too short to be busy all the time! If you could spend the day any way you wanted to, what would you do?

_____

_____

_____

_____

_____

_____

_____

_____

_____

_____

_____

What is the best quality that
you feel you exemplify?

_____

_____

_____

_____

_____

_____

_____

_____

_____

_____

_____

WE ALL HAVE SOME REALLY GREAT MOMENTS, AND THOSE SHOULD BE REMEMBERED. WHAT WAS ONE OF THE GREATEST MOMENTS OF YOUR LIFE?

_____

_____

_____

_____

_____

_____

_____

_____

_____

_____

"For I know the plans I have for you," declares the Lord,
"plans to prosper you and not to harm you,
plans to give you hope and a future."

JEREMIAH 29:11 NIV

_____

_____

_____

_____

_____

_____

_____

_____

_____

_____

_____

Write about one thing that truly inspires you.

_____

_____

_____

_____

_____

_____

_____

_____

_____

_____

_____

_____

THE WORLD IS A BEAUTIFUL PLACE FILLED
WITH WONDER. IF YOU COULD GO ANYWHERE
IN THE WORLD, WHERE WOULD IT BE?

_____

_____

_____

_____

_____

_____

_____

_____

_____

_____

Do you know that smiling when you don't feel like it can actually change your mood? Write down five things that make you smile.

1. _____

2. _____

3. _____

4. _____

5. _____

What is something you are
hoping for right now?

LAUGH

– what can you laugh about today?

_____

_____

_____

_____

_____

_____

_____

_____

_____

_____

You don't have to be willing and able; just be willing because God is able.

Who do you feel completely loved by and why?

_____

_____

_____

_____

_____

_____

_____

_____

_____

_____

_____

_____

Are there people in your life who really know you? What are a few things you wish people knew about you?

_____

_____

_____

_____

_____

_____

_____

_____

_____

_____

_____

_____

On a scale of 1 to 10, how happy do you feel today?

1 **2** **3** **4** **5** **6** **7** **8** **9** **10**

_____

_____

_____

_____

_____

_____

_____

_____

_____

_____

_____

How do you find peace when everything
around you feels chaotic?

_____

_____

_____

_____

_____

_____

_____

_____

_____

_____

_____

> You might be imperfect,
> but you are perfectly you.

I can do all this through him who gives me strength.

PHILIPPIANS 4:13 NIV

_____

_____

_____

_____

_____

_____

_____

_____

_____

_____

_____

What is the color you wear most often? Why?

_____

_____

_____

_____

_____

_____

_____

_____

_____

_____

It's important to have boundaries in life.
What are some things you are learning to say no to?

_____

_____

_____

_____

_____

_____

_____

_____

_____

_____

_____

If you could describe yourself in five words,
what would they be?

1. _____

2. _____

3. _____

4. _____

5. _____

Who is the most intriguing person you have read or heard about? Why?

_____

_____

_____

_____

_____

_____

_____

_____

_____

_____

_____

It is not that we think we are qualified to do anything on our own.
Our qualification comes from God.

2 CORINTHIANS 3:5 NLT

_____

_____

_____

_____

_____

_____

_____

_____

_____

_____

_____

_____

FOCUS

– what do you need to focus on today?

_____

_____

_____

_____

_____

_____

_____

_____

_____

_____

_____

What is your favorite childhood memory?

_____

_____

_____

_____

_____

_____

_____

_____

_____

_____

_____

THE OLDER WE GET, THE MORE WE REALIZE WE DON'T KNOW. WHAT IS SOMETHING YOU WOULD LIKE TO LEARN MORE ABOUT?

_____

_____

_____

_____

_____

_____

_____

_____

_____

_____

God has
given you
everything
you need.

If you had to write a book, what would you call it,
and what would it be about?

_____

_____

_____

_____

_____

_____

_____

_____

_____

_____

> **If you never chase your dreams,
> you will never catch them.**

_____

_____

_____

_____

_____

_____

_____

_____

_____

_____

_____

THE BOOK OF PROVERBS BY SOLOMON
HOLDS PROFOUND WISDOM.
WHAT IS A PROVERB YOU LIVE BY?

_____

_____

_____

_____

_____

_____

_____

_____

_____

_____

What is your favorite song?
What do you love about it?

On a scale of 1 to 10, how brave do you feel today?

1 2 3 4 5 6 7 8 9 10

_____

_____

_____

_____

_____

_____

_____

_____

_____

_____

Use this acrostic to consider the ways
you could serve others.

S
_____

E
_____

R
_____

V
_____

E
_____

Do you find it difficult to ask for help?
Why or why not?

_____

_____

_____

_____

_____

_____

_____

_____

_____

_____

_____

Family. There's really nothing quite like it. What are five things you love about your family?

1. _____

2. _____

3. _____

4. _____

5. _____

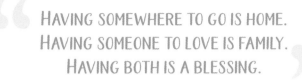

> HAVING SOMEWHERE TO GO IS HOME.
> HAVING SOMEONE TO LOVE IS FAMILY.
> HAVING BOTH IS A BLESSING.

_____

_____

_____

_____

_____

_____

_____

_____

_____

_____

_____

WHO WOULD YOU MOST LIKE TO MEET, AND WHY?

_____

_____

_____

_____

_____

_____

_____

_____

_____

_____

_____

_____

Change is a part of life. Change is what we do as we mature. If you could change one thing about yourself, what would it be?

_____

_____

_____

_____

_____

_____

_____

_____

_____

_____

_____

BLESSED

– how blessed do you feel today?

_____

_____

_____

_____

_____

_____

_____

_____

_____

_____

What can you do to bless someone today?

_____

_____

_____

_____

_____

_____

_____

_____

_____

_____

_____

What dream have you almost given up on?
Can you dare to keep dreaming?

_____

_____

_____

_____

_____

_____

_____

_____

_____

_____

_____

_____

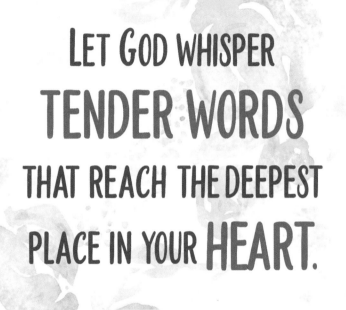

LET GOD WHISPER **TENDER WORDS** THAT REACH THE DEEPEST PLACE IN YOUR **HEART.**

What is your favorite day of the week? Why?

_____

_____

_____

_____

_____

_____

_____

_____

_____

_____

_____

"Don't let your hearts be troubled. Trust in God, and trust also in me."

JOHN 14:1 NLT

_____

_____

_____

_____

_____

_____

_____

_____

_____

_____

_____

> LIVE IN SUCH A WAY THAT IF SOMEONE
> SPOKE BADLY OF YOU, NO ONE WOULD BELIEVE IT.

_____

_____

_____

_____

_____

_____

_____

_____

_____

_____

_____

If you had to paint a picture, what would it be of? What would you title it?

_____

_____

_____

_____

_____

_____

_____

_____

_____

_____

_____

On a scale of 1 to 10, how beautiful do you feel today?

1 2 3 4 5 6 7 8 9 10

_____

_____

_____

_____

_____

_____

_____

_____

_____

_____

_____

WHAT IS YOUR FAVORITE THING TO DO WHEN THE SUN IS SHINING?

_____

_____

_____

_____

_____

_____

_____

_____

_____

_____

_____

Write down three obstacles you are facing and then list how you can make them opportunities instead.

OBSTACLE

1. _____

_____

_____

2. _____

_____

_____

3. _____

_____

_____

OPPORTUNITY

1. _____

_____

_____

2. _____

_____

_____

3. _____

_____

_____

Priorities help you manage your time well.
What are your top five priorities?

1. _____

2. _____

3. _____

4. _____

5. _____

We all need encouragement.
What are the words you most need to hear?

_____

_____

_____

_____

_____

_____

_____

_____

_____

_____

_____

Some people love being alone.
Others thrive on being with people. How does
spending quiet time on your own make you feel?

_____

_____

_____

_____

_____

_____

_____

_____

_____

_____

_____

> **IT'S EASY TO LOOK AT OURSELVES AND SEE OURSELVES AS WHAT WE ARE NOW. GOD LOOKS AT US AND SEES WHAT WE CAN BECOME.**

_____

_____

_____

_____

_____

_____

_____

_____

_____

_____

What is one of the most satisfying jobs you have done?

_____

_____

_____

_____

_____

_____

_____

_____

_____

_____

_____

THANKFUL
– what are you eternally thankful for?

_____

_____

_____

_____

_____

_____

_____

_____

_____

_____

Who do you trust with your every secret?
Why do you think they are so trustworthy?

_____

_____

_____

_____

_____

_____

_____

_____

_____

_____

_____

_____

A life of victory isn't a life without disappointment or hard work.

What does it look like to consider yourself a citizen of heaven?

_____

_____

_____

_____

_____

_____

_____

_____

_____

_____

_____

Rejoice in the Lord always. I will say it again: Rejoice!

PHILIPPIANS 4:4 NIV

_____

_____

_____

_____

_____

_____

_____

_____

_____

_____

_____

WHAT TRUTHS OF GOD CAN YOU DECLARE RIGHT NOW?

_____

_____

_____

_____

_____

_____

_____

_____

_____

_____

_____

_____

Do you need to create more margin
in your life? How can you do that?

_____

_____

_____

_____

_____

_____

_____

_____

_____

_____

_____

Words are powerful. Which five words
are among your favorites?

1. _____

2. _____

3. _____

4. _____

5. _____

What is your biggest
challenge to freedom?

_____

_____

_____

_____

_____

_____

_____

_____

_____

_____

_____

"WHEN YOU CHOOSE TO LOOK AT EACH MOMENT AS A MOMENT IN WHICH TO BE THANKFUL, YOU WILL FIND IN EACH MOMENT BEAUTY, JOY, AND SATISFACTION."

_____

_____

_____

_____

_____

_____

_____

_____

_____

_____

_____

On a scale of 1 to 10, how confident do you feel today?

①　②　③　④　⑤　⑥　⑦　⑧　⑨　⑩

_____

_____

_____

_____

_____

_____

_____

_____

_____

_____

How do you see gentleness
affecting your daily life?

_____

_____

_____

_____

_____

_____

_____

_____

_____

_____

_____

God's Word is full of encouragement and hope.
What is your favorite Scripture?

_____

_____

_____

_____

_____

_____

_____

_____

_____

_____

_____

COURAGE
– what makes you feel brave?

_____

_____

_____

_____

_____

_____

_____

_____

_____

_____

Use this acrostic to consider the ways you could love others.

L _____

O _____

V _____

E _____

ARE YOU HOLDING ON TO OFFENSE?
CAN YOU LET GO OF IT TODAY?

_____

_____

_____

_____

_____

_____

_____

_____

_____

_____

_____

_____

You have so much to give! How do you participate in your community so others can see your light?

_____

_____

_____

_____

_____

_____

_____

_____

_____

_____

_____

_____

EVERY
SITUATION
HAS THE
POTENTIAL
TO CREATE
beauty
IN YOU.

How is what you are doing right now preparing you for eternity?

_____

_____

_____

_____

_____

_____

_____

_____

_____

_____

_____

"TODAY'S TRIAL IS TOMORROW'S TESTIMONY."

_____

_____

_____

_____

_____

_____

_____

_____

_____

_____

_____

Most of us spend a lot of time running errands. What five errands do you run the most?

1. _____

2. _____

3. _____

4. _____

5. _____

What are you doing right now that you see God has called you to?

_____

_____

_____

_____

_____

_____

_____

_____

_____

_____

_____

Role models and mentors are critical in all stages of life.
Who is the person you most look up to right now?

_____

_____

_____

_____

_____

_____

_____

_____

_____

_____

_____

"Those the Father has given me will come to me,
and I will never reject them."

JOHN 6:37 NLT

_____

_____

_____

_____

_____

_____

_____

_____

_____

_____

_____

_____

WHAT CAN YOU DO TO START CULTIVATING A HEART OF GRATITUDE?

_____

_____

_____

_____

_____

_____

_____

_____

_____

_____

_____

Laughter is good medicine.
What has made you laugh out loud recently?

_____

_____

_____

_____

_____

_____

_____

_____

_____

_____

_____

_____

WORTHY

– where do you find your worth?

_____

_____

_____

_____

_____

_____

_____

_____

_____

Do you believe God hears you when you talk to him? Why or why not?

_____

_____

_____

_____

_____

_____

_____

_____

_____

_____

_____

On a scale of 1 to 10, how hopeful do you feel today?

1 2 3 4 5 6 7 8 9 10

_____

_____

_____

_____

_____

_____

_____

_____

_____

_____

GOD DOESN'T WANT YOU TO SETTLE FOR "GOOD ENOUGH." HE WANTS YOU TO GO FORWARD IN LIFE, ALWAYS PUTTING YOUR HEART AND MIND IN A POSITION TO LEARN AND GROW.

_____

_____

_____

_____

_____

_____

_____

_____

_____

_____

In which areas of your life do you need
to practice more self-control?

_____

_____

_____

_____

_____

_____

_____

_____

_____

_____

_____

_____

Is there someone who needs your forgiveness today?
Can you put aside your hurt and offer grace?

_____

_____

_____

_____

_____

_____

_____

_____

_____

_____

_____

What can you be grateful for today? Vibrant colors, bursting flavors, moving melodies... begin there.

Do you know the goodness of God?
How have you seen it in your life lately?

_____

_____

_____

_____

_____

_____

_____

_____

_____

_____

_____

Friends are critical for healthy social development. Who are your five closest friends?

1. _____

2. _____

3. _____

4. _____

5. _____

"Be still, and know that I am God. I will be exalted among the nations, I will be exalted in the earth!"

PSALM 46:10 ESV

_____

_____

_____

_____

_____

_____

_____

_____

_____

_____

_____

How do you put your hope and
confidence in God's love?

_____

_____

_____

_____

_____

_____

_____

_____

_____

_____

_____

Even if you don't think so, you do have at least an ounce of creativity! What is your creative outlet?

_____

_____

_____

_____

_____

_____

_____

_____

_____

_____

_____

_____

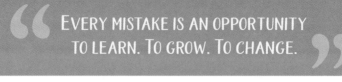

EVERY MISTAKE IS AN OPPORTUNITY TO LEARN. TO GROW. TO CHANGE.

_____

_____

_____

_____

_____

_____

_____

_____

_____

_____

_____

How do you see God's purpose
working in your life?

_____

_____

_____

_____

_____

_____

_____

_____

_____

_____

_____

_____

Within your heart you can make plans for your future,
but the Lord chooses the steps you take to get there.

PROVERBS 16:9 TPT

_____

_____

_____

_____

_____

_____

_____

_____

_____

_____

_____

PEACE

– how can you make peace a part of your day?

_____

_____

_____

_____

_____

_____

_____

_____

_____

_____

WHEN DO YOU FIND YOURSELF MOST AT A LOSS FOR WORDS?

_____

_____

_____

_____

_____

_____

_____

_____

_____

_____

_____

What is something you would like to change about yourself, or the situation you are in, within the next year?

_____

_____

_____

_____

_____

_____

_____

_____

_____

_____

_____

On a scale of 1 to 10, how strong do you feel today?

(1) (2) (3) (4) (5) (6) (7) (8) (9) (10)

_____

_____

_____

_____

_____

_____

_____

_____

_____

_____

What kind of success are you currently pursuing?

_____

_____

_____

_____

_____

_____

_____

_____

_____

_____

_____

Write down three areas of weakness and
then list how they can be turned into strengths.

WEAKNESS

1. _____

_____

_____

2. _____

_____

_____

3. _____

_____

_____

STRENGTH

1. _____

_____

_____

2. _____

_____

_____

3. _____

_____

_____

GOD WILL NOT FAIL YOU.

WHAT IS YOUR STORY OF GOD'S WORK IN YOUR LIFE?

_____

_____

_____

_____

_____

_____

_____

_____

_____

_____

_____

Do you cherish family traditions? Have you made some of your own? What are the five family traditions that you treasure the most?

1.
_____

2.
_____

3.
_____

4.
_____

5.
_____

How do you feel your faith being tested right now?

_____

_____

_____

_____

_____

_____

_____

_____

_____

_____

Use this acrostic to consider the ways you could help someone in need.

H _____

E _____

L _____

P _____

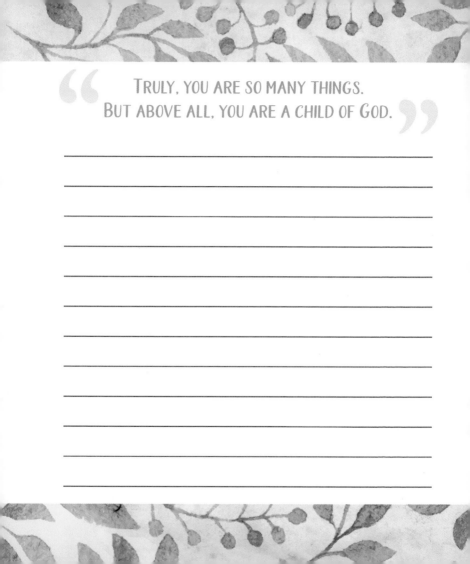

> **TRULY, YOU ARE SO MANY THINGS.
> BUT ABOVE ALL, YOU ARE A CHILD OF GOD.**

_____

_____

_____

_____

_____

_____

_____

_____

_____

_____

_____

_____

Do you find it difficult to trust God in certain areas?
What are they, and why do you think that is?

_____

_____

_____

_____

_____

_____

_____

_____

_____

_____

Are you afraid to be fully known?
Why or why not?

_____

_____

_____

_____

_____

_____

_____

_____

_____

_____

_____

_____

VALUE

– what made you feel valued today?

_____

_____

_____

_____

_____

_____

_____

_____

_____

_____

Strange things happen every day. What unusual thing has happened to you recently?

_____

_____

_____

_____

_____

_____

_____

_____

_____

_____

_____

_____

_____

What would it take for you to see yourself as beautiful?

_____

_____

_____

_____

_____

_____

_____

_____

_____

_____

_____

_____

Give all your worries and cares to God, for he cares for you.

1 PETER 5:7 NLT

_____

_____

_____

_____

_____

_____

_____

_____

_____

_____

_____

> LIGHT. JOY. PEACE. THESE ARE THINGS THAT PEOPLE CRAVE. YOUR INFLUENCE CAN BE IN THE SIMPLE, EVERYDAY WAY YOU HANDLE YOURSELF.

_____

_____

_____

_____

_____

_____

_____

_____

_____

_____

_____

Of all the parables in Scripture, what is your favorite?

_____

_____

_____

_____

_____

_____

_____

_____

_____

_____

Science says that opposites attract, but that's not always true in relationships. What are the five qualities you look for most in a friend?

1. _____

2. _____

3. _____

4. _____

5. _____

Joy flows
in the middle of
the darkness as
you trust in God's
perfect ways.

When do you feel most alive?

_____

_____

_____

_____

_____

_____

_____

_____

_____

_____

_____

On a scale of 1 to 10, how brilliant do you feel today?

1 2 3 4 5 6 7 8 9 10

_____

_____

_____

_____

_____

_____

_____

_____

_____

_____

Who are the people in your life that fully support you?
How do they show it?

_____

_____

_____

_____

_____

_____

_____

_____

_____

_____

_____

_____

How have you seen God move
in your life lately?

_____

_____

_____

_____

_____

_____

_____

_____

_____

_____

_____

> GIFTS FROM GOD ARE ALL AROUND YOU. LIFT UP YOUR HEAD AND ALLOW YOURSELF TO BE INSPIRED.

_____

_____

_____

_____

_____

_____

_____

_____

_____

_____

We need to have more fun in life.
What is the most fun you've had lately?

_____

_____

_____

_____

_____

_____

_____

_____

_____

_____

HOW DO YOU SHOW YOUR LOVE TO OTHERS?

_____

_____

_____

_____

_____

_____

_____

_____

_____

_____

_____

SEEK

– what are you looking for today?

_____

_____

_____

_____

_____

_____

_____

_____

_____

_____

Watch your words and be careful what you say,
and you'll be surprised how few troubles you'll have.

PROVERBS 21:23 TPT

_____

_____

_____

_____

_____

_____

_____

_____

_____

_____

_____

What is a characteristic you would love to possess, and why?

_____

_____

_____

_____

_____

_____

_____

_____

_____

_____

_____

We know that joy and happiness are not the same thing. How do you have joy even when circumstances are not ideal?

_____

_____

_____

_____

_____

_____

_____

_____

_____

_____

_____

_____

There are so many beautiful places in
this world. Which five destinations
would you most like to explore?

1. _____

2. _____

3. _____

4. _____

5. _____

Are you being honest with yourself today?
How do you really feel?

_____

_____

_____

_____

_____

_____

_____

_____

_____

_____

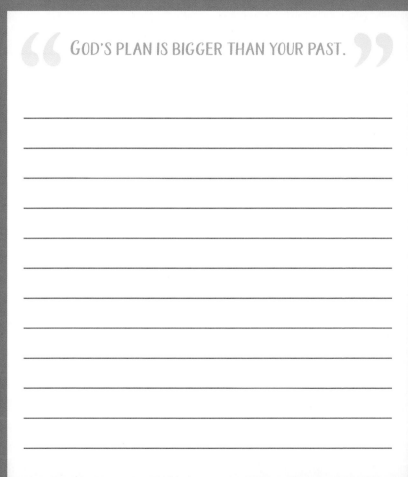

GOD'S PLAN IS BIGGER THAN YOUR PAST.

_____

_____

_____

_____

_____

_____

_____

_____

_____

_____

Your message to God is never lost in translation.

What are your dreams mostly about?
Why do you think that is?

_____

_____

_____

_____

_____

_____

_____

_____

_____

_____

_____

You've heard it said a thousand times: a glass with water in it up to the middle is either half empty or half full. Do you tend to focus on the positive or negative? Why?

_____

_____

_____

_____

_____

_____

_____

_____

_____

_____

_____

This is the confidence we have in approaching God:
that if we ask anything according to his will, he hears us.

1 JOHN 5:14 NIV

_____

_____

_____

_____

_____

_____

_____

_____

_____

_____

_____

_____

HAVE YOU WALKED THROUGH A SEASON OF GRIEF? HOW DID YOU MAINTAIN HOPE?

_____

_____

_____

_____

_____

_____

_____

_____

_____

_____

_____

_____

_____

Take an honest look at the things you long for, dream about, and desire. What do they reveal about your relationship with God?

_____

_____

_____

_____

_____

_____

_____

_____

_____

_____

_____

On a scale of 1 to 10, how loved do you feel today?

(1) (2) (3) (4) (5) (6) (7) (8) (9) (10)

_____

_____

_____

_____

_____

_____

_____

_____

_____

_____

What is something you need
God's guidance for right now?

_____

_____

_____

_____

_____

_____

_____

_____

_____

_____

TRUTH

– do you know the truth deep inside your heart?

_____

_____

_____

_____

_____

_____

_____

_____

_____

_____

What is a story you tell over and over?

_____

_____

_____

_____

_____

_____

_____

_____

_____

_____

_____

Use this acrostic to consider the ways you could stir up joy in you and others.

S _____

M _____

I _____

L _____

E _____

We should never let our fears drive us, but to say we fear nothing is likely not true (even if we want it to be). Write down five things that terrify you the most, and then ponder whether or not those fears are rational.

1.

2.

3.

4.

5.

> **DON'T JUST SAY YES. IT IS ALWAYS BETTER TO THINK CAREFULLY ABOUT A NEW VENTURE OR OPPORTUNITY BEFORE YOU COMMIT TO IT.**

_____

_____

_____

_____

_____

_____

_____

_____

_____

How have you changed in the last five years?

_____

_____

_____

_____

_____

_____

_____

_____

_____

_____

_____

Who can you uplift in prayer today?
Bring a friend before the Lord in prayer.

_____

_____

_____

_____

_____

_____

_____

_____

_____

_____

_____

_____

_____

ABUNDANCE,
OPULENCE, SPLENDOR,
IMMEASURABLE LOVE —
*it's your
inheritance!*

WHAT DO YOU FIND MOST INTERESTING ABOUT PEOPLE?

_____

_____

_____

_____

_____

_____

_____

_____

_____

_____

_____

> **NOTHING GOOD COMES OUT OF NOT TRYING YOUR BEST.**

May God, the inspiration and fountain of hope, fill you to overflowing
with uncontainable joy and perfect peace as you trust in him.

ROMANS 15:13 TPT

_____

_____

_____

_____

_____

_____

_____

_____

_____

_____

_____

What hurts you the most?

_____

_____

_____

_____

_____

_____

_____

_____

_____

_____

_____

_____

What are your priorities? Would they be obvious
to someone observing a day in your life?

_____

_____

_____

_____

_____

_____

_____

_____

_____

_____

Write down three things you are struggling with and
then list how they could be blessings in disguise.

STRUGGLE

1. _____

_____

_____

2. _____

_____

_____

3. _____

_____

_____

BLESSING

1. _____

_____

_____

2. _____

_____

_____

3. _____

_____

_____

What is something you are
truly proud of?

_____

_____

_____

_____

_____

_____

_____

_____

_____

_____

_____

CHALLENGE
– what are you challenging yourself to do today?

_____

_____

_____

_____

_____

_____

_____

_____

_____

_____

On a scale of 1 to 10, how determined do you feel today?

1 2 3 4 5 6 7 8 9 10

_____

_____

_____

_____

_____

_____

_____

_____

_____

_____

_____

Where is your favorite place in the world, and why?

_____

_____

_____

_____

_____

_____

_____

_____

_____

_____

Colors give vibrancy to the world around us.
What five colors do you love to wear and why?

1. _____

2. _____

3. _____

4. _____

5. _____

> "YOU ARE NOT A MISTAKE. YOUR HAIR COLOR, YOUR SMILE, YOUR INTERESTS, YOUR ABILITIES, THEY WERE ALL ORCHESTRATED BY THE CREATOR."

_____

_____

_____

_____

_____

_____

_____

_____

_____

_____

WHAT DO YOU GET YOUR VALUE FROM?

_____

_____

_____

_____

_____

_____

_____

_____

_____

_____

_____

_____

Working consistently with enthusiasm can become wearying. Are you feeling drained today? What can help you push through these feelings and enjoy your day?

_____

_____

_____

_____

_____

_____

_____

_____

_____

_____

What was the best gift you ever received? What made it the best?

_____

_____

_____

_____

_____

_____

_____

_____

_____

_____

_____

_____

Refusing constructive criticism shows you have no interest in improving your life. For revelation-insight only comes as you accept correction and the wisdom that it brings.

PROVERBS 15:32 TPT

_____

_____

_____

_____

_____

_____

_____

_____

_____

_____

_____

In what places, or to which people do you feel
God calling you to share his love?

_____

_____

_____

_____

_____

_____

_____

_____

_____

_____

_____

_____

_____

Do you find it difficult to accept compliments? Why or why not?

_____

_____

_____

_____

_____

_____

_____

_____

_____

_____

_____

On a scale of 1 to 10, how blessed do you feel today?

1 2 3 4 5 6 7 8 9 10

_____

_____

_____

_____

_____

_____

_____

_____

_____

_____

There is no fear in love. But perfect love drives out fear,
because fear has to do with punishment. The one who fears
is not made perfect in love.

1 JOHN 4:18 NIV

_____

_____

_____

_____

_____

_____

_____

_____

_____

_____

_____

What do you need God to
illuminate for you right now?

_____

_____

_____

_____

_____

_____

_____

_____

_____

_____

_____

_____

ENDURANCE

– what do you need endurance for today?

_____

_____

_____

_____

_____

_____

_____

_____

_____

_____

There are just some things we can't live
without. List your top five!

1. _____

2. _____

3. _____

4. _____

5. _____

In what ways do you need God's comfort today?

_____

_____

_____

_____

_____

_____

_____

_____

_____

_____

_____

Submitting decisions to God and others is wise.
How do you make big decisions?

_____

_____

_____

_____

_____

_____

_____

_____

_____

_____

_____

_____

STAY TRUE TO YOURSELF AND KNOW THAT
WHAT GOD HAS PLACED IN YOU IS ENOUGH.

_____

_____

_____

_____

_____

_____

_____

_____

_____

_____

_____

_____

What do you need God to breathe life back into today?

_____

_____

_____

_____

_____

_____

_____

_____

_____

_____

_____

Put your heart and soul into every activity you do, as though you are doing it for the Lord himself and not merely for others.

COLOSSIANS 3:23 TPT

_____

_____

_____

_____

_____

_____

_____

_____

_____

_____

_____

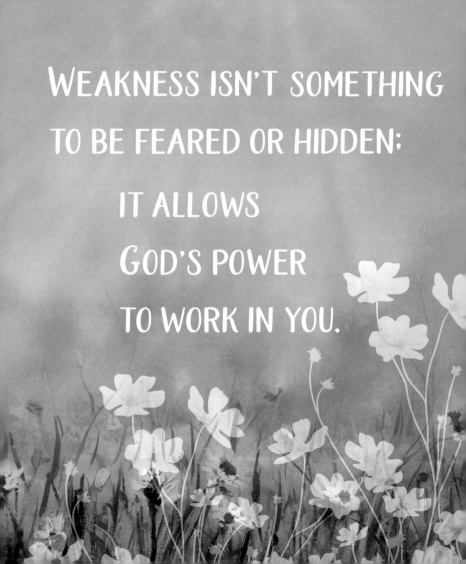

WHAT GIFTS HAS GOD BLESSED YOU WITH TO GET YOU TO WHERE YOU ARE NOW?

_____

_____

_____

_____

_____

_____

_____

_____

_____

_____

_____

_____

Use this acrostic to consider the ways you could find peace in your life.

P
_____

E
_____

A
_____

C
_____

E
_____

We are told we can boldly approach God
with our requests. What opportunities feel
impossible to you right now?

_____

_____

_____

_____

_____

_____

_____

_____

_____

_____

_____

Where can you see God's perfection
shining through your imperfection?

_____

_____

_____

_____

_____

_____

_____

_____

_____

_____

FAITH

– what level of faith do you have today?

_____

_____

_____

_____

_____

_____

_____

_____

_____

_____

Here's an age-old question that will likely never happen to you, but it's worth considering. You are going to a deserted island and can only take five things with you. What are they?

1. _____

2. _____

3. _____

4. _____

5. _____

WHAT PART OF YOUR LIFE NEEDS TO EXPERIENCE THE WARMTH OF GOD'S LOVE?

_____

_____

_____

_____

_____

_____

_____

_____

_____

_____

_____

_____

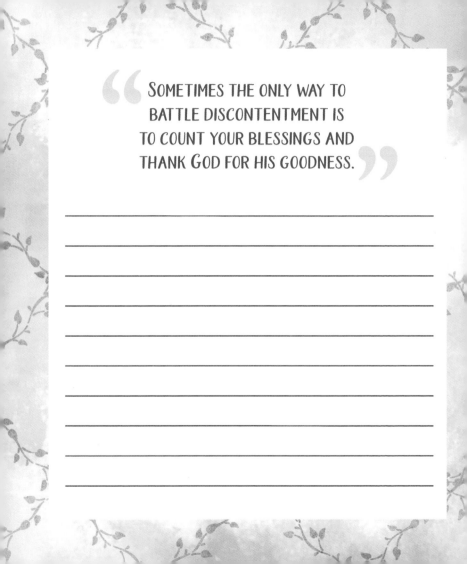

> SOMETIMES THE ONLY WAY TO
> BATTLE DISCONTENTMENT IS
> TO COUNT YOUR BLESSINGS AND
> THANK GOD FOR HIS GOODNESS.

_____

_____

_____

_____

_____

_____

_____

_____

_____

_____

On a scale of 1 to 10, how peaceful do you feel today?

1 2 3 4 5 6 7 8 9 10

_____

_____

_____

_____

_____

_____

_____

_____

_____

_____

What is the most relaxing way for
you to spend an hour or two?

_____

_____

_____

_____

_____

_____

_____

_____

_____

_____

_____

Surprises are exciting for some and anxiety-provoking for others. Do you like surprises? Why or why not?

_____

_____

_____

_____

_____

_____

_____

_____

_____

_____

_____

_____

The LORD directs the steps of the godly. He delights
in every detail of their lives.

PSALM 37:23 NLT

_____

_____

_____

_____

_____

_____

_____

_____

_____

_____

_____

_____

_____

HOW DO YOU BRING LIGHT TO A WORLD CLOAKED IN DARKNESS?

_____

_____

_____

_____

_____

_____

_____

_____

_____

_____

_____

> STUDY A FLOWER. READ ABOUT THE HUMAN EYE. WATCH THE SUN RISE OR SET. WRITE DOWN YOUR DREAMS. SPEND SOME TIME JUST SOAKING IN THE AWESOMENESS OF THE CREATOR.

_____

_____

_____

_____

_____

_____

_____

_____

_____

_____

Let no doubt take root; God cares deeply and loves fully.

What good things are happening around you in this moment?

_____

_____

_____

_____

_____

_____

_____

_____

_____

_____

_____

What are five things that make you happy?

1. _____

2. _____

3. _____

4. _____

5. _____

God understands our weaknesses and doesn't expect perfection. What can you let go of today that makes you feel like you are failing?

_____

_____

_____

_____

_____

_____

_____

_____

_____

_____

_____

What is your favorite season of the year?
Why?

_____

_____

_____

_____

_____

_____

_____

_____

_____

_____

_____

WISDOM

– how can you seek wisdom today?

_____

_____

_____

_____

_____

_____

_____

_____

_____

_____

"Does worry add anything to your life?
Can it add one more year, or even one day?"

LUKE 12:25 TPT

_____

_____

_____

_____

_____

_____

_____

_____

_____

_____

_____

How do you best receive love?

_____

_____

_____

_____

_____

_____

_____

_____

_____

_____

_____

EVERYTHING ON EARTH IS A FLEETING
TREASURE, A MOMENTARY COMFORT
THAT CAN BE LOST IN A FLASH. BUT THE
ASSURANCE OF YOUR ETERNAL PLACE
IN HIS KINGDOM IS INDESTRUCTIBLE.

Do you take time to really listen to others?
How could you do this better?

_____

_____

_____

_____

_____

_____

_____

_____

_____

_____

_____

WRITE DOWN YOUR FAVORITE PSALM.

_____

_____

_____

_____

_____

_____

_____

_____

_____

_____

_____

Faith is the confidence that what we hope for will actually happen;
it gives us assurance about things we cannot see.

HEBREWS 11:1 NLT

_____

_____

_____

_____

_____

_____

_____

_____

_____

_____

_____

_____

What do you love reading about, and why?

_____

_____

_____

_____

_____

_____

_____

_____

_____

_____

_____

_____

_____

Write down three things you are finding difficult and then list how those things can create beauty in you.

DIFFICULTY

BEAUTY

1. _____

1. _____

_____

_____

_____

_____

2. _____

2. _____

_____

_____

_____

_____

3. _____

3. _____

_____

_____

_____

_____

On a scale of 1 to 10, how valued do you feel today?

1 2 3 4 5 6 7 8 9 10

_____

_____

_____

_____

_____

_____

_____

_____

_____

_____

_____

You are a strong and graceful oak, flourishing and resilient!

What is your favorite thing to do
when the sun is out?

_____

_____

_____

_____

_____

_____

_____

_____

_____

_____

_____

You can't control people or circumstances, but you can control your response. What five things could steal your joy if you let them?

1. _____

2. _____

3. _____

4. _____

5. _____

If money weren't an issue, what would you buy for whom, and why?

_____

_____

_____

_____

_____

_____

_____

_____

_____

_____

_____

Navigating our obligations in life is sometimes not much different than juggling glass inside a room of bouncing rubber balls. What are you juggling today? Can you hand it all over to God and allow him to put back in your hands only that which he wants you to carry?

_____

_____

_____

_____

_____

_____

_____

_____

_____

_____

INTEGRITY

– does integrity play a role in your daily life?

_____

_____

_____

_____

_____

_____

_____

_____

_____

_____

WHERE DO YOU GO WHEN YOU JUST NEED TO GET AWAY?

_____

_____

_____

_____

_____

_____

_____

_____

_____

_____

GOD LOVES US WITH A SACRIFICIAL
LOVE THAT ESCAPES OUR HUMAN
UNDERSTANDING, OVERWHELMS
OUR HUMAN SELFISHNESS, AND
HUMBLES OUR HUMAN PRIDE.

_____

_____

_____

_____

_____

_____

_____

_____

_____

_____

Use this acrostic to consider how you could demonstrate humility in your life.

H _____

U _____

M _____

B _____

L _____

E _____

What makes you totally unique?

_____

_____

_____

_____

_____

_____

_____

_____

_____

_____

_____

_____

"You will know the truth, and the truth will set you free."

JOHN 8:32 ESV

_____

_____

_____

_____

_____

_____

_____

_____

_____

_____

_____

> EVER ENCOURAGING,
> OUR GOD BECKONS US:
> COME TO ME. YOU CAN MAKE IT.
> YOU'RE ALMOST THERE.

_____

_____

_____

_____

_____

_____

_____

_____

_____

_____

What does it look like for you
to honor your parents?

_____

_____

_____

_____

_____

_____

_____

_____

_____

_____

_____

What things are most concerning in this season?
Can you reflect on the bigger picture and
set your heart on future glory?

_____

_____

_____

_____

_____

_____

_____

_____

_____

_____

_____

What do you think are your greatest strengths?

_____

_____

_____

_____

_____

_____

_____

_____

_____

_____

_____

Hope
starts with
the promises
of God.

Whether you work outside the home or at home, there have to be some things you love about your current job. Name five.

1. _____

2. _____

3. _____

4. _____

5. _____

The most powerful force in the universe is also the most gentle. How can you grasp hold of God's powerful love today?

_____

_____

_____

_____

_____

_____

_____

_____

_____

_____

_____

WHAT DOES GRACE LOOK LIKE TO YOU?

_____

_____

_____

_____

_____

_____

_____

_____

_____

_____

_____

_____

BELIEVE

– what do you truly believe?

_____

_____

_____

_____

_____

_____

_____

_____

_____

_____

Truthful words will stand the test of time,
but one day every lie will be seen for what it is.

PROVERBS 12:19 TPT

_____

_____

_____

_____

_____

_____

_____

_____

_____

_____

When do you feel most aware
of God's presence?

_____

_____

_____

_____

_____

_____

_____

_____

_____

_____

_____

On a scale of 1 to 10, how relaxed do you feel today?

1 2 3 4 5 6 7 8 9 10

_____

_____

_____

_____

_____

_____

_____

_____

_____

_____

Do you feel like you are owed a platform?
How can you choose love over your opinions today?

_____

_____

_____

_____

_____

_____

_____

_____

_____

_____

_____

What are your priorities in life right now?

_____

_____

_____

_____

_____

_____

_____

_____

_____

_____

_____

> TIME GIVES US BETTER PERSPECTIVE ON THE TRUE DEFINITION OF BEAUTY. SPENDING TIME WITH THOSE WE LOVE AFFORDS US A GLIMPSE INTO THE DEPTH OF BEAUTY THAT LIES WITHIN.

_____

_____

_____

_____

_____

_____

_____

_____

_____

_____

We are vessels without lids, made to overflow so God's joy can be seen by everyone. Do you need to be filled up today? What's the best way for that to happen?

_____

_____

_____

_____

_____

_____

_____

_____

_____

_____

_____

_____

_____

_____

_____

How can you build your spiritual house
on a solid foundation?

_____

_____

_____

_____

_____

_____

_____

_____

_____

_____

_____

Give thanks in all circumstances; for this is
the will of God in Christ Jesus for you.

1 THESSALONIANS 5:18 ESV

It has been said that home is where your heart is. What are five things you love about your home—wherever that is to you right now.

1.

2.

3.

4.

5.

TODAY IS A NEW DAY, FULL OF PROMISE AND LIFE.

WHAT HAVE YOU WORKED REALLY HARD TO BE?

_____

_____

_____

_____

_____

_____

_____

_____

_____

_____

_____

IF WE CAN LEARN TO FULLY TRUST GOD, HE WILL CALM
OUR FEARS AND STILL OUR QUICKENED HEARTS.

_____

_____

_____

_____

_____

_____

_____

_____

_____

_____

_____

How do you want to be remembered?

_____

_____

_____

_____

_____

_____

_____

_____

_____

_____

_____

GRACE

– how can you demonstrate grace today?

_____

_____

_____

_____

_____

_____

_____

_____

_____

_____

What are you putting your time, energy, and talents into?
Are they being used for God's glory?

_____

_____

_____

_____

_____

_____

_____

_____

_____

_____

_____

_____

What does a typical day look like for you?

_____

_____

_____

_____

_____

_____

_____

_____

_____

_____

_____

_____

We know that in all things God works for the good of those who love him, who have been called according to his purpose.

ROMANS 8:28 NIV

_____

_____

_____

_____

_____

_____

_____

_____

_____

_____

_____

_____

> " WHEN YOU SPEND TIME WITH GOD, THERE IS NO NEED TO HIDE. YOU CAN BE EXACTLY WHO YOU ARE. YOU CAN SAY EVERYTHING YOU WANT TO SAY. THERE IS FREEDOM IN HIS PRESENCE. "

_____

_____

_____

_____

_____

_____

_____

_____

WHAT IS SOMETHING NEW YOU HAVE LEARNED FROM GOD'S WORD RECENTLY?

_____

_____

_____

_____

_____

_____

_____

_____

_____

_____

_____

On a scale of 1 to 10, how special do you feel today?

1 2 3 4 5 6 7 8 9 10

_____

_____

_____

_____

_____

_____

_____

_____

_____

_____

Do you ever laugh so hard your cheeks hurt?
What are five things that make you
laugh like that?

1. _____

2. _____

3. _____

4. _____

5. _____

What recent experience has made you feel deeply loved?

_____

_____

_____

_____

_____

_____

_____

_____

_____

_____

_____

When was the last time someone went out of their way to be nice to you? How did it make you feel?

_____

_____

_____

_____

_____

_____

_____

_____

_____

_____

_____

HOW COULD YOU BETTER
MANAGE YOUR TIME?

_____

_____

_____

_____

_____

_____

_____

_____

_____

_____

_____

GOD LOVES YOU WITH A

FIERCELY PROTECTIVE,

ETERNALLY FAITHFUL,

INESCAPABLE LOVE.

If anyone longs to be wise, ask God for wisdom and he will give it!
JAMES 1:5 TPT

_____

_____

_____

_____

_____

_____

_____

_____

_____

_____

_____

_____

Use this acrostic to consider how you could gain wisdom and understanding.

S
_____

M
_____

A
_____

R
_____

T
_____

CONFIDENCE

– where does your confidence lie today?

_____

_____

_____

_____

_____

_____

_____

_____

_____

_____

What is the most amazing thing you have experienced lately?

_____

_____

_____

_____

_____

_____

_____

_____

_____

_____

_____

_____

Write down three mistakes you've made and then list
what those mistakes have taught you.

MISTAKE

1. _____

_____

_____

2. _____

_____

_____

3. _____

_____

_____

LESSON

1. _____

_____

_____

2. _____

_____

_____

3. _____

_____

_____

> " **TRAIN YOUR HEART TO RUN FIRST TO GOD WITH YOUR PAIN, JOY, FRUSTRATION, AND EXCITEMENT. HIS FRIENDSHIP WILL NEVER LET YOU DOWN!** "

_____

_____

_____

_____

_____

_____

_____

_____

_____

_____

DO YOU FEEL THE NEED TO ALWAYS BE PREPARED? WHY OR WHY NOT?

_____

_____

_____

_____

_____

_____

_____

_____

_____

_____

_____

If you had all the courage in the world,
what are five things you would do?

1. _____

2. _____

3. _____

4. _____

5. _____

What is stopping you from sharing God's good news with others? How can you take down that barrier?

_____

_____

_____

_____

_____

_____

_____

_____

_____

_____

_____

Write about something that changed
your life significantly.

_____

_____

_____

_____

_____

_____

_____

_____

_____

_____

_____

_____

_____

Let's not get tired of doing what is good. At just the right time we will reap a harvest of blessing if we don't give up.

GALATIANS 6:9 NLT

_____

_____

_____

_____

_____

_____

_____

_____

_____

_____

_____

On a scale of 1 to 10, how inspired do you feel today?

1   2   3   4   5   6   7   8   9   10

_____

_____

_____

_____

_____

_____

_____

_____

_____

_____

_____

WHAT FASCINATES YOU ABOUT GOD'S CREATION?

_____

_____

_____

_____

_____

_____

_____

_____

_____

_____

_____

Waiting is not easy, but it's often worth it.
What has been worth the wait for you?

_____

_____

_____

_____

_____

_____

_____

_____

_____

_____

_____

_____

God is
faithful
to the
deepest
needs
of your
heart.

What story in the Bible captures
your attention? Why?

_____

_____

_____

_____

_____

_____

_____

_____

_____

_____

_____

_____

> **YOUR PATH HAS BEEN CHOSEN AND YOUR FEET HAVE BEEN SET UPON IT. TRULY, IT IS A PATH OF LOVE AND FAITHFULNESS.**

_____

_____

_____

_____

_____

_____

_____

_____

_____

_____

HOPE

– what are you hoping for today?

_____

_____

_____

_____

_____

_____

_____

_____

_____

_____

What would you love to do with your life?

_____

_____

_____

_____

_____

_____

_____

_____

_____

_____

Who do you typically feel compassion toward?
Can you extend compassion today?

_____

_____

_____

_____

_____

_____

_____

_____

_____

_____

_____

Time is often our greatest inhibitor. If time were unlimited, what would you do?

_____

_____

_____

_____

_____

_____

_____

_____

_____

_____

_____

_____

HOW DO YOU BELIEVE GOD SEES YOU?

_____

_____

_____

_____

_____

_____

_____

_____

_____

_____

_____

_____

God revives, rebuilds, recovers, and renews. He takes what was, strips it away, and creates something completely new. How do you feel like a new person?

_____

_____

_____

_____

_____

_____

_____

_____

_____

_____

_____

HOPE STARTS WITH THE PROMISES OF GOD.

_____

_____

_____

_____

_____

_____

_____

_____

_____

_____

_____

_____

WHAT IS ONE OF THE BIGGEST TRANSFORMATIONS YOU HAVE BEEN THROUGH?

_____

_____

_____

_____

_____

_____

_____

_____

_____

_____

Those who hope in the LORD will renew their strength.
They will soar on wings like eagles; they will run and not grow weary,
they will walk and not be faint.

ISAIAH 40:31 NIV

_____

_____

_____

_____

_____

_____

_____

_____

_____

_____

When you recognize that you belong to God,
trusting him with everything becomes your new normal.
Where is God leading you today?

_____

_____

_____

_____

_____

_____

_____

_____

_____

_____

_____

Do you find it easy to trust people? Why or why not?

_____

_____

_____

_____

_____

_____

_____

_____

_____

_____

_____

_____

On a scale of 1 to 10, how encouraged do you feel today?

1 2 3 4 5 6 7 8 9 10

_____

_____

_____

_____

_____

_____

_____

_____

_____

_____

_____

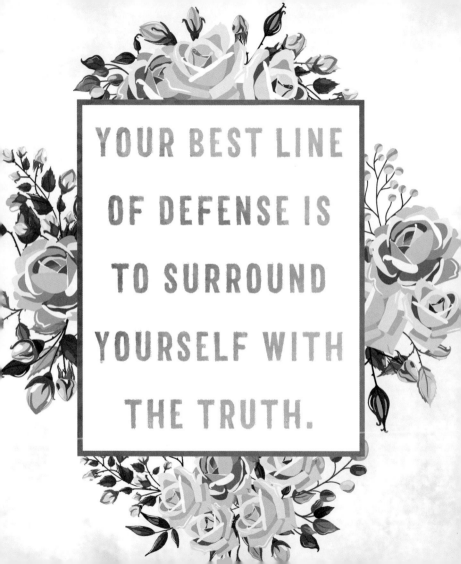

What is one of the hardest things
you've ever had to do?

_____

_____

_____

_____

_____

_____

_____

_____

_____

_____

_____

_____

WONDER

– what can you stop and be in awe of today?

_____

_____

_____

_____

_____

_____

_____

_____

_____

_____

Getting a literal breath of fresh air
is great for your health! What are five things
you love to do outside?

1. _____

2. _____

3. _____

4. _____

5. _____

Where do you feel God is leading your next step?

_____

_____

_____

_____

_____

_____

_____

_____

_____

_____

_____

_____

> GOD DOESN'T TAKE A STAB IN THE DARK WHEN YOU ARE APPROACHING HIM, GUESSING A NAME AND HOPING HE GETS IT RIGHT. HE KNOWS EXACTLY WHO YOU ARE AND WHY YOU ARE COMING TO HIM.

_____

_____

_____

_____

_____

_____

_____

_____

_____

Use this acrostic to consider how you could
find courage in the face of fear.

B
_____

R
_____

A
_____

V
_____

E
_____

WHAT MOTIVATES YOU TO LEARN MORE ABOUT GOD?

_____

_____

_____

_____

_____

_____

_____

_____

_____

_____

_____

Stand on the promise that there is nothing in your history—no past or present sin—that can separate you from God's love. Can you believe your total acceptance in God?

_____

_____

_____

_____

_____

_____

_____

_____

_____

_____

If your faith remains strong, even while surrounded by life's difficulties, you will continue to experience the untold blessings of God!

JAMES 1:12 TPT

_____

_____

_____

_____

_____

_____

_____

_____

_____

_____

_____

How do you usually face your fears?

What situations facing you right now cause you to want to run away and hide? Can you see God's hand in those situations and trust in his perfect plan?

_____

_____

_____

_____

_____

_____

_____

_____

_____

_____

_____

_____

JOY

– where is the depth of your joy found today?

_____

_____

_____

_____

_____

_____

_____

_____

_____

_____

When do you find it
most difficult to be patient?

_____

_____

_____

_____

_____

_____

_____

_____

_____

_____

_____

_____

Desire without hope is empty, but together they bring joy and expectancy. What are you hoping for in this season?

_____

_____

_____

_____

_____

_____

_____

_____

_____

_____

_____

THE RICHNESS OF

God's love

IS DEEPLY

SATISFYING.

What does absolute faith look like to you?

_____

_____

_____

_____

_____

_____

_____

_____

_____

_____

_____

There are many magnificent wonders in nature. From butterflies to mountains, all shout of a marvelous Creator. What five things have you seen that have left you in awe of God?

1. _____

2. _____

3. _____

4. _____

5. _____

On a scale of 1 to 10, how passionate do you feel today?

1 2 3 4 5 6 7 8 9 10

WHAT MAKES YOU FEEL LIKE SINGING?

_____

_____

_____

_____

_____

_____

_____

_____

_____

_____

_____

> " WE DON'T LEAVE OUR JUDGMENT IN THE HANDS OF A JURY. EVEN THE MOST EXPERIENCED PROSECUTOR CAN'T MAKE A CASE AGAINST US THAT WILL LAST INTO ETERNITY. GOD KNOWS WHAT HAPPENED, AND, MORE IMPORTANTLY, HE KNOWS OUR HEARTS. "

_____

_____

_____

_____

_____

_____

_____

_____

Who are you in the face of conflict?
Do you avoid apologizing in an attempt to save face?
What can you do today to humble yourself
for the sake of a restored relationship?

_____

_____

_____

_____

_____

_____

_____

_____

_____

_____

_____

When do you feel most at peace?

_____

_____

_____

_____

_____

_____

_____

_____

_____

_____

_____

Trust in the Lord with all your heart; do not depend on your own understanding. Seek his will in all you do, and he will show you which path to take.

PROVERBS 3:5-6 NLT

_____

_____

_____

_____

_____

_____

_____

_____

_____

_____

_____

BEAUTY

– how do you display beauty in your life?

_____

_____

_____

_____

_____

_____

_____

_____

_____

_____

What has surprised you most in life?

_____

_____

_____

_____

_____

_____

_____

_____

_____

_____

_____

God has created us each with a unique skill set. How can you use your gifts to benefit the church, the community, and the world?

_____

_____

_____

_____

_____

_____

_____

_____

_____

_____

_____

Write down three lies you find yourself believing.
Then list the truth.

LIE

TRUTH

1.
_____
_____
_____

1.
_____
_____
_____

2.
_____
_____
_____

2.
_____
_____
_____

3.
_____
_____
_____

3.
_____
_____
_____

What does a life of unconditional love look like to you?

_____

_____

_____

_____

_____

_____

_____

_____

_____

_____

_____

_____

_____

What five random acts of kindness could you see yourself completing in the next few weeks?

1. _____

2. _____

3. _____

4. _____

5. _____

Every day
is worth
celebrating.

WHAT IS YOUR FAVORITE
TIME OF THE DAY? WHY?

_____

_____

_____

_____

_____

_____

_____

_____

_____

_____

_____

Our thoughts determine our actions and our words.
What thoughts govern your mind?

_____

_____

_____

_____

_____

_____

_____

_____

_____

_____

_____

> **WE LOVE TO THE DEGREE THAT WE UNDERSTAND GOD'S LOVE FOR US.**

_____

_____

_____

_____

_____

_____

_____

_____

_____

_____

_____

If you could ask God one question, what would it be?

_____

_____

_____

_____

_____

_____

_____

_____

_____

_____

On a scale of 1 to 10, how appreciated do you feel today?

1 2 3 4 5 6 7 8 9 10

_____

_____

_____

_____

_____

_____

_____

_____

_____

_____

"Be strong and courageous. Do not be afraid; do not be discouraged, for the LORD your God will be with you wherever you go."

JOSHUA 1:9 NIV

_____

_____

_____

_____

_____

_____

_____

_____

_____

_____

_____

What are you thankful for today?

_____

_____

_____

_____

_____

_____

_____

_____

_____

_____

_____

STRENGTH

– what do you need strength for today?

_____

_____

_____

_____

_____

_____

_____

_____

_____

_____

What work are you waiting for God to complete in you?
How can you be patient while continuing to hope
for his promises?

_____

_____

_____

_____

_____

_____

_____

_____

_____

_____

_____

_____

Where could you use a little, or a lot, of God's strength right now?

_____

_____

_____

_____

_____

_____

_____

_____

_____

_____

_____

_____

Use this acrostic to consider how God
gives you strength in your weakness.

S _____

T _____

R _____

O _____

N _____

G _____

Who are the top five historical figures
you admire and why?

1.

2.

3.

4.

5.

HOW DO YOU WANT OTHERS TO SEE GOD'S BEAUTY DISPLAYED THROUGH YOUR LIFE?

_____

_____

_____

_____

_____

_____

_____

_____

_____

_____

Turn your face to the sun. Let its warmth embrace you. God is working in all things. In what ways do you see him moving today?

_____

_____

_____

_____

_____

_____

_____

_____

_____

_____

_____

Choose to be content with what you have.

Have you seen the fruit
of God's promises lately?

_____

_____

_____

_____

_____

_____

_____

_____

_____

_____

_____

_____

What five characteristics do you love most about God?

1. _____

2. _____

3. _____

4. _____

5. _____

You have been created to enjoy all that is exquisite, beautiful, and captivating. What can you enjoy today?

_____

_____

_____

_____

_____

_____

_____

_____

_____

_____

_____

_____

What word is God speaking
to you in this season?

_____

_____

_____

_____

_____

_____

_____

_____

_____

_____

_____

_____

> AS IF ETERNITY IN HIS KINGDOM WEREN'T ENOUGH, GOD BLESSES US EACH AND EVERY DAY, WHETHER WE ACKNOWLEDGE IT OR NOT.

_____

_____

_____

_____

_____

_____

_____

_____

_____

_____

RELAX

– how can you take a moment to relax today?

_____

_____

_____

_____

_____

_____

_____

_____

_____

How do you like to spend your weekends?

_____

_____

_____

_____

_____

_____

_____

_____

_____

_____

_____

On a scale of 1 to 10, how successful do you feel today?

① ② ③ ④ ⑤ ⑥ ⑦ ⑧ ⑨ ⑩

_____

_____

_____

_____

_____

_____

_____

_____

_____

What are the top five things you would
love to do on a rainy day?

1. _____

2. _____

3. _____

4. _____

5. _____

HOW IS GOD BETTER THAN ANY FRIEND YOU COULD HAVE?

_____

_____

_____

_____

_____

_____

_____

_____

_____

_____

_____

Are there people in your life that you find hard to love?
How does understanding God's love help you with this?

_____

_____

_____

_____

_____

_____

_____

_____

_____

_____

_____

_____

There's a journey of joy in waking up every morning knowing it's another day to breathe in the fresh air. What moment can you find joy in today?

_____

_____

_____

_____

_____

_____

_____

_____

_____

_____

_____

In which aspect of your walk do you feel most steady and certain?

_____

_____

_____

_____

_____

_____

_____

_____

_____

_____

_____

_____

**The season of your greatest rejoicing can be now when
you consider the strength God provides.
What is worth rejoicing about today?**

_____

_____

_____

_____

_____

_____

_____

_____

_____

_____

_____

Don't miss the joy of the current season by wishing it were a different one.

How can you replace frustration
with praise today?

_____

_____

_____

_____

_____

_____

_____

_____

_____

_____

_____

_____

_____

God delights in your voice, your laughter, and your ideas.
How do you share your life with God?

_____

_____

_____

_____

_____

_____

_____

_____

_____

_____

_____

> WHEN THE WORLD AROUND YOU SEEMS TO HAVE COLLAPSED, AND YOU FIND YOURSELF FLOUNDERING AROUND LOOKING FOR SOMETHING FIRM TO TAKE HOLD OF, GRAB GOD'S HAND. HE IS STEADY AND SURE, AND HIS LOVE IS SAFE.

_____

_____

_____

_____

_____

_____

_____

_____

ACCEPTANCE

– when do you feel most accepted?

_____

_____

_____

_____

_____

_____

_____

_____

_____

_____

What five decisions do you need to make soon?

1. _____

2. _____

3. _____

4. _____

5. _____

What are you doing right now
to have the life you want?

_____

_____

_____

_____

_____

_____

_____

_____

_____

_____

_____

_____

Establishing the right patterns begins with the renewing of our minds. What habits are you trying to break?

_____

_____

_____

_____

_____

_____

_____

_____

_____

_____

"Until now you have asked nothing in my name.
Ask, and you will receive, that your joy may be full."

JOHN 16:24 ESV

_____

_____

_____

_____

_____

_____

_____

_____

_____

_____

_____

_____

HOW DO YOU FEEL UNDER THE LOVING GAZE OF GOD?

_____

_____

_____

_____

_____

_____

_____

_____

_____

_____

_____

God created us to be relational. He knows that life is better when shared with others. How do you give yourself opportunities to be uplifted by other believers or to be an encouragement to them?

_____

_____

_____

_____

_____

_____

_____

_____

_____

_____

If we confess our sins, he is faithful and just and will forgive us our sins and purify us from all unrighteousness.

1 JOHN 1:9 NIV

_____

_____

_____

_____

_____

_____

_____

_____

_____

_____

_____

On a scale of 1 to 10, how understood do you feel today?

1 2 3 4 5 6 7 8 9 10

_____

_____

_____

_____

_____

_____

_____

_____

_____

_____

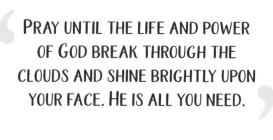

> **PRAY UNTIL THE LIFE AND POWER OF GOD BREAK THROUGH THE CLOUDS AND SHINE BRIGHTLY UPON YOUR FACE. HE IS ALL YOU NEED.**

_____

_____

_____

_____

_____

_____

_____

_____

_____

Use this acrostic to consider how
you could be full of life
and energy today.

L

——————————————————————

I

——————————————————————

F

——————————————————————

E

——————————————————————

True love
releases past
mistakes and
genuinely
believes for
the best
next time.

List five things you want to pray for regularly.

1. _____

2. _____

3. _____

4. _____

5. _____

DETERMINATION

– how determined are you today?

_____

_____

_____

_____

_____

_____

_____

_____

_____

_____

_____

Wealth is rarely what we hope it will be; the more we have, the more we want, and the more we have to lose. Do finances consume a lot of your thoughts? Why do you think this is?

_____

_____

_____

_____

_____

_____

_____

_____

_____

_____

Write down three things you feel are impossible to accomplish. Then show how they are possible with God.

IMPOSSIBLE

1.
_____

_____

_____

2.
_____

_____

_____

3.
_____

_____

_____

POSSIBLE

1.
_____

_____

_____

2.
_____

_____

_____

3.
_____

_____

_____

Let the sunrise of your love end our dark night.
Break through our clouded dawn again! Only you can satisfy our
hearts, filling us with songs of joy to the end of our days.

PSALM 90:14 TPT

_____

_____

_____

_____

_____

_____

_____

_____

_____

_____

_____

_____

How can you choose to pursue peace
in a relationship instead of being
caught up in emotions?

_____

_____

_____

_____

_____

_____

_____

_____

_____

_____

_____

What are five things you highly value?

1. _____

2. _____

3. _____

4. _____

5. _____

When you dive into your unique life, you are saying yes to contentment and joy and moving forward into greater fulfillment and happiness. What does your unique life look like?

_____

_____

_____

_____

_____

_____

_____

_____

_____

_____

_____